TWENTY FIRST CENTURY
SCIENCE

GCSE Separate Sciences

Project Directors
Jenifer Burden Peter Campbell
John Holman Andrew Hunt
Robin Millar

Project Officers
Angela Hall John Lazonby
Peter Nicolson

Authors and Editors
Jenifer Burden Peter Campbell
Anna Grayson Andrew Hunt
Pam Large Robin Millar
David Sang

Contributors
Simon Carson Angela Hall
John Miller Michael Reiss
Elizabeth Swinbank Carol Tear
Charles Tracy

OCR
RECOGNISING ACHIEVEMENT

Nuffield
Curriculum Centre

THE UNIVERSITY *of York*

OXFORD

Contents

Introduction

Welcome to *Twenty First Century Science*

This book covers modules B7, C7, and P7 from GCSE Biology, GCSE Chemistry, and GCSE Physics.

Module B7 has six topics. The first explores how all living things on Earth are dependent on others for their survival. The second topic looks at some of the closest relationships between living things – symbiotes and parasites. The third topic is about new ways to tackle problems using our growing knowledge of inheritance – new DNA technologies. The last three topics take a deeper look at human anatomy – how blood provides a transport system for your body, how energy is released from food in your cells, and how your body uses this energy for movement. Stories of biology in action in this module show how biological ideas are researched and put to use in the twenty-first century.

Module C7 has four topics. The first topic introduces organic chemistry and the importance of carbon compounds. The second topic tackles three challenging questions for chemists: How much?, How fast?, and How far? The third topic is about analytical chemistry, which has a vital part to play in making sure that the food we eat and the air we breathe are safe. The final topic, about green chemistry, shows how modern industry is reinventing the processes it uses to make our use of chemicals more sustainable. Stories of chemists in action in this module show how these chemical ideas are put to use in the twenty-first century.

Module P7 has four topics. The first topic introduces observatories and telescopes. The second topic describes the mapping of the heavens – what astronomers have been able to discover using both naked-eye observation and telescopes. The third topic looks inside stars to understand what they are made of and how they work. The last topic looks at the life cycle of stars, describing how they change and why. You will see that dying stars can be extremely violent and that some produce black holes. Stories of physics in action in this module take you to the frontiers of astronomy today.

How to use this book

If you want to find a particular topic, use the **Contents** and **Index** pages. You can also use the **Glossary**. This explains all the key words used in the book.

Each module has two introduction pages, which tell you the main ideas you will study. They look like this:

Why study biology?
Why it is useful to know about this topic.

The science
The scientific information you will learn about in this module.

Biology in action
What you will learn from this module about how science works.

Why study biology?
Biology is the study of living things. Biologists explore all aspects of life – from the chemical reactions of individual cells to the interactions within an ecosystem. Astrobiologists are involved in the search for life beyond Earth. Knowledge of biology informs any science which affects living things, such as the medical and environmental sciences. Engineers sometimes copy design solutions from the natural world, and modify natural organisms to make products we can use.

The science
No organism lives in isolation. Understanding life processes such as photosynthesis and respiration helps to explain how living things interact with each other. Some biologists study human body systems, and develop new technologies with the potential to improve our quality of life.

Biology in action
Biotechnologists modify microorganisms to produce medicines, and engineer plants to give higher yields. Geneticists analyse genes to find family links, and look for genes which affect our risk of certain diseases, or which may affect our response to certain medicines. Sports scientists help people maintain good health and improve their fitness. And if you suffer a sporting injury, physiotherapists treat damage to the skeleton and muscles.

176

Find out about:
▷ how living things depend on other species for survival
▷ photosynthesis and heterotrophic nutrition
▷ modern genetic technologies
▷ respiration – releasing energy from food
▷ transport around the human body
▷ the structure of the human skeleton and how it moves

Find out about
The main ideas explored in this module.

Each module is split into sections. Pages in a section look like this:

Heading
Each section looks at a different part of the module.

Find out about
The key points explored in the section.

Higher Tier
The 'H' flag next to something on the page means that it refers to Higher Tier material in the specification.

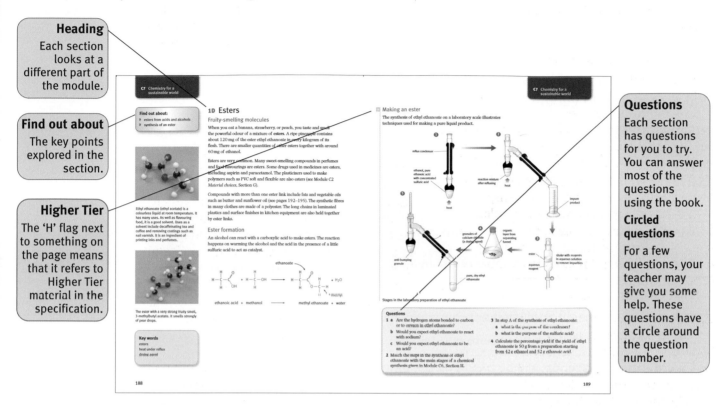

Questions
Each section has questions for you to try. You can answer most of the questions using the book.

Circled questions
For a few questions, your teacher may give you some help. These questions have a circle around the question number.

Each module ends with a summary, and some also have questions. Here is an example:

Summary
A checklist of key points explained in this module.

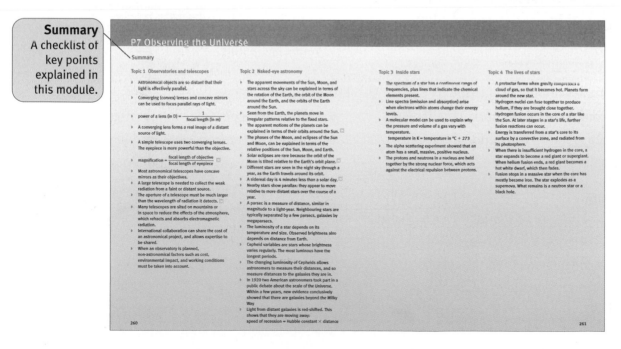

Internal assessment

In each of GCSE Biology, GCSE Chemistry, and GCSE Physics your internal assessment counts for 33.3% of your total grade. Marks are given for:

- *either* a practical investigation
- *or* a case study and a data analysis

Your school or college will decide on the type of internal assessment. You may be given the marking schemes to help you understand how to get the most credit for your work.

Internal assessment (33.3% of total marks)

EITHER: Investigation (33.3%)

Investigations are carried out by scientists to try and find the answers to scientific questions. The skills you learn from this work will help prepare you to study any science course after GCSE.

To succeed with any investigation you will need to:

- choose a question to explore
- select equipment and use it appropriately and safely
- design ways of making accurate and reliable observations

Your investigation report will be based on the data you collect from your own experiments. You may also use information from other people's work. This is called secondary data.

Marks will be awarded under five different headings.

Strategy

- Choose the task for your investigation.
- Decide how much data you need to collect.
- Choose a procedure to give you reliable data.

Collecting data

- Take careful, accurate measurements safely.
- Collect enough data and check its reliability.
- Collect data across a wide enough range.
- Control factors that might affect the results.

Interpreting data

- Present your data to make clear patterns in the results.
- State your conclusions from the results.
- Use chemical knowledge to explain your conclusion.

Evaluation

- Say how you could improve your method.
- Explain how reliable your evidence is.
- Suggest ways to increase the confidence in your conclusions.

Presentation

- Write a full report of your investigation.
- Lay out your report clearly and logically.
- Describe you apparatus and procedure.
- Show all units correctly.
- Take care with spelling, grammar, and scientific terms.

OR: Case study and data analysis (33.3%)

A **case study** is a report which weighs up evidence about a scientific question. You find out what different people have said about the issue. Then you evaluate the information and make your own conclusions.

You choose a topic from one of these categories:

- ▶ A question where the scientific knowledge is not certain.
- ▶ A question about decision-making using scientific information.
- ▶ A question about a personal issue involving science.

Selecting information

- ▶ Collect information from a range of sources.
- ▶ Decide how reliable each source is.
- ▶ Choose relevant information.
- ▶ Say where your information came from.

Understanding the question

- ▶ Use science knowledge to explain your topic.
- ▶ Report on the scientific evidence used by people with views on the issue.

Making your own conclusion

- ▶ Compare different evidence and points of view.
- ▶ Weigh the risks and benefits of different courses of action.

- ▶ Say what you think should be done based on the evidence.

Presenting your study

- ▶ Set out your report clearly and logically.
- ▶ Use an appropriate style of presentation.
- ▶ Illustrate your report.
- ▶ Take care with spelling, grammar, and scientific terms.

A **data analysis** task is based on a practical experiment which you carry out. You may do this alone or work in groups and pool all your data. Then you interpret and evaluate the data.

Interpreting data

- ▶ Present your data in tables, charts, or graphs.
- ▶ State your conclusions from the data.
- ▶ Use chemical knowledge to explain your conclusions.

Evaluation

- ▶ Say how you could improve your method.
- ▶ Explain how reliable your evidence is.
- ▶ Suggest ways to increase the confidence in your conclusions.

Why study biology?

Biology is the study of living things. Biologists explore all aspects of life – from the chemical reactions of individual cells to the interactions within an ecosystem. Astrobiologists are involved in the search for life beyond Earth. Knowledge of biology informs any science which affects living things, such as the medical and environmental sciences. Engineers sometimes copy design solutions from the natural world, and modify natural organisms to make products we can use.

The science

No organism lives in isolation. Understanding life processes such as photosynthesis and respiration helps to explain how living things interact with each other. Some biologists study human body systems, and develop new technologies with the potential to improve our quality of life.

Biology in action

Biotechnologists modify microorganisms to produce medicines, and engineer plants to give higher yields. Geneticists analyse genes to find family links, and look for genes which affect our risk of certain diseases, or which may affect our response to certain medicines. Sports scientists help people maintain good health and improve their fitness. And if you suffer a sporting injury, physiotherapists treat damage to the skeleton and muscles.

Biology across the ecosystem

Find out about:

- how living things depend on other species for survival
- photosynthesis and heterotrophic nutrition
- modern genetic technologies
- respiration – releasing energy from food
- transport around the human body
- the structure of the human skeleton and how it moves

Topic 1

Interdependence

Wherever you go on Earth, you are never alone. Other species are everywhere – in the rock and soil beneath your feet, the air around you, even inside and on the surface of your body. You depend on some of these organisms for your survival. Some of them depend on you. This is the **interdependence** of life.

Life exists in even the harshest of environments.

Ultimate dependence – the Sun

All life on Earth depends on the Sun. It provides energy

▶ to keep the Earth's atmosphere warm
▶ to drive the production of food chemicals

All living things need a continual supply of energy. Plants capture energy from the Sun during photosynthesis. They use photosynthesis to produce food chemicals. This energy flows through the rest of the ecosystem as the plants are eaten or decompose.

Webs of life

The need for energy from food is behind many interactions between living things. Food webs show the story of food in an ecosystem – what eats what. This helps us understand more about how organisms affect each other.

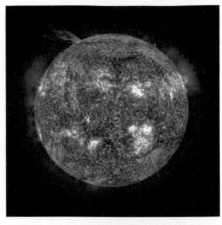

The Sun gives out 386 billion billion megawatts of energy every second. It would take 2500 million of the largest power stations on Earth a year to generate this amount.

Energy passes from the rose bush to the aphids and then to the ladybird.

Nature's recycling

Living things are made up of a rich diversity of chemicals. Many of these are **organic** compounds, such as glucose. Organic compounds contain two or more carbon atoms. Almost all organic compounds are made by living things. Biochemists study biological molecules, and develop processes to make them artificially.

When living things die, the carbon in their bodies must be recycled to produce the bodies of new organisms. Microorganisms play a crucial role in recycling carbon and other elements on Earth.

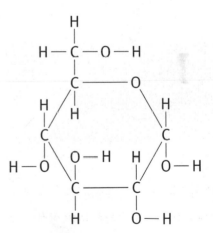

The formula for a glucose molecule

Key words

interdependence
organic

Find out about:

▶ how photosynthesis captures energy for life on Earth

1A Harvesting the Sun

How is the Sun's energy harnessed by living organisms?

Plants capture energy from sunlight. This may look as easy as sunbathing, but the process is one of nature's cleverest tricks. Many complex chemical reactions are involved.

This sunbather is enjoying warmth from the Sun, but he does not rely directly on the Sun's energy for his life processes. The lizard is using energy from the Sun to raise its body temperature. The plant is harnessing light energy to drive food production.

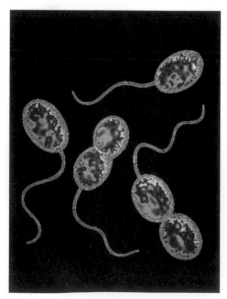

This bacterium uses sulfur from the environment for chemical reactions that release energy. (× 7500)

Plants use energy from sunlight to build up carbon dioxide and water into organic compounds such as glucose. This is the process of **photosynthesis**. Energy from sunlight is transferred to chemical energy in the new compounds. So these compounds act as an energy store. They can be used as food molecules which are broken down to release energy. They also provide raw materials to build new plant cells for growing.

Living things that can make their own food are called **autotrophs**. Most autotrophs are types of plant, but there are some bacteria which also make their own food chemicals. These bacteria do not use energy from light to drive this process. Instead they obtain energy from chemical reactions using raw materials from their environment.

Most living things cannot make their food

Animals have to eat. They cannot make their own food, so they need to take in organic molecules. Organisms that rely on other living things for food are called **heterotrophs**.

Just passing through

Some plant material passes to other organisms as they eat the plant. Energy stored in the chemicals making up the plant cells is passed on to other organisms along food chains. In this way energy moves through the ecosystem. This is similar to how elements like carbon and nitrogen move through an ecosystem. But there is a big difference.

Carbon and nitrogen are always being recycled in an ecosystem. When an animal or plant dies, its organic compounds are broken down by decay. The carbon and nitrogen atoms become part of a new organism in the cycle.

When energy is passed through an ecosystem, some is lost at every stage of a food chain. This is because all living things release energy from food by respiration. Land plants use half the organic compounds they make for respiration. Some of the energy released in respiration is transferred to the environment. This energy warms the air or water around the plants and animals, and eventually radiates back into space.

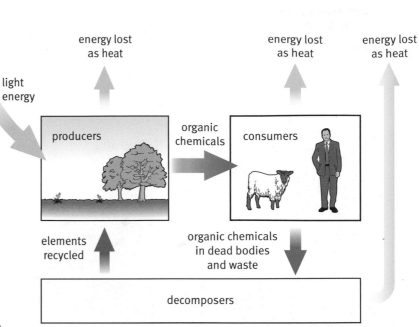

Transfer of energy and elements through an ecosystem

Questions

1 Give two reasons why sunlight is essential for life on Earth.

2 Write down definitions for the terms

   a autotroph

   b heterotroph

3 Identify two autotrophs and two heterotrophs on this double page.

4 Explain how energy is transferred from

   a the grass to sheep

   b the tree to decomposers

5 Some animals rely on energy from the Sun to raise their body temperature. Others, including human beings, do not use the Sun's energy in this way. Why is this?

Key words

organic
photosynthesis
autotroph
heterotroph

Find out about:

▶ how photosynthesis captures energy for life on Earth

1B Trapping light energy

Less than one-billionth of the Sun's energy reaches the plants on Earth. Plants convert only about 1–3% of this light energy into new plant material. This might sound very small, but remember that the Sun's energy output is enormous. So this 1–3% is still enough energy to drive life on Earth.

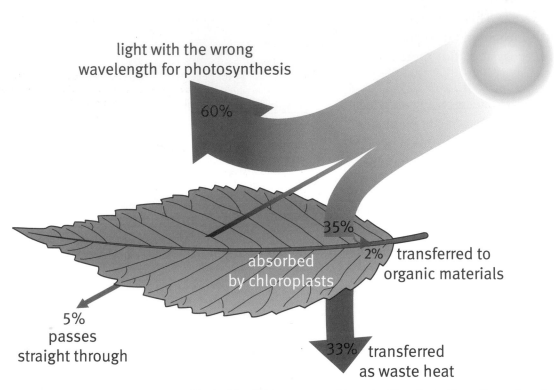

light with the wrong wavelength for photosynthesis

60%

35% absorbed by chloroplasts

2% transferred to organic materials

5% passes straight through

33% transferred as waste heat

Most of the light energy reaching a leaf is reflected from the surface, is transferred as waste heat, or passes straight through the leaf.

What happens during photosynthesis?

The chemical equation for photosynthesis is:

$$6CO_2 + 6H_2O \xrightarrow[\text{chlorophyll}]{\text{light energy}} C_6H_{12}O_6 + 6O_2$$

carbon dioxide   water   glucose   oxygen

Do not let the equation mislead you. The reaction does not happen in one go – it has lots of smaller steps. The equation is a convenient way of summing up the process.

A glucose molecule is made up of carbon, hydrogen, and oxygen atoms. So glucose is a **carbohydrate**.

Photosynthesis takes place in **chloroplasts**. They contain a green pigment called **chlorophyll**. Chlorophyll absorbs light and uses the energy to kick-start photosynthesis.

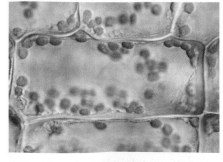

Chloroplasts contain the green pigment chlorophyll and the enzymes that are needed for photosynthesis. (× 2000)

The light energy splits water molecules into hydrogen and oxygen atoms. The hydrogen is combined with carbon dioxide from the air to make glucose. The oxygen is released as a waste product. It passes out of the plant into the air. Given enough raw materials, light, and the right temperature, a large tree can make 2000 kg of glucose in a day.

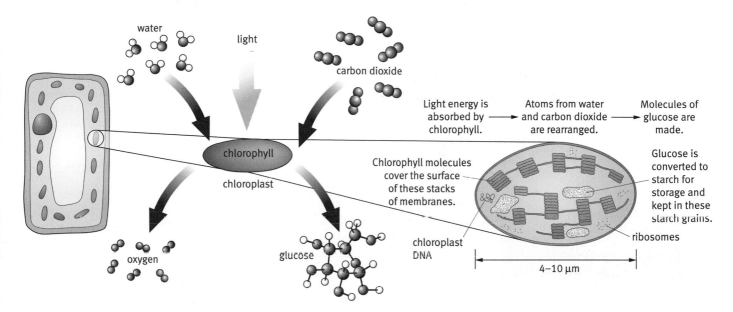

Light energy is absorbed by chlorophyll. → Atoms from water and carbon dioxide are rearranged. → Molecules of glucose are made.

Chlorophyll molecules cover the surface of these stacks of membranes.

Glucose is converted to starch for storage and kept in these starch grains.

Glucose is made by photosynthesis.

Why are plants green?

Most leaves are green because of the chlorophyll in plant cells.

Chlorophyll absorbs energy from visible light. Visible light is part of the electromagnetic spectrum.

Not all of visible light can be used for photosynthesis. Chlorophyll absorbs red light and blue light. So these are the most useful parts of the light spectrum for photosynthesis. Green light is not absorbed. It is reflected by the chlorophyll. This is why most leaves are green.

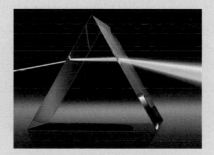

White light is split into its different wavelengths in a prism.

Key words

carbohydrate
chloroplast
chlorophyll

Questions

1 Draw a diagram to show the flow of chemicals in and out of leaves during photosynthesis.

2 Describe the main stages in making glucose by photosynthesis.

3 Write down the word equation that sums up photosynthesis.

4 What property of glucose makes it a carbohydrate?

5 Explain why only a small percentage of light energy from sunlight is used in photosynthesis.

6 Explain why chlorophyll is green in colour.

1C Using glucose from photosynthesis

Glucose made during photosynthesis is used by plant cells in three ways.

(1) Making other chemicals needed for cell growth

Like all larger living things, plants are made up of different types of cell. But every cell is made up of the same basic chemicals. The diagram below shows the chemicals in a typical plant cell.

Glucose has to be converted into the other chemicals needed for cell growth. Cells need other carbohydrates, as well as **fats** and **proteins**. Two important carbohydrates in plants are **cellulose** and **starch**. Both of these are large molecules made up of thousands of glucose molecules linked together. Large molecules made up of many smaller molecules of the same type linked together are called **polymers**. So cellulose and starch are both polymers of glucose.

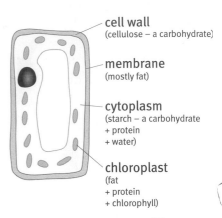

cell wall
(cellulose – a carbohydrate)

membrane
(mostly fat)

cytoplasm
(starch – a carbohydrate
+ protein
+ water)

chloroplast
(fat
+ protein
+ chlorophyll)

A plant cell contains many different chemicals.

Cellulose molecules are long straight chains of glucose molecules. These chains are linked together to make a strong material for cell walls.

(2) Storing energy in starch molecules

Sometimes photosynthesis produces glucose faster than the plant needs it at the time. This extra glucose is converted into starch. Starch is a storage molecule. When photosynthesis cannot keep up with the demand for glucose, the starch can be converted back. Starch may be stored in leaf cells, but some plants have special organs such as the tubers of a potato which have cells that are filled with starch.

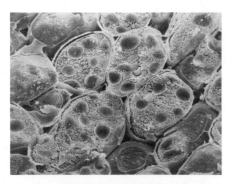

Starch grains in a plant cell store glucose as starch (× 200).

(3) Releasing energy in respiration

Plant cells use glucose in **respiration**. The glucose molecules are broken down, releasing the energy stored in the molecules. The equation for respiration is:

$$C_6H_{12}O_6 \quad + \quad 6O_2 \longrightarrow 6CO_2 \quad + \quad 6H_2O \text{ (+ energy released)}$$

glucose   oxygen   carbon dioxide   water

This energy is used to power chemical reactions in the cells, such as converting glucose to cellulose, starch, or proteins.

Making proteins needs nitrogen

On pages 136 and 142–3 you learnt about the structure of proteins. Remember that proteins are long chains of amino acids. Every amino acid contains atoms of carbon, hydrogen, oxygen, and at least one nitrogen atom. To make amino acids, nitrogen must be combined with carbon, hydrogen, and oxygen atoms from glucose.

Most of the Earth's nitrogen is in the air, but plants mainly take in nitrogen from the soil as **nitrate ions**. The nitrate ions are absorbed by the plant roots.

Nitrates are not the only minerals that plants need. For example, they need magnesium to make chlorophyll, and phosphates to make DNA. But they need nitrogen in the largest quantities, because proteins are used to build cells and to make enzymes.

Nitrate ions are absorbed by active transport

Nitrate ions are at higher concentration inside root cells than outside. This means the ions will move by diffusion out of the cell, not into it. To move nitrate ions into the root cells, active transport is needed. This requires energy. You can read more about how this is done on page 110.

Why is glucose stored as starch?

Glucose is a soluble carbohydrate. Cell cytoplasm is mainly water. So glucose made by photosynthesis dissolves in the cytoplasm.

This causes a problem for cells. If the concentration of glucose in the cell cytoplasm becomes too high, then too much water moves into the cell. This happens by osmosis. So the glucose cannot be stored in cells because it upsets the cell's **osmotic balance**, as shown in this diagram:

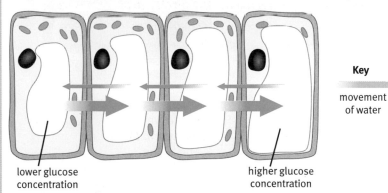

Key

→ movement of water

lower glucose concentration

higher glucose concentration

Too much dissolved glucose in a plant cell would cause overall water movement from neighbouring cells by osmosis.

Large carbohydrates like starch are insoluble. They have very little effect on the osmotic balance of a plant cell. This makes them ideal for storing glucose. The starch is kept in small membrane-surrounded bags in the cell called starch grains. You can read more about osmosis on page 109.

Nitrates contain this group of atoms:

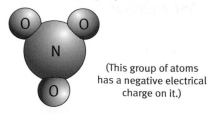

(This group of atoms has a negative electrical charge on it.)

Nitrate ions are found dissolved in soil water, and in rivers and seas.

Key words

fats
proteins
cellulose
starch
polymers
respiration
nitrate ions
osmotic balance

Questions

1 Glucose from photosynthesis has three roles in the plant cell. Explain what these are.

2 Why do plant cells need a source of nitrate ions?

3 Explain why starch is needed to store glucose in plant cells.

4 Water moves into root cells by osmosis. What does this tell you about the water in the soil?

5 Leguminous plants, such as clover, are able to survive in soil low in nitrate ions. Explain why.

Find out about:

▶ what limits the rate of photosynthesis

Intensive tomato farming takes place all year round in this greenhouse.

1D The rate of photosynthesis

The conditions inside the greenhouse in the photograph on the left are kept under very careful control. The tomato plants growing here have the optimum conditions for photosynthesis. They are making glucose at their highest rate, so they are growing quickly. All this is planned by the farmer so that the **yield** from the tomato plants will be as high as possible. Yield is the amount of product the farmer has to sell.

All reactions speed up when the temperature rises, and photosynthesis is no exception. The greenhouse is kept warm at 26 °C. This is the optimum temperature for photosynthesis to take place in these plants.

Faster photosynthesis – light

Other factors have an effect on the rate of photosynthesis. Light energy drives photosynthesis, so increasing the amount of light a plant receives increases the rate of photosynthesis.

The diagram shows an experiment to investigate how changing light intensity affects the rate of photosynthesis in a piece of pondweed. The results from the experiment are shown in the graph. The graph shows that

▶ At low light intensities, increasing the amount of light increases the rate of photosynthesis.

▶ At a certain point increasing the amount of light stops having an effect on rate of photosynthesis.

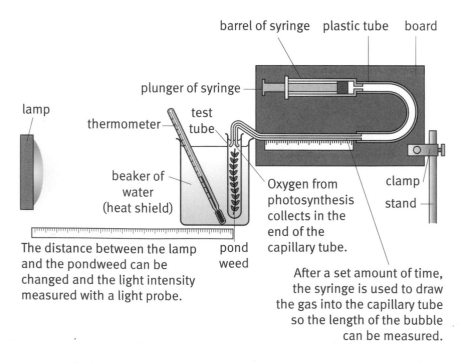

This experiment investigates the effect of light intensity on the rate of photosynthesis.

Why does the rate not keep on rising?

Photosynthesis needs more than light energy. Extra light makes no difference to the rate of photosynthesis if the plant does not have the carbon dioxide, water, or chlorophyll to use the energy to the full. The temperature must also be high enough for photosynthesis reactions to speed up. Increasing the light intensity stops having an effect on the rate of photosynthesis because one of these other factors is in short supply. This factor is called the **limiting factor**.

H Limiting factors

In a British summer the limiting factor for photosynthesis is often water. Stomata close to prevent water diffusing out of the leaves, and this also has the unavoidable consequence of reducing carbon dioxide diffusion into the leaf.

The graph below shows the effect of increasing light intensity on the rate of photosynthesis at two different carbon dioxide concentrations. At 0.04% CO_2, more light increases the rate of photosynthesis up to a point, until light is no longer the limiting factor. Increasing the CO_2 level to 0.4% makes the rate of photosynthesis higher – carbon dioxide must have been the limiting factor. But even this graph levels off as another factor becomes in short supply.

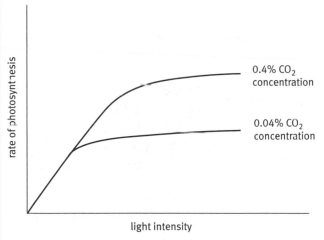

At the higher carbon dioxide concentration, photosynthesis takes place faster. But the rate still levels off. Another factor must be limiting photosynthesis.

Carbon dioxide levels in the greenhouse

Carbon dioxide forms 0.04% of normal air. Levels over about 1% are toxic to plants and animals. The levels in the tomato greenhouse are kept at 0.1%. Raising the concentration higher than this has no effect on the rate of photosynthesis. So it would not be cost effective for the farmer to add more carbon dioxide than this to the greenhouse.

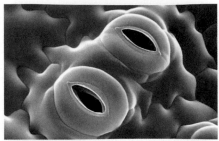

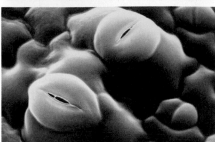

Top: The stomata on the underside of leaves open to allow gases to move in and out of the leaf. *Bottom:* They close to conserve water. (× 400)

Key words

yield
limiting factor

Questions

1 Write down four factors that can affect the rate of photosynthesis.

2 Explain what is meant by a limiting factor.

3 Suggest a factor that could be limiting bluebells growing on a woodland floor in spring.

4 **a** Sketch a graph showing how increasing light intensity affects the rate of photosynthesis.

   b Label the graph line 0.04% CO_2.

   c Draw a second line on the graph to show the rate of photosynthesis for the same plant at 0.1% CO_2.

1E Balancing respiration and photosynthesis

There is only a certain amount of carbon on Earth. Much of the carbon is in molecules that make up the bodies of living things. A lot is also in the atmosphere and oceans as carbon dioxide, and in molecules of fossil fuels.

Carbon dioxide is taken out of the atmosphere by photosynthesis. The carbon is used to produce glucose molecules. The glucose is broken down during respiration. This releases carbon dioxide back into the atmosphere.

Compensation point

Plants only carry out photosynthesis when they are in light. But respiration happens 24 hours a day. So for part of each 24-hour period, plants are actually net producers of carbon dioxide:

▶ Plants take in carbon dioxide for photosynthesis during the day.
▶ They make carbon dioxide in respiration 24 hours a day.
▶ During the day they take in more carbon dioxide for photosynthesis than they make in respiration.

When photosynthesis and respiration are taking place at the same rate, glucose production and use in the plant are balanced. This is called a plant's **compensation point**.

Rising carbon dioxide levels

Carbon dioxide is also added to the atmosphere by the burning of wood and fossil fuels, such as oil, gas, coal, and petrol. The stages in recycling carbon on Earth are explained in the diagram of the **carbon cycle** on the opposite page.

If the amount of carbon dioxide released into the air does not balance the amount taken up by photosynthesis, atmospheric carbon dioxide levels will change.

Most scientists agree that the average carbon dioxide level in the atmosphere is rising. The official figure in 2005 was 0.04% carbon dioxide. It is expected to be 0.05% by the end of the century.

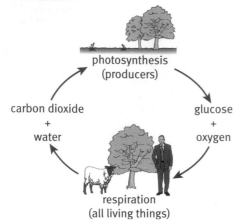

How respiration and photosynthesis are linked

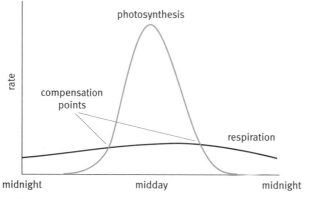

At the compensation points, there is no net movement of carbon dioxide into or out of the plant.

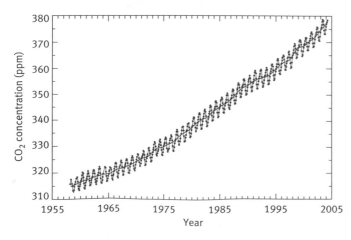

Carbon dioxide concentrations have been recorded at Mauna Loa in Hawaii since 1958. They rise and fall each year, but the overall trend has been an increase of about 1.5 ppm per year since 1980.

Why is the level of carbon dioxide rising?

Increasing carbon dioxide levels in the air are considered by most scientists to be due to human activity. The main sources of this additional carbon dioxide are the combustion of fossil fuels, cement manufacture, and loss of rainforests. Trees store carbon in their wood, and this is released as carbon dioxide when forests are cut down and burned. The loss of rainforest also reduces the plants available to take carbon dioxide out of the atmosphere for photosynthesis.

Why is the extra carbon dioxide not used up?

Some of the extra carbon dioxide from human activity is stored in the oceans, but almost half stays in the atmosphere. But this extra CO_2 is not used up by photosynthesis. If the Earth's vegetation behaved like plants in a greenhouse, the extra carbon dioxide would increase the rate of photosynthesis and so be used up. Tests have been carried out on maize, rice, soya bean, and wheat – the four main food crops. The results have shown a smaller increase in the rate of photosynthesis than expected with higher CO_2 levels. There were other factors limiting the rate of photosynthesis, so the plants could not use the extra carbon dioxide.

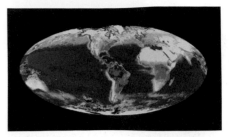

A false-colour satellite image showing the distribution of vegetation on land and phytoplankton in the oceans. The colours represent chlorophyll densities: from red (most dense) through yellow and blue to pink (least dense) in the oceans, and from dark green to pale yellow on land.

Key words

compensation point
carbon cycle

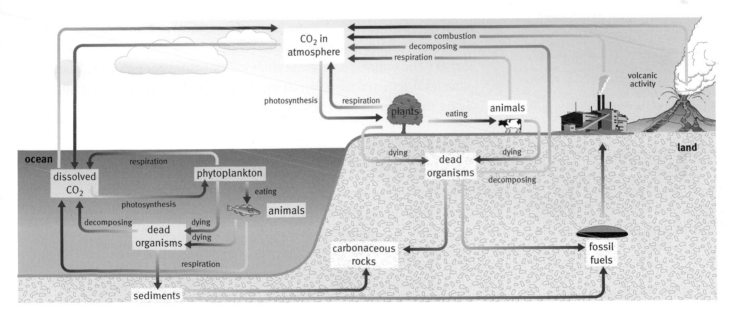

The carbon cycle

Questions

1 List ways in which carbon dioxide is

   a added to the atmosphere

   b taken out of the atmosphere

2 How is human activity causing the amount of CO_2 in the atmosphere to rise?

3 At what times of the day does a plant reach its compensation point?

4 Explain what is happening inside the plant at this point.

Find out about:

▶ how energy and nutrients move through food webs
▶ what pyramid diagrams show

1F Feeding relationships

Food chains

Food chains like the one on page 87 all follow the same pattern. They start with autotrophs. These are the **producers** which use carbon dioxide to make organic chemicals. These chemicals then pass to the heterotrophs. First herbivores eat the producers, and then the herbivores are eaten by carnivores.

One very important group of heterotrophs is often overlooked in a food chain. **Decomposers** may be smaller and less attractive than other organisms, but they do an essential job. A lot of nutrients and energy in an ecosystem pass through them.

Any ecosystem has many food chains interlinked in a food web.

Pyramid of numbers

One way of summing up how living things in an ecosystem are interlinked is to use a pyramid diagram.

The simplest diagram is a **pyramid of numbers**. The different living things in a given area are counted. They are grouped into different **trophic levels**: producers, primary **consumers** (herbivores), secondary consumers, and tertiary consumers. A diagram showing the number of living things at each level is then drawn. For example, a pyramid of numbers for all the living things in an open field is shown opposite.

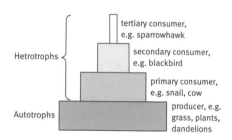

A pyramid of numbers.

Why a pyramid shape?

A pyramid of numbers usually shows more producers than herbivores. This makes sense because not all the nutrients in the producers end up in herbivores. So herbivores do not get all the energy stored in producers.

▶ Most herbivores don't eat the whole plant. For example, they may leave the roots.
▶ Not all of the plant material will be digested by the herbivores – some will pass out of their bodies in faeces.
▶ Plants use at least half of the glucose they make for respiration. Some of the energy released during respiration is used to make new plant cells. Energy stored in the chemicals of these cells is passed along the food chain to the herbivores. But some of the energy released in respiration escapes into the environment as heat energy, so this is not passed on to herbivores.

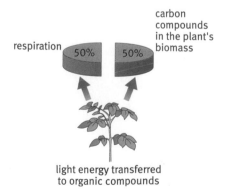

Plants use at least half the carbohydrate they make for respiration.

Energy use in consumers

Herbivores and carnivores break down food molecules in respiration as well. Some of this energy is used for growth, where food molecules become part of the structure of new cells.

Animals also use energy released by respiration for other life processes, for example, movement and keeping warm. So the number of organisms usually gets less at each level of an ecosystem. This is because on average only about 10% of the energy at each stage of a food chain gets passed on to the next level. The rest

> ▶ is used for life processes in the organism, e.g. movement, keeping warm
> ▶ escapes into the environment as heat energy
> ▶ is excreted as waste – passes to decomposers
> ▶ is uneaten – passes to decomposers

The diagram shows the efficiency of energy flow through an ecosystem.

When pyramids of numbers are a different shape

Pyramids of numbers may not always show the shape you expect. For example, look at the pyramid of numbers for an oak woodland.

Because oak trees are so large, each one has many small herbivores feeding on it. There may be thousands of caterpillars on every oak tree in this ecosystem. Using a **pyramid of biomass** instead shows the situation more clearly.

This diagram shows the biomass of all the organisms in an ecosystem. Biomass is the total mass of the living organisms. Obviously each oak tree has a much larger biomass than each herbivore (e.g. a caterpillar!), so the pyramid of biomass for this ecosystem has a normal pyramid shape.

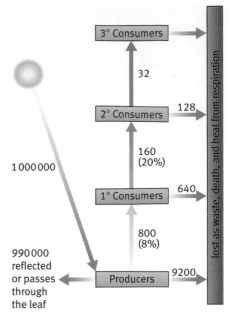

Energy flows through an ecosystem.

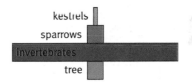

Oak woodland pyramid of numbers

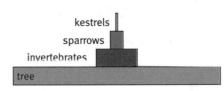

Oak woodland pyramid of biomass

Questions

1 Ecosystems contain different trophic levels. Look at the food web on page 87. Identify two

  a producers   **b** primary consumers (herbivores)

  c secondary consumers   **d** tertiary consumers

2 Explain why the energy in a producer will not all be transferred to a carnivore in the same food chain.

3 Calculate the percentage efficiency of energy transfer between the secondary and tertiary consumers in the ecosystem above (shown in the diagram at the top of page).

4 Explain why a pyramid of biomass may give a more accurate picture of an ecosystem than a pyramid of numbers.

Key words

producers
decomposers
pyramid of numbers
trophic levels
consumers
pyramid of biomass

Canada geese migrate to the UK in winter and leave in the spring.

When pyramids of biomass are a different shape

Untangling a food web is a complicated business. Not all pyramids of biomass will be the same shape. For example, some organisms are only in the ecosystem for part of the year. They may be missing when the measurements are taken.

Other organisms in an ecosystem may be eaten almost as fast as they are reproducing. Any pyramid records only a 'snapshot' of the ecosystem at the time when the measurements are taken. If the measurements were taken over a longer period of time, the results could be very different. For example, look at the pyramid for an ocean ecosystem.

This pyramid shows that at the time these measurements were made there was less phytoplankton producer biomass than the zooplankton feeding on them. Common sense tells you that this could not work, but the pyramid was correct when the measurements were taken. Phytoplankton have a much faster reproduction rate than zooplankton. Over a year the total biomass of phytoplankton in this ecosystem will be greater than the biomass of the zooplankton feeding on them.

Pyramids of biomass also have other limitations. For example, living things contain different amounts of water. Biomass can only be compared fairly if the material is dried first.

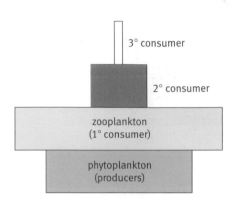

Ocean pyramid of biomass

Our impact on ecosystems

At the moment humans are using about 10–20% of the biomass produced on land. Some is used for food and the rest as a source of animal feed, fuels, and raw materials for building. Tropical swamps and rainforests produce more biomass than any other natural ecosystems. Their removal limits the biomass left for other animals. You can read more about the impact of deforestation and habitat change on page 86.

Underground in an ecosystem

The Earth's total biomass is difficult to measure. A lot of it is under water or in the soil. Soil can take thousands of years to form, which makes it virtually non-renewable, so soil conservation is crucial. If vegetation is cleared from an area, the soil is no longer held in place by the plants' roots. Rain and winds can wash and blow the soil away.

Soil has four main components:

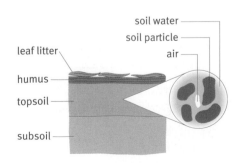

Components of soil

- inorganic particles of sand, silt, and clay
- air
- water (with dissolved mineral ions)
- biomass (living organisms and decaying material)

The air and water in soil are essential for life underground. Air provides oxygen for aerobic microorganisms. Water is held within soil by the small inorganic particles of sand, silt, and clay. Organic material in the soil also has a very important role in holding water in the soil. Some of the minerals forming inorganic particles in soils are soluble. These gradually dissolve in the soil water, providing mineral ions which are taken up by plant roots.

Most of the soil's biomass is not as obvious as this earthworm. A fertile soil contains plenty of decaying plant materials and a huge variety of microorganisms.

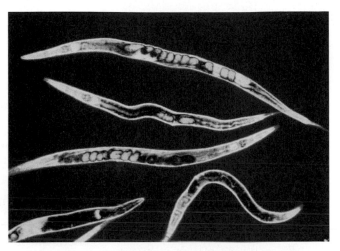

The films of water around soil particles are home to these microscopic worms and the bacteria they feed on. (× 120)

Underground biomass

Soil has two sorts of biomass – living organisms and decaying material. A fertile soil is packed with living roots, invertebrates, fungi, and bacteria. There can be a billion bacteria in one gram of soil, forming the bulk of its biomass.

The biomass in decaying material is attacked by a huge range of bacteria and is unable to resist this onslaught. Between them the different species of bacteria have enzymes for a wide range of possible chemical reactions. These convert the decaying biomass into inorganic raw materials, such as carbon dioxide and nitrate ions, which plants can recycle.

Soil microbes	Approximate number per gram of soil
bacteria	1 000 000 000
fungi	1 000 000
nematodes	500 000
flatworms	100 000
insects	5000

Questions

5 Explain why the pyramid of biomass for the ocean ecosystem is not a typical pyramid shape.

6 Describe the different components of soil.

7 a Explain why it is more sensible to compare dry mass than wet mass of biomass in an ecosystem.

b Why do you think it is not always possible to use dry mass when measuring biomass?

Life in the soil

A single gram of soil contains millions of microorganisms. These bacteria and fungi play a vital role in plant growth. Lucy Gilliam is using genetic techniques to investigate the biodiversity of soil. She also investigates the importance of microorganisms in soil to the rest of the ecosystem.

Lucy works as a microbial ecologist at Rothamsted Research. Rothamsted is the largest agricultural research centre in the UK. She is part of a team looking at the different types of bacteria and fungi in soil. 'People think it's just dirt,' says Lucy, 'but we've got a great diversity of life under our feet and it's very important to understand how the soil ecosystem works.'

Soil bacteria improve the soil

Microbes improve the condition of soil. They provide essential nutrients to plants, and even help break down pollutants like oil or petrol. Some bacteria and fungi in the soil cause plant diseases but others help plants to resist disease. Soil bacteria are also very important for recycling of chemicals in the ecosystem. For example, soil bacteria have an essential role in the carbon and nitrogen cycles.

We need to learn more about the different microorganisms in soil. Scientists believe that a wide diversity of microorganisms is important to maintaining the health of the soil. They think that soils with a wide diversity of bacteria are more productive and have greater resistance to stresses such as pollution or flooding. Human activities, such as intensive agriculture, tend to reduce the biodiversity of the soil.

Lucy Gilliam at work in the lab

Even the smallest speck of soil contains tens of thousands of different species of bacteria. Most of them are only visible under a powerful electron microscope. Lucy studies the area of soil surrounding the roots of the plants. This is called the rhizosphere.

Around the roots

A recent experiment involved analysing the diversity of bacteria surrounding the roots of potato plants. Lucy took samples of the soil from the rhizosphere and extracted the genetic material. She analysed this DNA to identify different species of microorganisms. These data showed that growing different varieties of potato plant affects the amounts and types of bacteria in the soil.

'We are discovering new species of microbes in soils all the time and we really don't understand what they're doing there,' explains Lucy. 'We've only just got the tools to tap into this diversity of bacteria to figure out how it works.'

Lucy enjoys the fact that there is more to learn. 'It's really exciting work. I love trying to discover something that no one has ever known before.'

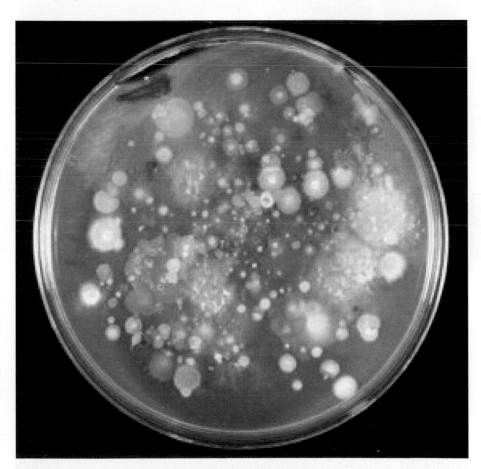

Different species of soil bacteria growing on an agar plate

Topic 2 Further up the food chain

Most species of living thing cannot produce their own food. They must eat other organisms for nutrients and energy. These organisms are called **heterotrophs,** and they have evolved a variety of feeding relationships.

Clown fish and giant anemone.

Living in harmony

The clown fish and anemone have a close relationship, based on food and survival. The clown fish sleeps, eats, and lays its eggs between the tentacles of the giant anemone. The fish is covered in a slime which protects it from the anemone's poisonous tentacles.

Living in the tentacles protects the fish from predators. It darts out quickly to catch other fish, which it eats back in the safety of the tentacles. Bits of this food fall into the tentacles, providing a meal for the anemone. When both organisms benefit from a relationship it is called **mutualism**.

Parasites

Not all relationships are as pleasant as mutualism. Some organisms feed off others without offering anything in return. They are **parasites**, for example, insects that feed on plant sap or blood, or worms that grow inside plant roots or inside our guts. These parasites may cause disease, or threaten people's lives by destroying the crops and animals they rely on for food. A lot of scientific ingenuity is devoted to fighting organisms that cause disease.

A parasite cannot survive without its host. Over millions of years the host has gradually evolved. The parasite's own evolution must have been closely linked to that of its host, so it could survive these changes in its environment.

Key words

heterotrophs
mutualism
parasites

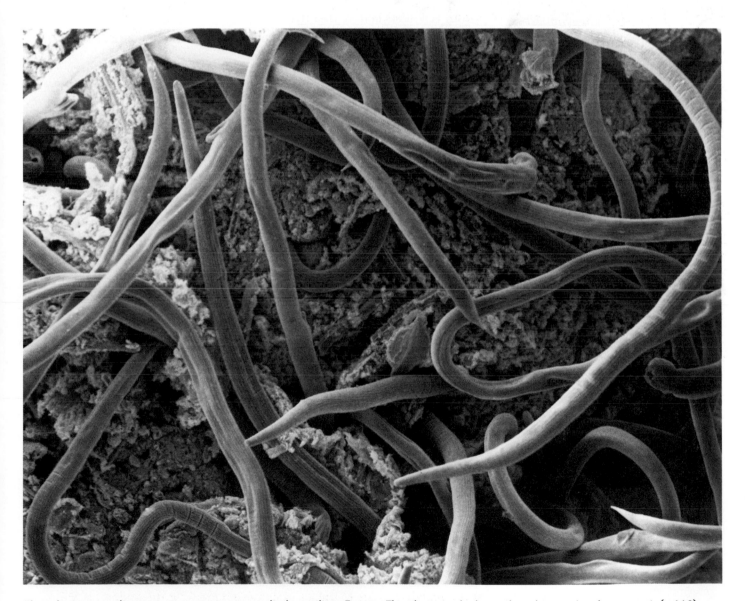

Threadworms are the most common worm parasite in northern Europe. The photograph shows threadworms in a human gut. (× 110)

Find out about:

▶ examples of symbiosis and commensalism

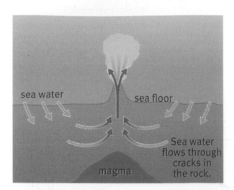

A hydrothermal vent. The average water temperature is 12 °C, but superheated water can gush out at 400 °C. Away from the vent the temperature drops to 2 °C.

2A Living together

Heterotrophs all rely on getting ready-made organic compounds to provide their food. But they have several different ways of doing this.

Dotted along the mid-ocean ridges are hydrothermal vents. Superheated water from the vents flows out into the ocean. Clustered around each vent are colonies of tube worms. They do not have mouths or guts – but closer investigation explains why these aren't needed.

Inside the worms are species of autotrophic bacteria. The bacteria convert carbon dioxide to glucose, using chemical energy instead of light. The worms have specialized blood which transports sulfide as well as oxygen. The worm's blood system transports sulfide to the bacteria, which use it to release energy.

Some scientists believe that hydrothermal vents are where life first originated on Earth. You can read more about this on page 80.

Mutual benefits

The conditions around a vent are harsh and unforgiving. The vent water is rich in minerals which the bacteria need, but the surrounding ocean contains very few nutrients. The flow of water from the vents shifts from moment to moment, so the tube worms provide an ideal environment for the bacteria.

Tube worms and the bacteria within them live in mutualism. The bacteria get a supply of sulfide and warmth. The worms get organic food molecules produced by the bacteria. The relationship benefits both organisms.

Tube worms are about 2 m in length. The total biomass of worms and bacteria in this ecosystem is 10 kg per m².

Mutualism is a common arrangement, for example:

- Sponges, sea anemones, and clams all have a close association with algae. The algal cells provide extra food in return for protection from herbivores.

The clam looks green because the soft lining of the shell's edges is full of algae.

- Leguminous plants have nitrogen-fixing bacteria in their root cells. The bacteria supply the plant with nitrates in return for the low-oxygen environment which they require, and sugar from plant photosynthesis.

The root nodules contain nitrogen-fixing bacteria.

One-sided relationships

Some species take advantage of others and give nothing in return. For example, sticky seed pods may cling to your clothes until you brush them off. This might be annoying, but there's no harm done, and the seeds catch a ride to a potential new home. This is an example of **commensalism**. Only one species benefits from the relationship, but the other is unharmed.

Key words

commensalism

- Cows have cellulose-digesting bacteria in their gut. The bacteria digest cellulose in plant material eaten by the cows. This releases glucose which the cow can absorb from their gut. In return the bacteria have a constant supply of plant material and a warm environment.

Bacteria help these cows digest the cellulose in the grass.

Organisms do not have to live as one to be mutualistic. For example, some mutualistic species will swim into the mouth of a particular species of larger fish. The smaller animal clears the fish's mouth of parasites, which in return gives them a meal in return.

The red cod is a carnivore but it will not eat this shrimp.

Questions

1 Tube worms do not 'eat' in the way many other animal species do. Why are they classified as heterotrophs?

2 Explain the difference between mutualism and commensalism. Give one example of each relationship in your answer.

Dr Ben Heath of Bath University

Sex, reproduction, and parasites

'Sex and reproduction are usually thought of as being linked together, but to a biologist they are entirely separate and in one sense almost the reverse of each other,' explains Dr Ben Heath, a research scientist at Bath University.

'If you think about it, sexual reproduction is actually very inefficient. One female reproducing asexually can produce just as many offspring as a male and female reproducing sexually.'

So, why isn't the world filled with asexual organisms?

'Many ideas have been put forward by different scientists to explain why sexual reproduction happens in so many species. These ideas fall into two main categories:

▶ Sex helps to remove "bad genes" from a population.
▶ Sex helps to spread "good genes" through a population.'

Removing 'bad genes'

'In an asexual population all offspring are exact copies of their parents, so any "bad genes" or mistakes in the DNA of parents will be added to the mistakes of all previous generations and passed on. Eventually these mistakes can build up to a lethal level. This is a bit like making photocopies of photocopies and so on – the quality of the reproduction gets worse each time, and eventually you can't recognize the original document.'

Sexual reproduction mixes genes from two parents. This means that there is variation between the individuals in the population – they're not all the same, as they are in asexual reproduction. Individuals with harmful genes are less likely to survive, so these genes are less likely to be passed on to the next generation.

'Natural selection weeds out harmful genes so the population is better able to survive. In this way it is thought that over millions of years asexual populations have died out leaving the sexual ones we see all around us today.'

Spreading 'good genes'

'In addition to removing "bad genes", sex can also promote the spread of "good genes" and allow populations to adapt to their environment more rapidly. In a changing environment it can greatly increase the chance of having at least one offspring who is well adapted to the prevailing conditions. It's a bit like increasing your chances of winning a lottery by buying lots of tickets. If you're asexual you could still buy lots of tickets but they'd all have the same number, which wouldn't improve your chances of winning, now would it?'

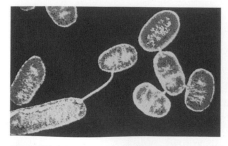

Plasmids normally move between bacteria in a primitive version of sex called conjugation. This is how antibiotic resistance genes can spread so quickly through a bacterial population.

Repelling parasites

Ben is interested in a third idea about the benefits of sexual reproduction. Some scientists think sex can help the fight against by parasites.

'The environment that an organism lives in and adapts to over many generations is also made up of other living things. These include many parasites that are constantly evolving new ways of overcoming their hosts' defences.

'These defences, which include the immune system in higher animals, must constantly change (like changing your password or the combination lock of a safe) in order to keep parasites out and minimize the harm they do.

'In this way every living organism is in a perpetual race against parasites. But it is a race they cannot win. The only way to survive is to keep "running" because their defences are constantly being overcome. Continually trying out new combinations of genes over the generations and throughout the centuries and millennia is the only way to stay one step ahead of the parasites.'

Ben's own research is on *Wolbachia*, which is a bacterial parasite that lives inside the cells of an estimated 76% of all insects, as well as some other important animal groups.

'*Wolbachia* is fascinating to evolutionary biologists, because it can hijack the reproductive system of its host in order to further its own transmission. In addition to shedding light on some fascinating areas of basic reproductive biology, there is currently great interest in using *Wolbachia* as a new way of combating important tropical diseases including malaria which affects 500 million people every year and kills a person every 15 seconds. Any approach that impacts on the transmission of malaria could potentially improve the lives of millions of the world's poorest people.'

A male fruit fly (actual length 3.5 mm)

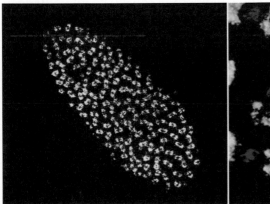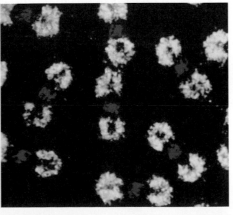

The micrographs show an early fruit fly embryo infected with *Wolbachia* bacteria. Nuclear DNA is stained red, and the *Wolbachia* are visible as yellow/green dots. The *Wolbachia* position themselves either side of the dividing DNA which ensures they get into both daughter cells during development. The entire embryo (left) is approximately 1 mm long. The right image shows an area 100 μm (0.1 mm) across.

Find out about:

▸ parasites and what makes them successful

2B Tapeworms and other parasites

Life on Earth exists on land, in water, and also in or on other living things. Every plant and animal on Earth is home to other organisms. Many of these organisms are parasites. Parasites are not good company. They benefit from the relationship, but cause harm to their host.

Human parasites

Parasites have several ways of getting in or onto the human body. They can be transferred

- ▸ by food or water
- ▸ through the nose, mouth, anus, and genital and urinary tracts
- ▸ by insect bites
- ▸ by burrowing under the skin

Most parasites are small and hidden, so it is hard to know they are there until symptoms start to appear. Some parasites can establish chronic infections which last for the host's entire lifetime.

Tapeworms

Mites living on human eyelashes. (× 170)

Even a healthy human body houses an amazing number of other species – at least 200. Your own body cells are outnumbered by cells of other species by about 10:1.

Fortunately most of your residents are not parasites. The majority are bacterial cells which live in your large intestines and usually do not cause you any harm. If all the bacteria in your body could be gathered together, they would just squeeze into an empty drink can.

Perhaps the most gruesome human parasites are **tapeworms**. These live in the human gut and can be up to 9 metres long. In humans the adult tapeworm itself stays in the gut, which is the hollow tube running through the body from mouth to anus. The tapeworm competes with the **host** for digested food. The tapeworm does not enter the host's body tissues, so symptoms are usually just a mild stomach ache. However, in some cases the tapeworm larvae may move within the body to the brain and eyes, and cause very serious damage.

Parasites have specific features which enable them to survive in or on their host. Tapeworms have a number of adaptations:

- ▸ Their heads have suckers and stickers to grip the gut wall.
- ▸ They are protected from digestion by a thick, enzyme-resistant cuticle.
- ▸ They use anaerobic respiration so they can survive without oxygen.
- ▸ Each tapeworm has male and female sex organs so it can reproduce without a mate.
- ▸ They produce very large numbers of eggs (a cow tapeworm produces approximately 600 million eggs each year). This increases the chance that some will survive to find a new host.

The most sophisticated adaptation of a tapeworm is its life cycle. This helps the tapeworm to infect new hosts. Human tapeworms use a second host (pigs, cows, or fish) to transfer them to new human hosts. When the eggs are eaten by this second host they hatch into larvae. The tapeworm larvae tunnel into the herbivore's blood and migrate to the muscle tissue. They form a cyst and wait. They will only become adult tapeworms if humans eat them in undercooked meat. Stomach acid then releases the larvae from the cyst.

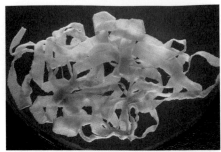

Human tapeworms like this one may be 2 m to 7 m in length.

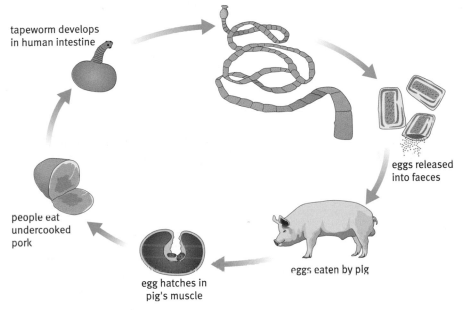

tapeworm develops in human intestine

eggs released into faeces

people eat undercooked pork

egg hatches in pig's muscle

eggs eaten by pig

DNA evidence shows that tapeworms evolved alongside humans. As our ancestors changed their way of life the tapeworm adapted to use different herbivores to transmit their larvae.

This may seem a complicated lifecycle, but it is a very effective way for the tapeworm to spread from human to human. Humans are much more likely to eat infected meat than faeces. If human food is contaminated by infected faeces the lifecycle is short-circuited. The tapeworm larvae find their way to the person's muscles and brain. They form cysts which can be life threatening.

Parasitic worms

Parasites are an important cause of human disease. They also have an indirect effect on humans by damaging food production.

- A quarter of the world's human population carry some sort of parasitic worm. The worms feed on nutrients from a person's gut, causing malnutrition and other illnesses.
- Other worm species cause damage indirectly by limiting human food supplies. They cause illness in farm animals and also attack crop plants, blocking water and mineral uptake. This causes stunted growth, which reduces crop yields.

Key words

tapeworms
host

Questions

1 Write a short definition of a parasite relationship.

2 Describe how three features of a tapeworm enable it to survive as a parasite.

3 Explain how parasites cause damage to humans

   a directly

   b indirectly

4 Scientists believe that the evolution of a parasite and its host are closely linked. Use the example of a tapeworm to suggest evidence for this view.

Find out about:

▶ malaria
▶ the relationship between malaria and sickle-cell anaemia

The parasite that causes malaria is transferred into human blood with a drop of saliva when a female *Anopheles* mosquito bites the skin.

2c Parasites that cause disease

Malaria

The disease **malaria** is a major cause of ill health and death in countries where it thrives. Malaria is caused by a **protozoan**. This protozoan parasite is a single-celled animal. Blood-sucking mosquitoes carry this protozoan from host to host. As many as 300–500 million people worldwide are infected with this protozoan, and malaria kills more than two million people every year. The protozoan also relies on a complicated life cycle to survive.

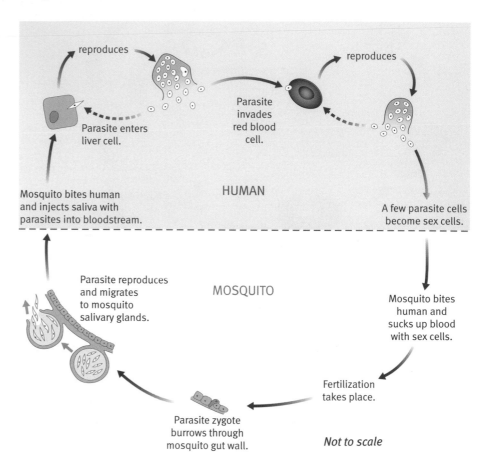

reproduces

reproduces

Parasite enters liver cell.

Parasite invades red blood cell.

Mosquito bites human and injects saliva with parasites into bloodstream.

HUMAN

A few parasite cells become sex cells.

Parasite reproduces and migrates to mosquito salivary glands.

MOSQUITO

Mosquito bites human and sucks up blood with sex cells.

Fertilization takes place.

Parasite zygote burrows through mosquito gut wall.

Not to scale

In the human body the parasites which cause malaria spend most time inside red blood cells, feeding on haemoglobin.

The malaria parasite's life cycle protects it from our immune system. The parasites have different markers on their cells at every stage of the life cycle. This makes it difficult for white blood cells to identify and attack them. The parasites also spend most of their time feeding inside our red blood cells. When one red blood cell is used up the parasites burst out and infect new cells. Toxins are released from the used-up cells, and these cause a very dangerous fever. You can read more about the human immune system in Module B2 *Keeping healthy*.

Key words

malaria
protozoan
sickle-cell anaemia
haemoglobin

Questions

1 Explain how the parasite that causes malaria is adapted to survive.

Sickle-cell anaemia

Sickle-cell anaemia is a genetic disorder. It is caused by a faulty allele of the gene which codes for the **haemoglobin**. Haemoglobin is the protein that carries oxygen molecules in red blood cells.

Sickle-cell haemoglobin proteins have a different shape from normal haemoglobin. When faulty haemoglobin gives up oxygen to body cells, the shape of the haemoglobin molecule changes. The haemoglobin molecules form long rods which stretch red blood cells into a rigid 'sickle' shape. These rigid red blood cells get stuck in small blood vessels, causing acute pain and extreme tiredness. This is called 'sickling'. Body cells don't get the oxygen they need, and over time this damages tissues and organs. 'Sickling' also damages red blood cells. The spleen removes damaged cells, but these cannot be replaced fast enough. Sickle-cell sufferers get severe **anaemia**.

How is sickle-cell anaemia inherited?

The sickle-cell allele is recessive. A person must inherit the allele from both parents to have the disease. A person with one sickle-cell allele and one normal allele is a carrier of sickle-cell anaemia. The diagram shows how two carriers of sickle-cell anaemia can pass the alleles on to their children.

Sickle-cell anaemia and malaria

The sickle-cell allele occurs occasionally as a random mutation. Without proper management of the disease many sufferers would die young. So you might expect that the sickle-cell allele would not occur very often – it would have a low frequency in the population.

But people in parts of Africa have known for hundreds of years that sickle-cell anaemia is more common in areas where malaria is common – there is a correlation. However, the explanation for this observation is still uncertain. What is known is that carriers of the sickle-cell allele have a much higher resistance to malaria than people who have two normal haemoglobin alleles. Their condition is known as sickle-cell trait. In regions where malaria is common they have a greater chance of survival than non-carriers. They are more likely to survive and have children, passing on their genes, including the sickle-cell allele. Where malaria is common, natural selection favours people with sickle-cell trait. So the frequency of the sickle-cell allele is higher in these areas.

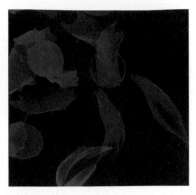

Red blood cells with normal haemoglobin

Red blood cells with sickle-cell haemoglobin

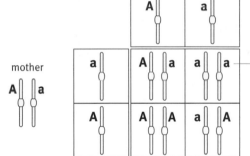

Key
A = normal allele
a = sickle-cell allele

father

mother

children who inherit two recessive genes will have sickle-cell anaemia

Children of two sickle-cell carriers each have a 25% chance of having the disease.

Questions

2 Describe the symptoms of sickle-cell anaemia.

3 Explain why the sickle-cell allele has a higher frequency in certain populations.

4 Scientists are not certain how sickle-cell trait gives protection against malaria. Find out how this may work.

Biology in action

Emily and Dr Chaud

Sickle-cell anaemia

Dr Meera Chaud first met Emily in the accident and emergency (A & E) department at Whittington Hospital, London. Emily was in great pain with a **sickle-cell crisis**. She was also pregnant at the time, so Meera had to identify a drug that would help the pain, and be safe for the baby. Today Emily has come with her new baby, Akila, for a follow-up visit to the **haematology** clinic. This clinic helps patients with diseases of the blood system.

What are the symptoms?

Meera explains the symptoms of sickle-cell anaemia: 'Usually patients go to their doctor because they are in severe pain. Normal red blood cells are nice and round and flexible, so they can squeeze through capillaries quite easily. But sickle-shaped red blood cells don't bend. The cells stack together and block the capillaries. Blood cannot pass through the capillary, and the tissues behind the blockage are deprived of oxygen. The tissue has to use anaerobic respiration, which causes the pain. This is a sickle-cell crisis.' (You can read more about anaerobic respiration on pages 240–241.)

Sickle-cell anaemia may cause very serious problems. It can be particularly dangerous if a blockage happens in capillaries of the lungs. This stops blood from the body getting to the lungs to collect fresh oxygen. The whole body becomes deprived of oxygen, and the patient needs intensive care.

Emily with her partner Wayne and baby Akila. Wayne has no sickle-cell alleles; Emily has two sickle-cell alleles. Akila has inherited one sickle-cell allele and one normal allele. She has sickle-cell trait.

Unfortunately at the moment there is no cure for sickle-cell anaemia. Meera describes some of the work she does with patients. 'It's all about managing the symptoms so people can have the best quality of life. A lot of it is about making sure they know how to reduce the chance of a crisis. The important things are to avoid dehydration and strenuous exercise – but gentle exercise is fine. There's quite a static population of sickle-cell families in this part of London, so usually it's a lifelong relationship between the clinic and the patient. I think it's great, a joint achievement between the doctor and the patient. It's wonderful to see Emily so well today with her new baby.'

Emily's story

Emily is twenty-two years old. She was born in Uganda, and moved to London when she was eight.

'My mum found out that I had sickle-cell disease when I was six months old. I was diagnosed back home in Uganda. I wasn't able to crawl and my feet, legs, and arms swelled up and I didn't want to be cuddled. She went to the hospital and was told I had sickle cell.

'I was in and out of hospital a lot and missed a lot of school. My symptoms included stress, dehydration, exhaustion, and when my haemoglobin dropped really low I'd have to go into hospital. In Uganda I was treated with a saline drip and pain relief. Sometimes I was in hospital for months. Since arriving in the UK I've been in intensive care twice and had pneumonia.

'I've had to deal with so much pain that my threshold is quite high. This means that I can walk into A & E in severe pain, but not always show it. Once a doctor didn't believe I was in pain, as I was joking with my Mum to take my mind off the pain! Usually, though, I can discuss with the doctor how much pain relief I use.

'Little things spark it off. When I was younger I could never go swimming, and it turned out to be the chlorine in the water that was triggering my symptoms. I conquered that by going with my brother during the summer for me to get my body used to the smell of the chlorine. I try to find ways of managing my pain and ways of coping with the problems.'

'Both my parents have sickle-cell trait and so does one of my brothers, but the rest are fine. I've always known if I had a baby, they would inherit a sickle-cell allele from me. When I met Wayne, it's the first thing I told him, that I had sickle cell. It's important that he knows. It's hard and emotional as it doesn't just affect me, it affects the people close around me. Wayne was tested and we knew he was fine. Akila does not have sickle-cell disease, he has sickle-cell trait. When he grows up and knocks a girl off her feet, she'll have to be tested. But I enjoy life and I feel the future holds promise. I'm fine, I have baby Akila and couldn't ask for anything more.'

Becoming a doctor – Meera's story

'Well, I started by doing GCSE biology, but I didn't decide on medicine until I did my A levels. I did my first degree in Cambridge and then came to London for the clinical training you need to do as part of your course. After that I became a house officer – that's the junior doctor who runs around doing all the menial jobs. It's a steep learning curve, but it's also a very sociable and fun job.

'Now I've started medical rotation, where I work around the medical departments (the hospital departments that don't do operations or surgery). At the moment I'm in the haematology department, but to start with I worked in A & E, which is where I met Emily.

'If I pass what feels like a few thousand exams, I hope to be a registrar in about three years' time. By then I'll be twenty-eight. I would like to be a consultant in my thirties.'

Topic 3

New technologies

Living things make complex molecules far more efficiently than they can be made in a lab. For thousands of years people have harnessed microorganisms to make products such as drinks, bread, yogurt, and cheese. Microorganisms are added to the food and kept in the right conditions. As they grow, their by-products create the desired product. For example, yeast produces alcohol in beer-making. Some microorganisms also make non-food products, for example, natural antibiotics.

Fermenting beer

Making new products

The microorganisms used for these processes are carefully chosen from natural organisms. But it is now possible to alter the genes of a microorganism so that it produces an altered product, or even a completely new product. This is **genetic modification**. Genetically modified organisms include bacteria that make drugs and hormones for human use, and crops which have better resistance to disease.

Looking at genes

Genetic tests can give people information about the genes they carry. You read about some uses of genetic tests in Module B1 *You and your genes*. Genetic tests can also help to match a suspect to the scene of a crime, or show whether two people are related to each other. Many new applications of **DNA technology** are being developed.

The bacteria growing in this tank have been genetically modified to make a protein for use in drug manufacture.

Analysis of a person's DNA can provide useful information.

Key words

genetic modification
DNA technology

41

Find out about:

▶ how microorganisms can be grown to produce useful chemicals

3A Living factories

Bacteria and fungi make many useful organic chemicals very efficiently.

Microorganisms show amazing variety. The different species have a great variety of microbial enzymes at their disposal. Many of the proteins they make are difficult to produce in the laboratory. In biotechnology, microbial enzymes are harnessed on a huge scale. Scientists look for the correct species of microorganism and ensure that they have optimum conditions for growth.

Antibiotics

On pages 50–51 you learnt about the use of antibiotics to treat certain infections. Antibiotics are produced naturally by microorganisms. For example, the fungus *Penicillium* produces the antibiotic penicillin.

In optimum conditions *Penicillium* can double its mass every six hours. When the fungus grows in a tank of nutrient solution, the antibiotic is secreted into the solution. It is then a simple task to extract the antibiotic.

Microorganisms are usually grown in batches using huge industrial tanks called **fermenters**. The main difficulty is keeping the conditions inside the fermenter right for the microorganism. Fast-growing microorganisms take in a lot of oxygen and nutrients, and produce waste products and heat. The solution inside the fermenter must be carefully monitored and controlled.

Harvesting enzymes

Microbial enzymes are very important in food production. They are used to control the flavour, aroma, texture, and rate of production for many food products. **Rennin** is one example of an enzyme used in food production. It is a very important enzyme in cheesemaking.

Rennin is made in the stomachs of all young mammals. It causes the milk they feed on to lump together. This slows the food down as it passes through the gut, giving more time for enzymes to digest the food and for useful molecules to be absorbed.

Originally rennin for cheesemaking was taken from calf stomachs, but these are in short supply. Now most rennin comes from industrially grown fungi. Cheese made using rennin from fungi is labelled 'vegetarian cheese'.

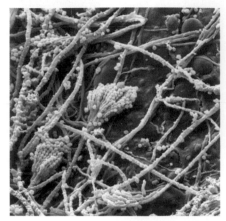

A photograph of *Penicillium*. You can see a photograph of a colony of this fungus on page 50. It produces penicillin and secretes it outside its cells.

Early stages of cheese production – churn milk.

Rennin causes the milk to form into solid lumps – the start of cheese.

Growing microorganisms for food

Microbial cells contain the same building blocks as cells from other organisms – carbohydrates, fats, and proteins. Bacterial proteins are similar to those in fish. Protein in yeast, a fungus, is similar to soya protein. Eating some microorganisms can provide a useful source of protein. Microbial cells are also low in fat and high in fibre from their cell walls. These nutrients add to their value as a food source. Microorganisms can be grown from simple starting nutrients, and they reproduce rapidly. Microbial biomass grown for food is called **single-cell protein (SCP)**.

Surprisingly, the technology for producing SCP was not developed by food companies. It was developed by oil companies. They wanted to use low value fuels as food for microorganisms, and make a more valuable product – SCP. The process works, but it has not been a commercial success. Oil prices have risen, and other protein sources, such as soya, have become cheaper.

Several types of SCP are used in animal feed, but only one type has been cleared for human consumption. Quorn is made from a fungus. The fungus isn't really a single cell. It grows as a cluster of interwoven fungal **hyphae**. When these are pressed together, the fungus looks like pastry. It is treated to match the taste and texture of meat and sold as mince and pieces for cooking. It is also made into convenience foods such as burgers and sausages, and used in ready-made meals.

Not all microorganisms can be eaten. Eating just a small amount of this fungus would be fatal.

Key words

fermenter
rennin
single-cell protein (SCP)
hyphae

Quorn provides a high-protein food grown by microbial cells.

Questions

1 Name three types of product which can be produced by the fermentation of microorganisms. Give one example of each.

2 Produce a flow chart to explain the main steps in the fermentation of microorganisms to produce antibiotics.

3 Why is it important to control the conditions inside a fermenter?

4 Why do microorganisms produce antibiotics naturally?

Pharmacogenetics – a look into the future

'In five to ten years' time a visit to your GP could routinely involve a genetic test before you are given a prescription,' says Dr Alice Rebeck, a scientist working in pharmacogenetics for GlaxoSmithKline (GSK). This is already happening for some medicines. Pharmacogenetics is the study of how people's responses to medicines vary due to differences in their genes. By understanding these differences, we will in the future be better able to predict how people will respond to a particular medicine.

Why do people respond differently to medicines?

People with the same disease will not all respond to the same medicine in the same way. For example, imagine four patients suffering from an illness such as asthma. Each patient has similar symptoms. They are all prescribed the same medicine at the exact same dosage, but they respond differently:

Large amounts of data are collected from clinical trials. Alice reviews and analyses this data and talks to other research scientists and physicians about how they can put the data to good use. Their aim is to develop safer and more effective medicines to meet the needs of patients.

◗ The first person recovers from the illness.
◗ The second does not notice any improvement in how they feel.
◗ The third person recovers, but develops an adverse reaction to the medicine – an itchy rash.
◗ The fourth person only feels better after another visit to their GP, who increases the dosage of the medicine.

It is possible that these different outcomes for each patient are the result of differences in their genes. On pages 142–3 you read about the relationship between genes and proteins. Genes are the coded instructions for the production of proteins in a cell. Each gene is the code for a different protein. If two people have different versions of a gene (called alleles) they may not make exactly the same protein. For example, if a gene codes for a specific enzyme, differences in this gene between people could result in differences in this enzyme.

◗ Some people may not produce it at all.
◗ Others may produce it, but in different amounts.
◗ Others may make a non-working form of the enzyme.

These differences in the structure or amount of a protein may change the way a particular medicine works in the body.

Clinical trials

Like all pharmaceutical companies, GSK conducts clinical trials to investigate how safe and effective new medicines are. (You can read more about clinical trials on page 53.) During the trial, blood samples are taken from each participant and different measurements are made to monitor their response to the new medicine. This sometimes includes extracting DNA from the blood samples to look at variation in the participants' genes. Scientists investigate whether these genetic variations are associated with different responses to the new medicine. This is **pharmacogenetics**.

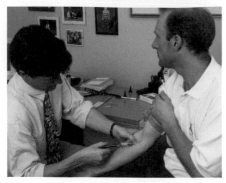

A clinical trial.

Alice describes a recent example. 'We tested a new medicine being developed to treat obesity in the US. At first there didn't seem to be any difference in weight loss between those taking the new medicine and the control group taking the placebo. However, some of the patients receiving the new medicine did show a significant weight loss. We looked at genes that are related to the way this new medicine was thought to work in the body. We were able to show that most of the patients who achieved weight loss had a version of a gene that was different from patients who did not lose weight. This data suggested that we could use pharmacogenetics to predict which patients would obtain the most benefit from taking this new medicine.'

GSK has had similar results with another new medicine under investigation for treating Alzheimer's disease. Alzheimer's is a form of dementia which can affect older people. People with the disease gradually become very forgetful, making everyday tasks very difficult. They may not recognize familiar faces, and have problems speaking, understanding, reading, or writing. A new medicine was tested on patients with Alzheimer's. Unfortunately these patients did not improve.

Could pharmacogenetics help? Scientists working on this new medicine knew that a gene called APOE is associated with Alzheimer's disease. People with different versions of the APOE gene have a different level of risk of developing Alzheimer's. Scientists looked at the APOE gene of the patients on the early clinical trials. Patients with particular versions of the APOE gene did improve when they were given the new medicine. Clinical trials are now continuing to confirm these findings.

'Pharmacogenetic studies like this will enable new medicines to be targeted at those people who are most likely to benefit from a medicine. I really enjoy my work and feel privileged to be part of a team that can make a difference to patients' lives,' says Alice.

Find out about:

▶ genetic modification of bacteria

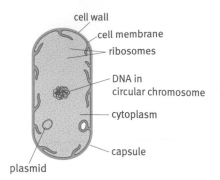

A typical bacterial cell

cell wall
cell membrane
ribosomes
DNA in circular chromosome
cytoplasm
capsule
plasmid

Plants are sprayed with chemicals to reduce disease and pest damage. The chemicals are expensive to make and can cause pollution.

GM varieties of crops could transform farming by cutting the use of chemical sprays.

3B Genetic modification

Bacterial cells make proteins

Bacterial cells are about one-tenth the length of typical animal cells. They have no nucleus, but they have one large circular chromosome in their cytoplasm. Most bacteria also have rings of DNA, which contain extra genes. These DNA rings are called **plasmids**.

Bacteria produce a wide variety of proteins. Some of these do similar jobs to proteins in human cells, e.g. proteins in cell membranes. However, they are not identical to the equivalent human protein. Bacteria don't make many proteins which human cells produce. How can we make bacteria produce a protein which they don't normally make? Any cell can only make a protein if it has the gene which codes for it. Scientists can add a human gene to bacterial cells so that they make the human protein.

Genetic modification

Changing the genes of an organism is called genetic modification. Bacterial cells can be modified by adding genes from other microorganisms, plants, or animals.

Many drugs used to treat diseases are proteins that can be made using these genetically modified (**GM**) bacteria. An example of such a drug is human insulin. Before genetic modification these proteins used to be extracted from animals. For example, pig insulin was given to people with diabetes. This worked, but there could be unwanted harmful effects. The insulin produced from GM bacteria does not cause these side effects.

Genetic modification of plants

Another use of genetic modification is to add new genes to plants. An estimated one-third of all crops are lost to pests, disease, and weeds. Plant diseases account for at least 10% of crops lost. Selective breeding has been used to produce crop plants which have more resistance to diseases. Genetic modification takes this one stage further. Plants can be given genes from other species, including genes from microorganisms. These genes often code for proteins that will protect the plant from common diseases.

Page 28 explains another type of genetic modification – gene therapy.

Putting new genes into cells

Getting new genes into the cells is the most difficult step of genetic modification. A **vector** is needed to carry the gene into the cell. To modify bacteria scientists make use of bacterial plasmids. Plasmids are easier to manipulate than a bacterial cell's main chromosome. They are small and are designed to move in and out of cells.

How can you tell which cells have been modified?

Not all the bacterial cells in a population will take up the modified plasmid. Scientists need a way of identifying which cells have been genetically modified. They do this by attaching a second gene to the plasmid. For example, this could be a gene from jellyfish which codes for a green fluorescent protein which is very easy to spot. Alternatively a gene for antibiotic resistance could be used. This gene can be used to separate out the GM bacteria from cells which have not taken up the plasmid:

> Make a modified plasmid that contains the human insulin gene and also a gene for antibiotic resistance.
> Add the modified plasmid to a bacteria population.
> Treat the population with the specific antibiotic.
> The bacteria which survive must contain the plasmid, so they will also make insulin.
> Grow these bacteria and harvest the insulin.

Large genes are too big to fit into a plasmid. Fortunately plasmids aren't the only things that can get through bacterial cells walls. Bacteria are infected by viruses called **bacteriophages**. Scientists use bacteriophages to carry larger genes into bacterial cells. This may sound odd, because viruses usually cause disease. However, the bacteriophages are disabled before they are used for genetic modification.

Vectors are also used to get new genes into plant cells. You can read more about this in the following Biology in action pages.

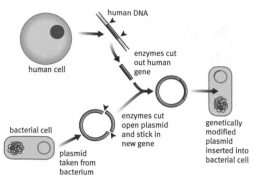

Plasmids are used as vectors in genetic modification of bacteria.

Key words

plasmids
GM
vector
bacteriophage

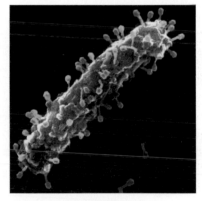

Bacteriophages attacking a bacterium (× 15 000)

Questions

1 Draw a labelled diagram of a bacterial cell.

2 Write a flow chart to explain the main stages in genetic modification of bacteria.

3 Give one example of genetic modification in

   a bacteria   b plants

4 Explain how vectors are used to transfer new genes into

   a bacterial cells   b plant cells

5 When the insulin gene is attached to a plasmid, a gene for antibiotic resistance may also be added. Explain why this second gene is needed.

Philippe Vain

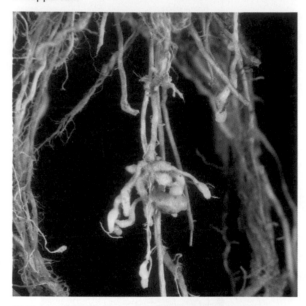

Philippe works on a species of root-knot nematode worm called *Meloidogyne* sp.

Designing for life

Philippe Vain is a plant biotechnologist at the John Innes Centre in Norwich. His team, along with researchers at the University of Leeds, has been designing genetically modified crops aimed at helping many of the world's poorest farmers. 'Our goal is to improve the pest resistance of key crops – rice, bananas, and potatoes – for developing countries,' says Philippe. 'In ten years' time there will still be more than half a billion people in the world without a reliable source of food. It is a much better strategy to give these people the means of food production instead of supplying food aid all the time.'

Nematode worms reduce crop yields

The target of his research is nematodes, microscopic worms that live in the soil. These worms attack the roots of crops, taking nutrients from the plant and laying their eggs inside the tissues. 'If you have a small infestation, you're going to get a reduced yield, a large infestation and you'll lose most of the crop.' For a poor farmer this can be a matter of life and death.

Farmers could kill the worms by spraying the crops using chemicals called nematicides, but these are expensive and highly toxic to humans and the environment. Instead, it was decided to develop a crop that was resistant to the pests.

Adding an extra gene

The plants already have genes for natural substances called cystatins. The cystatin genes are active in certain parts of the plant, for example, their seeds. Cystatins affect insect digestion, so insects cannot eat parts of the plant which contain them. Cystatins have no effect on humans. In fact we eat them all the time, in seeds from crops such as rice and maize.

When a particular gene is active in a cell we say that it is being expressed. This means that the protein which it codes for is being made in the cells. Philippe's team added another copy of the cystatin gene to the plants, which is expressed in the root cells.

Agrobacterium species cause cancer in plants. This plant is infected with *Agrobacterium tumifaciens*, which causes crown-gall disease.

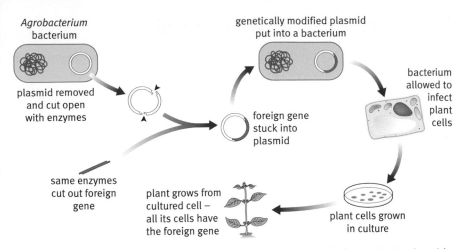

Agrobacterium bacterium

plasmid removed and cut open with enzymes

same enzymes cut out foreign gene

genetically modified plasmid put into a bacterium

foreign gene stuck into plasmid

bacterium allowed to infect plant cells

plant cells grown in culture

plant grows from cultured cell – all its cells have the foreign gene

Agrobacterium is used to transfer a gene into a plant's DNA. The bacterium's plasmid acts as the vector in this example of genetic modification.

This would make the roots indigestible to the nematodes. The researchers used the bacteria *Agrobacterium* as a vector to carry the extra gene into the plant's genetic material.

The only difference between the final genetically modified plant and the original is an extra copy of the cystatin gene. Nevertheless, by law, any genetically modified plant has to go through extensive testing and safety trials before it can be released into the environment.

The resulting plants show a high level of resistance to the nematode and are ready to be offered to farmers as part of a government aid project. Phillipe Vain: 'You want to make a contribution. It's very rare to have a crop improvement strategy that really works, so it's very exciting to see the outcome.

'For us, the best result will be people trying the crop and it making a difference to their lives.'

Much of Philippe's work is on banana plants and rice.

Find out about:

▶ concerns about GM plants

3C How risky are GM crops?

In the US a wide variety of genetically modified (GM) crops are grown and sold. Some of the genes which have been added to crops are for disease resistance, but other characteristics have also been modified. For example, tomatoes have been modified to grow larger and with a sweeter flavour to meet customer demands.

Opponents of GM crops are concerned about the possible effects that any genetically modified organism (GMO) could have. As a result of such concerns, European countries have stricter regulations controlling the release of GMOs.

Anyone who wishes to introduce a GMO into the UK environment must apply to Defra (the Department for Environment, Food and Rural Affairs). Each application is looked at by the Advisory Committee on Releases to the Environment (ACRE), an independent scientific expert committee. ACRE advises Defra on every GMO application. Very few GM crops are currently grown in the UK.

Why are some people concerned about GMOs?

GMOs are living things. They reproduce between themselves, and interbreed with non-GM organisms. It is impossible to predict with absolute certainty how GMOs will interact with other species. The potential risks of introducing GMOs into the ecosystem need to be balanced against the potential benefits.

The table outlines some of the arguments about GMOs:

Questions

1 A disease-resistance gene is added to a crop plant. What advantages could this bring for the

   a plant

   b farmer

   c environment

   d consumer?

2 What possible disadvantage could there be for each of these groups?

3 Give one argument which you agree with either for or against GM crops which is

   a social

   b environmental

   c economic

   d ethical

Arguments against the release of genetically modified organisms	Counter arguments
The added genes could make 'safe' plants produce toxins or allergens.	Food safety organizations can check for these.
Marker genes for antibiotic resistance could be taken up by disease organisms.	These antibiotics are not used in medicine, so it wouldn't matter.
Pesticides may 'leak' out of GM plant roots, and damage insects and microbes they were not designed to kill.	Insect-resistant plants reduce pesticide application so they benefit the environment.
GM crops may cause ecosystem changes that cannot be reversed.	Farmers may benefit from healthier crops and lower costs of production.
Multinationals will increase their domination of world markets.	Some GM technology has already been shared with developing nations.
Many consumers in EU countries refuse to buy GM products so farmers may lose markets.	Consumers in most countries are prepared to buy GM crops.
Poor farmers will not be able to afford the GM seeds.	Gene technology can develop more nutritious and higher-yielding plants that will benefit developing countries.

3D Genetic testing

Genetic tests are used to identify faulty alleles in adults, fetuses, and embryos. On pages 20–25 you found out about different views people may hold on genetic testing.

The first genetic tests were developed in the 1980s, and are now available for several genetic disorders, such as cystic fibrosis, haemophilia, and Huntington's disorder. More recently tests have been developed to provide information about a person's risk of developing certain **multifactorial** diseases. A multifactorial disease is caused by a number of factors. Genes may be part of the cause, but they are not the only reason the disease develops. Environmental factors also play a major part in determining whether a person develops the disease.

The technology behind genetic testing

Genetic tests use artificially made pieces of DNA called **gene probes**. A gene probe is a short piece of single-stranded DNA which has complementary bases to the allele being tested for. So the probe will stick to this allele. If the probe sticks to a person's DNA, then they have the disease allele. Scientists use two different techniques to find out whether the probe has stuck to a DNA sample:

- **UV** – a fluorescent molecule is attached to the gene probe when it is made. These molecules glow under ultraviolet (UV) light.
- **Autoradiography** – the gene probe is made from radioactive DNA bases. These blacken X-ray film.

The technique of using gene probes to identify disease alleles is very similar to the process of **DNA fingerprinting**. The only difference is in the gene probes which are used. You can read more about DNA fingerprinting in the next Biology in action pages.

Find out about:

- how DNA technology is used for genetic testing

Key words

multifactorial disease
gene probes
UV
autoradiography
genetic fingerprinting

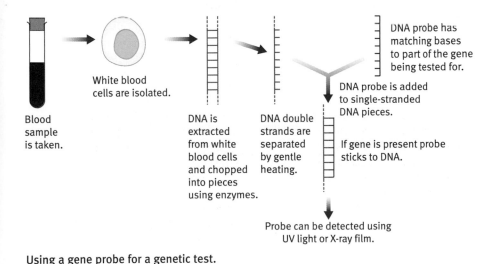

Using a gene probe for a genetic test.

Labels within the figure:

White blood cells are isolated.

Blood sample is taken.

DNA is extracted from white blood cells and chopped into pieces using enzymes.

DNA double strands are separated by gentle heating.

DNA probe has matching bases to part of the gene being tested for.

DNA probe is added to single-stranded DNA pieces.

If gene is present probe sticks to DNA.

Probe can be detected using UV light or X-ray film.

Questions

1 Suggest why white blood cells are used as the source of a DNA sample.

2 Describe the structure of a gene probe.

3 Why are DNA probes useful for genetic testing?

4 How do scientists find out if a gene probe has stuck to a person's DNA?

DNA fingerprinting

How are genes copied?

Genes are copied using a technique called **polymerase chain reaction (PCR)**. PCR uses enzymes to replicate the gene's DNA. The process is similar to DNA replication in cells, when chromosomes are copied before cell division. It takes just a few minutes for PCR to copy a piece of DNA, and 20 cycles will turn one DNA molecule into a million.

PCR is very useful in forensic DNA work. Often the amount of DNA found at a crime scene is very small. Before the PCR technique was introduced, this DNA was often not enough to give a reliable DNA fingerprint. PCR is also used to copy a gene for genetic modification (page 214).

Discovering DNA fingerprinting

Sir Alec Jeffreys in the 1980s

'My life changed on Monday morning at 09.05 am 10 September 1984. In science it is unusual to have such a "Eureka moment". We were getting extraordinary variable patterns of DNA including from our technician and her mother and father. My first reaction to the results was 'this is too complicated'; and then the penny dropped and I realized we had genetic fingerprinting."

Sir Alec Jeffreys is describing the discovery that made him one of the most famous scientists in the world. He had detected regions along the DNA molecule known as **minisatellites**. These are sections of DNA that are not genes. A unit of about 30 base pairs is repeated over and over again tens or even thousands of times. The same minisatellite can be different lengths in different people. DNA fingerprinting looks at the lengths of many different minisatellites throughout a person's DNA.

chromosome 21

CGCCTCGGCCTCCCAGAGTGCTGAGATTACAGGCGTGAACCACCATGCCTAGCCGTTAGCTCCCA
CTTATGAGTGAGAACAGGTGATGTTTGGTTTTCCATTCCTGAGTTACTTTACCCAGAATTGTTGT
CTCCAATCTCATCGAGGTCTCTGCGAATGCCAGTAATTCATTCCTTTTTATGGCTAAGTAGTATT
CCATCGTATATATACATATACATATATATGTATACACACATATACATATATATGTATACACACAT
ATACATATATATGTATACACACATATACATATATATGTATACACACATATACATATATATGTATA
CACACATATACATATATATGTATACACACATATACATATATATGTATACACACATATACATATAT
ATGTATACACACATATACATATATATGTATACACACATATACATATATATGTATACACACATATA
CATATATATGTATACACACATATACATATATATGTATACACACATATACATATATATGTATACAC
ACATATACATATATATGTATACACACATATACATATATATGTATACACACATATACATATATATG
TATACACACATATACATATATATGTATACACACATATACATATATAGTATACACACATATACATA
TATATGTATACACACATATACATATATATGTATACACACATATACATATATATGTATACACACAT
ATACATATATATGTATACACACATATACATATATATGTATACACACATATACATATATACATATA
TACACAAACACACATGCACCGCACTTTTTTTTTTTTTTTTTTTTTTGAGATGGGAGTCTCACTCTAT
CACCAGGCTGGAGTGCAGTGGTGTGATCTTGGCTCACTGCAACCTCTGTCTCCTGGGTTCAAGCT
ATTCTCCTGCTTCAGCCTCCTGAGTAGCTGGGATTACAGGTGCTCACCACCATGCCCAGCTAATT
TTTGTATTTTTACCATGTTGGCCAGGATGATCTCCATCTCCTGACCTCCTGATCCTCCTGCCTTG

part of the DNA code from chromosome 21 showing repeating minisatellite

The first human minisatellites were described in 1980. Four years later Sir Alec Jeffreys realized how they could be used in DNA fingerprinting.

Biology in action

How the technique works

Dr Tim Slingsby is a young scientist working with Sir Alec at Leicester University. He explains the basic techniques of DNA fingerprinting:

▶ *Extract DNA from the tissue sample:* break open the cells and purify the DNA.

▶ *Cut the DNA up into pieces:* **restriction enzymes** cut DNA at particular base sequences. One or two restriction enzymes that cut DNA at non-minisatellite sequences are added to the DNA sample. The pieces of cut-up DNA are different lengths in different people – because their minisatellites are different lengths.

▶ *Separate the fragments out:* gel electrophoresis separates the pieces of DNA out according to size. The cut-up DNA is put at one end of the gel and an electric current moves the pieces through the gel. Shorter pieces move faster than longer pieces, so they move further along the gel.

▶ *Make the pieces visible:* after gel electrophoresis the pieces of DNA have been separated, but we cannot see the different lengths. The DNA is transferred from the gel to a piece of membrane and a DNA probe is added that binds to the minisatellite sequences. The probe has a radioactive chemical attached to it. The membrane is placed next to an X-ray film. Where the probe has stuck to the DNA it causes the X-ray film to go black. So the final DNA fingerprint is a series of black lines on an X-ray film.

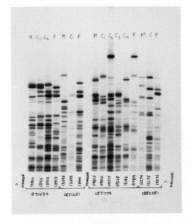

Each black line shows where pieces of DNA that contain minisatellite sequences have been separated out by gel electrophoresis.

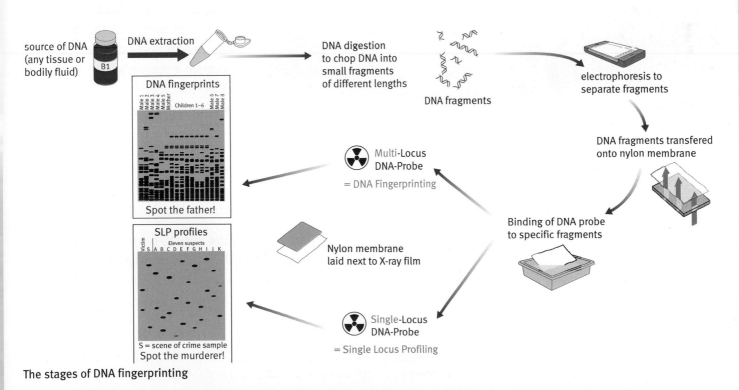

The stages of DNA fingerprinting

The impact of DNA fingerprinting

The first application of DNA fingerprinting was in an immigration dispute. In 1985 a young man was returning to the UK after a trip to Africa. He was refused re-entry to the UK on the grounds that he was not related to the people he claimed were his family. His solicitor had read about DNA fingerprinting. People from the same family share lots of their DNA, so there are similarities between their DNA fingerprint patterns. DNA fingerprinting proved that this man was a member of the family, and he was re-admitted to the UK. DNA fingerprinting is also used in paternity cases to show whether or not a man is the biological father of a child.

To begin with DNA fingerprinting was not used in criminal cases. A DNA fingerprint pattern was difficult to interpret, and needed too much high-quality DNA for the technique always to work. DNA from crime scenes is often only present in small amounts, e.g. a few drops of blood, or a single hair follicle. It may also be quite badly decomposed if the sample is old.

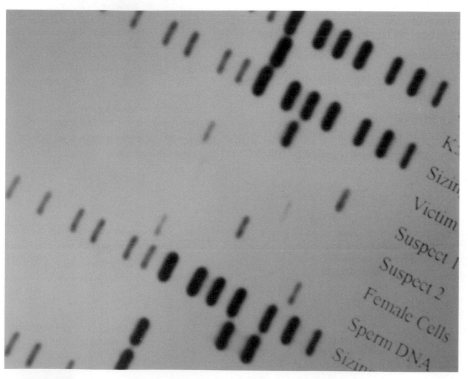

A DNA profile

So very quickly Sir Alec refined the technique and developed **DNA profiling**. This works in a very similar way to DNA fingerprinting, but only a few minisatellites are targeted. The pattern is much simpler, so it is easier to interpret. The technique can also be used with smaller samples of DNA. But Sir Alec points out that DNA profiling does not directly solve crimes. Just because a person's DNA is present at a crime scene does not necessarily mean they committed the crime. He says: 'It establishes whether sample X comes from person Y. It is then up to the court to interpret that in the context of other evidence in a criminal case.'

Perhaps surprisingly DNA profiling was first used to prove a person's innocence. In 1985 a man confessed to the brutal murder of a young girl. However, DNA profiling proved him innocent. DNA profiles were then taken of the local male population, and the man responsible for the crime was caught.

Looking to the future

Tim Slingsby is working on new applications of DNA technology: 'I am looking at DNA sequences in human sperm to investigate how variation is produced and maintained in humans from one generation to the next. I am particularly interested in **recombination**, a process that occurs during meiosis – cell division to produce sex cells. During recombination, pairs of chromosomes exchange sections of their DNA. This process leads to chromosomes in the sex cells that have a completely unique combination of alleles.'

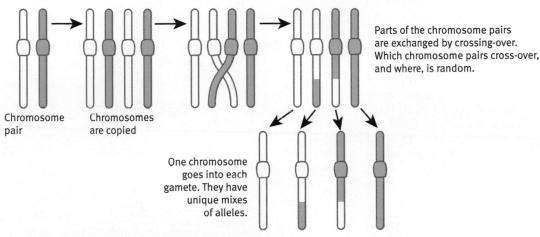

Parts of the chromosome pairs are exchanged by crossing-over. Which chromosome pairs cross-over, and where, is random.

Chromosome pair

Chromosomes are copied

One chromosome goes into each gamete. They have unique mixes of alleles.

After recombination the chromosomes still have the same genes – but they may have different combinations of alleles.

'A better understanding of recombination will be valuable to scientists who are trying to identify genes that make people more likely to develop particular genetic diseases. It will also help the study of diseases that are caused when recombination goes wrong, for example, thalassaemia. Knowing more about recombination helps us to understand more about human evolution, and it could also be helpful for cancer research.'

So why did Tim choose to work at Leicester University? He explains: 'Alec is wonderfully enthusiastic about science and despite all of his success, he remains very approachable and down to earth. He is one of the very few scientists in his position who still works at the bench – and he churns out important results at a rate that is both inspiring and intimidating! He recognises the importance of public understanding of science, and often gives up his time to present his work outside of the science community. Alec's success shows that he is clearly more than an ordinary scientist, but one of the first things that I picked up from him is that every scientist needs one basic skill – curiosity.'

Topic 4

Blood and circulation

In your body, every cell matters. Blood delivers nutrients and oxygen to each group of cells and takes away their waste. Your heart pumps throughout your life to keep the blood moving.

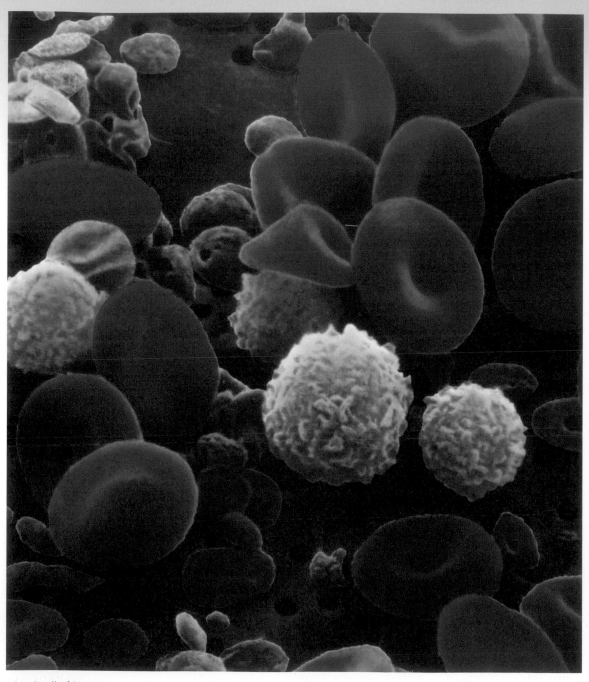

Blood cells (the colours in this photograph are computer-generated (false colour)). (× 2500)

Your heart

Your heart is a hollow sac of muscle. If you are at rest it beats about 60–80 times per minute, forcing blood through a network of blood vessels. Blood vessels carry blood to and from your body's cells. At the cells useful molecules pass from the blood into the cells, and waste products are taken away.

Blood

Blood tissue is made of several different types of cells floating in a clear liquid called **plasma**. Each type of cell has an important role in maintaining life. The plasma carries many dissolved chemicals around your body.

Blood groups

Blood donations save thousands of lives in the UK every day. Some people lose blood in accidents, and others need different parts of blood to treat particular illnesses. If you do have a blood transfusion, doctors and nurses will check carefully that you are given blood of a matching blood group. Your blood group is an inherited feature, determined by your genes.

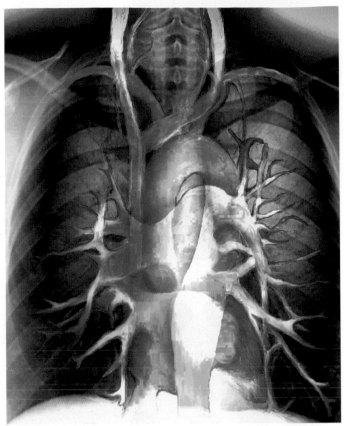

Artwork showing the heart and major blood vessels of the human chest.

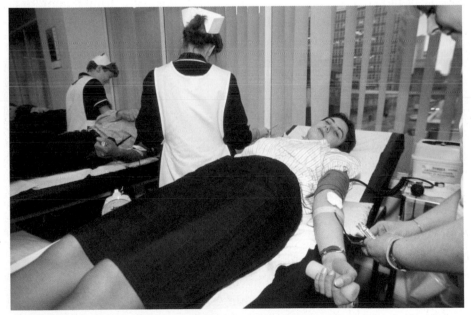

This woman is giving blood. Donated blood helps about one million people in the UK every year.

Key words

plasma

Find out about:

▶ the different parts of blood
▶ blood transfusions

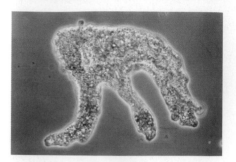

Amoeba

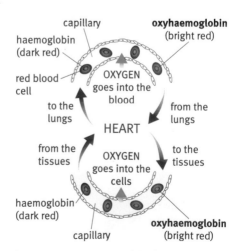

red blood cell

white blood cells (phagocytes)

platelet

white blood cell (produces antibodies)

This diagram shows the cells in blood, but not in the correct proportions. Each 1 mm³ of blood contains approximately 5 million red blood cells, 250 000 platelets, and 7000 white blood cells.

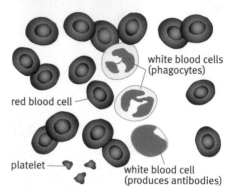

haemoglobin (dark red)

oxyhaemoglobin (bright red)

capillary

red blood cell

OXYGEN goes into the blood

to the lungs

from the lungs

HEART

from the tissues

OXYGEN goes into the cells

to the tissues

haemoglobin (dark red)

capillary

oxyhaemoglobin (bright red)

In the lungs oxygen is at high concentrations and binds to haemoglobin. At low oxygen concentrations in body tissues the oxygen is released. It diffuses into body cells which use the oxygen for respiration.

4A Blood

Systems for moving molecules

All living things need a way of moving materials around their body. Small organisms, for example a single-celled *Amoeba*, can rely on simple diffusion.

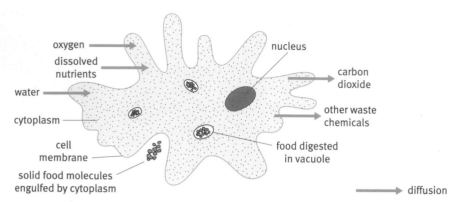

oxygen
dissolved nutrients
water
cytoplasm
cell membrane
solid food molecules engulfed by cytoplasm
nucleus
carbon dioxide
other waste chemicals
food digested in vacuole
diffusion

Amoeba is small enough for diffusion to transport substances in and out of the cell.

Diffusion is a slow process, so larger organisms need special transport systems. In most animals this is a **circulatory system**.

The human circulatory system

You have between 5 and 7 litres of blood circulating around your body. A sample of blood looks completely red. A closer look shows that it contains cells floating in a pale yellow fluid called plasma. Plasma is mainly water. It carries a wide range of dissolved materials including food molecules, hormones, and waste products from cells. Plasma also helps to distribute heat around the body.

There are three types of cell floating in plasma:

▶ **red blood cells** – to transport oxygen
▶ **white blood cells** – to fight infection
▶ **platelets** – which play an important role in blood clotting at an injury site

Red blood cells

Red cells are the most obvious blood components because of their colour. They are packed with the protein **haemoglobin**. Haemoglobin binds oxygen as blood passes through the lungs. The oxygen is released from haemoglobin as blood circulates through the tissues of the body.

Red blood cells have no nucleus, which allows more space for haemoglobin. The biconcave shape gives the cells a large surface area. This means that oxygen can diffuse in and out of the cells more rapidly. This shape also gives cells flexibility to squeeze through capillaries, which are only one cell wide.

White blood cells

White blood cells protect the body from infection by disease-causing microorganisms. They produce antibodies, and engulf and digest microorganisms by phagocytosis. You can read more about how white blood cells work on page 42.

Platelets

Platelets are fragments of cells which are made from the cytoplasm of large cells. When a blood vessel is damaged, for example when you are cut, platelets stick to the cut edge. They send out chemicals which trigger a series of reactions that form a clot at the cut site. Clotting helps to stop too much blood being lost from the body.

If you do suffer a major blood loss you will need a **blood transfusion**. There is a huge demand for donated blood – 9 000 **donors** a day are needed to keep UK hospitals fully supplied. The blood is stored in bags mixed with an anticoagulant to stop it clotting. The large capital letter on each bag shows the blood type. Getting the wrong blood type in a transfusion can be very serious.

The ABO blood types

Every cell carries markers on the outside. These markers are called antigens. Antigens are what white blood cells use to detect foreign cells. If your white blood cells detect foreign antigens on a cell, they produce antibodies to destroy it. Red blood cells can carry two different antigens, A and B. This determines your **ABO blood type**:

- just A antigens – blood type A
- just B antigens – blood type B
- both A and B antigens – blood type AB
- neither type of antigen – blood type O

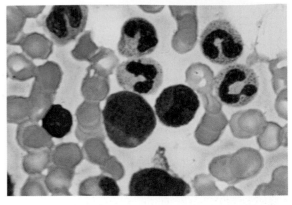

White blood cells

Donated blood

Your plasma contains antibodies against the red blood cell antigens you do not have. There are two types of antibody, anti-A and anti-B. So for example, someone with A antigens on their red blood cells will have anti-B antibodies in their blood plasma.

Blood type	Antigens	Antibodies
A	A	anti-B
B	B	anti-A
AB	A and B	none
O	neither	anti-B and anti-A

ABO blood types

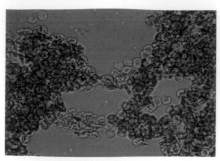

Clotted red blood cells

Blood transfusions

A person who gets a blood transfusion is called the **recipient**. It is essential to know the recipient's blood type. Anti-A antibodies have no effect on red blood cells carrying antigen B, but they will cause cells carrying antigen A to clot together in the bloodstream. These clots block blood vessels, stopping supplies of glucose and oxygen from reaching cells.

Before a blood transfusion the recipient's blood type is matched to suitable donated blood. Doctors check that the recipient's antibodies will not react with the donor's antigens. The antibodies in the donor's blood are present in much smaller amounts, and do not cause clotting in the recipient.

Donor \ Recipient	O anti-A + anti-B	A anti-B	B anti-A	AB none
O anti-A + anti-B	—	—	—	—
A anti-B		—		—
B anti-A			—	—
AB none				—

Key	
—	no clotting
(cell)	clotting

People with blood type AB don't have anti-A or anti-B antibodies. They can safely be given a transfusion of any blood type, so they are known as a **universal recipient**. Anyone with blood type O doesn't have A or B antigens. Their blood can be given to anyone – so they are known as a **universal donor**.

Questions

1 Write one sentence to describe the function of the four main components of blood.

2 List the different blood types in the ABO system.

3 For each type say which

   a antigens are present on the red blood cells

   b antibodies are present in the blood plasma

4 A patient has blood group O. Explain what would happen if they were given a transfusion of blood type A.

5 What blood type or types can a person with blood type O be given in a transfusion? Explain your answer.

6 Explain the meaning of the terms universal recipient and universal donor.

7 When blood is donated it is checked for blood type. Find out what other checks are made.

4B How blood types are inherited

Your ABO blood type is an inherited feature. It is determined by a single gene, like other features such as dimples, earlobe shape, and hairy ring fingers. You studied the inheritance of simple features such as these on page 14. For example, the dimples gene has two versions, called alleles. The allele for dimples is dominant, and the allele for no dimples is recessive. A person who inherits one of each of these alleles from their parents will have dimples.

There is an important difference in the control of blood type. The gene for ABO blood type has three different alleles:

- allele I^A – red cells have A antigens
- allele I^B – red cells have B antigens
- allele I^O – red cells have neither antigen A nor antigen B

Any person will only inherit two ABO type alleles – one from each parent. The table shows the possible combinations and the blood group these produce.

A person with the alleles I^A and I^B has both types of antigen on their red blood cells. These alleles are **codominant**. Allele I^O is recessive to both the I^A and I^B alleles.

Predicting blood groups

You can use a genetic cross diagram to predict a child's possible ABO blood type. For example, a man with blood type AB and a woman with blood type O have a child. What blood type could the child inherit?

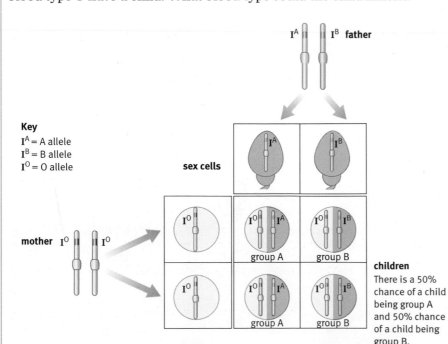

Key
I^A = A allele
I^B = B allele
I^O = O allele

children
There is a 50% chance of a child being group A and 50% chance of a child being group B.

Find out about:

- how blood types are inherited

Alleles	Blood type
$I^A I^A$	A
$I^A I^O$	A
$I^B I^B$	B
$I^B I^O$	B
$I^A I^B$	AB
$I^O I^O$	O

Key words

codominant

Questions

1 What blood type would a person with these alleles have:
   a I^A and I^O b I^A and I^B
   c I^B and I^B d I^B and I^O
   e I^O and I^O?

2 The I^A and I^B alleles are codominant. Explain what this means.

3 Use a genetic cross diagram to show the blood types that a child could have if their parents were

   a type AB and type A (with alleles I^A and I^O)

   b type O and type B (with alleles I^B and I^O)

Biology in action

Karen Sugden

Genes and environment

Almost all of our characteristics are affected by both our genes and our environment. Many scientists, such as Karen Sugden, are investigating the links between these two factors.

Does depression have a genetic cause?

Karen works in the new hi-tech laboratories of the Social, Genetic and Developmental Psychiatry Centre at King's College, London. She is part of a team looking at the genetic basis for depression.

'Depression is one of the most important disorders in terms of worldwide health,' says Karen. 'It's vital to get a better understanding of the disease.' About two out of every three people in the UK will suffer from depression at some point in their lives. It may be mild, or last just a few weeks. For some people the condition is very serious. They need medication and other treatment to help them recover.'

What is depression?

People often say that they feel 'depressed' when they're fed up because of something that has happened to them. For example, they may have done badly in an exam. These ups and downs are quite normal, and people usually get over them fairly quickly.

When a person has depression they feel a low mood which may last for several weeks. Everyday tasks, such as going to the shops or tidying up, may feel too much to manage. A person with depression may also suffer from physical symptoms, such as tiredness and headaches.

'I know now that depression affects different people in different ways. To start with I felt very down, but there were other things like I'd lose my temper easily, sometimes for nothing really. I couldn't focus on anything, nothing seemed worth doing, and I couldn't imagine being happy. I've had different treatments, some medication from my doctor, but also he's helped me to look after myself better generally and that really does help. I make sure that I eat properly, and do get out of the house. It's important for me to be active, because that helps me sleep. My doctor has really supported me, and helped me to get better.'

What causes depression?

Karen's experiments involve looking at a gene called 5-HTT, which helps to regulate a chemical in the brain known as serotonin. Serotonin acts as a chemical messenger between nerve cells.

The 5-HTT gene comes in two different alleles – a long version and a short version. We all inherit two copies of the gene, one from our mother and the other from our father.

'We knew from other studies that the 5-HTT gene was involved in depression and we also knew that stress causes depression,' explains Karen. 'What we didn't understand was why if bad things happen in people's lives, some people get depressed and some people don't.'

The scientists studied a group of 1000 people living in New Zealand. 'We got cheek swabs from the individuals,' says Karen. 'From these cheek cells we then extracted the DNA.' The DNA samples contained each person's entire genome – all their genes.

Using the latest DNA analysis equipment, the researchers were able to take a sample from each person's DNA and examine their 5-HTT genes. Karen's team compared this information against whether they had suffered stressful life events or depression.

They discovered that those people who had the short allele of the 5-HTT gene were more likely to get depression if they suffered stressful events in their lives.

This suggests that depression is a disease that is influenced by both genetic and environmental factors. Just because someone has the short 5-HTT allele does not mean that they will get depression. But if they suffer an extremely stressful event, it makes depression more likely.

Karen says that making the discovery made the hard work involved in the research worthwhile. 'To see the results come out, particularly when you have a theory and that theory is proved right, is very rewarding.' But when it comes to understanding depression, this work is only the start: 'There's still a huge way to go, lots and lots of things to find out yet!'

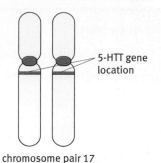

chromosome pair 17

The 5-HTT gene is found on human chromosome 17. Each person has two copies of the gene, one from each of their parents.

Find out about:

▶ the structure of the human heart

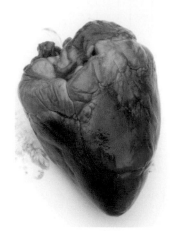

A sheep's heart is similar in structure to the human heart.

4C The heart

Your heart is a hollow muscle. It is a divided into two separate halves by a wall down the middle. Each half is about the size of a clenched fist. The heart pumps blood around the body, even when you are resting. On average your heart beats 100 000 times a day, which makes 35 million beats a year. To get an idea of the force each heartbeat produces, squeeze a tennis ball as hard as possible.

Inside the heart

Each side of the heart has two chambers – an **atrium** and a **ventricle**. Blood enters the atria which act as holding areas. The thin walls of the atria allow them to swell as blood arrives from the veins. The atria muscle then contracts, and blood is pushed into the ventricles. The ventricle walls have much thicker muscle. They contract with enough force to push blood out and away from the heart.

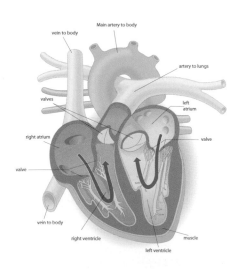

Diagram of a human heart. The artery leaving the right-hand side of the heart has been coloured blue to show that it is carrying blood which is short of oxygen.

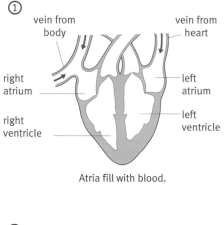

Atria fill with blood.

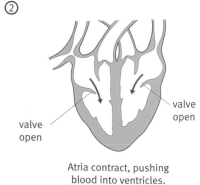

Atria contract, pushing blood into ventricles.

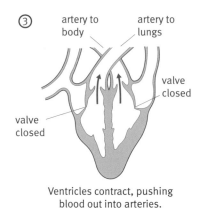

Ventricles contract, pushing blood out into arteries.

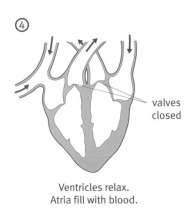

Ventricles relax. Atria fill with blood.

The sequence of events in a heartbeat. Both sides of the heart contract at the same time.

A double circulation

Blood from the body enters the right atrium of the heart. It is pumped out of the right ventricle towards the lungs to pick up oxygen. The blood is now **oxygenated**. It returns to the left atrium and passes into the left ventricle. Here it gets another, harder pump which carries it around the rest of the body. The left ventricle has a thicker wall of muscle than the right, because it has to pump blood to the whole of the body. The right ventricle only pumps blood as far as the lungs. As the blood passes around the body it gradually gives up its oxygen to the cells. It becomes **deoxygenated**. The blood then returns to the right atrium again. So blood passes through the heart twice on every circuit of the body. This is called a **double circulation**.

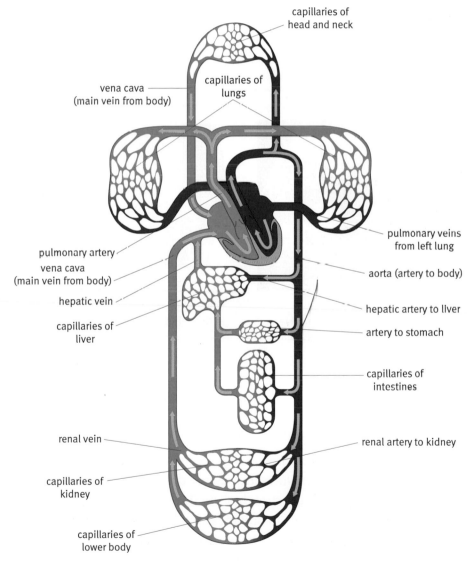

Blood is carried away from the heart by arteries, and towards the heart in veins. You can read more about the structure and function of blood vessels in Module B2 *Keeping healthy*.

Key words

atrium
ventricle
oxygenated
deoxygenated
double circulation

Questions

1 Explain what is meant by a double circulatory system.

2 Explain the difference in wall thickness between
  a atria and ventricles
  b the right and left ventricles

Find out about:

▶ the function of valves in the heart and veins

▶ why tissue fluid is important

4D Valves and tissue fluid

Valves – a one-way system

When the ventricles contract they push blood out of the heart. But what stops blood going backwards? This is the job of the heart **valves**. They act like one-way doors to keep the blood flowing in one direction. There are two sets of valves in the heart:

▶ Between each atrium and ventricle. These valves stop blood flowing backwards from the ventricles into the atria.

▶ Between the ventricle and the arteries leaving the heart. These valves stop blood flowing backwards from the arteries into the ventricles.

Valves are also found in veins. Blood pressure is lower in veins than in arteries. Valves stop blood from flowing backwards in the veins in between each pump from the heart.

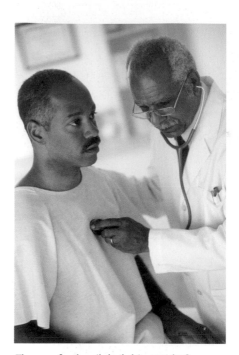

The comforting 'lub-dub' sound of a heartbeat is the sound of heart valves snapping shut. The 'lub' sound is caused by the valves between the atria and ventricles shutting. The 'dub' sound is made as the valves between the ventricles and the arteries close.

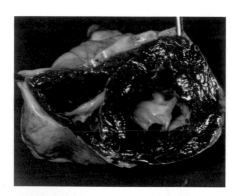

A valve between a ventricle and an artery. Strong tendons hold the valve flaps in place, preventing blood from flowing backwards.

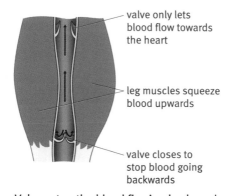

valve only lets blood flow towards the heart

leg muscles squeeze blood upwards

valve closes to stop blood going backwards

Valves stop the blood flowing backwards in the veins.

Why is a double circulation important?

The lungs and other body organs contain a **capillary network**. As blood squeezes through these capillaries its pressure drops. It has less force moving it along. If blood went straight from the lungs to the rest of the body, it would move too slowly to provide enough oxygen for the body's cells. The double circulation gives the blood a pump to get through each network of capillaries – the right ventricle pumps it through the lungs, and the left ventricle pumps it through the rest of the body.

Key words

valves
capillary network

Capillary networks

On average you will have 6 litres of blood in your body which is all pumped through the heart three times each minute. But the blood spends most of that time in capillary networks. Capillaries are where chemicals in the body's cells and in the blood are exchanged. The structure of capillaries makes them ideally suited for this function.

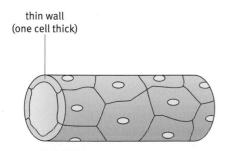

thin wall (one cell thick)

Capillary walls are very thin and porous.

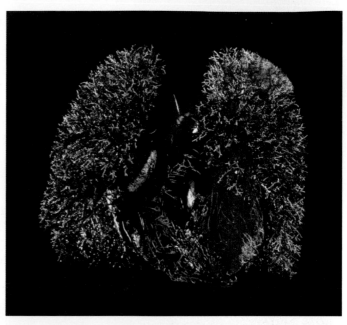

A resin cast of the capillary network of an adult human's lungs.

When blood enters a capillary network from an artery it is at high pressure. Blood plasma is squeezed out of the capillary. It forms a liquid called **tissue fluid**, which bathes all of your cells.

Tissue fluid contains all the dissolved raw materials being carried by blood plasma. These chemicals diffuse from the tissue fluid into cells. Waste products from cells diffuse out into the tissue fluid.

As blood passes through the capillary network its pressure drops. Plasma stops being squeezed out, and tissue fluid with waste products from cells moves back into the capillaries.

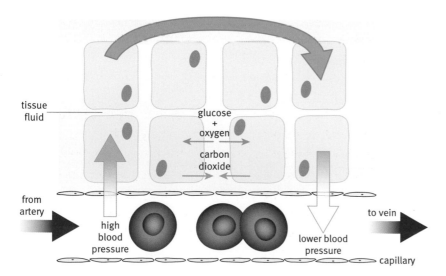

tissue fluid

glucose + oxygen

carbon dioxide

from artery

high blood pressure

lower blood pressure

to vein

capillary

Capillary actions

Questions

1 Draw a flow chart to show the route blood takes on its journey around the body. Include all the key words on pages 230–234 in your description. Start with:

Blood leaves the left ventricle ➜

2 Describe the job of valves in the heart and veins.

3 What is tissue fluid made from?

4 Explain why tissue fluid leaks out at the start of capillaries, and moves back in towards the end of the capillary network.

5 Explain how tissue fluid helps the exchange of chemicals between the capillaries and body tissues.

6 Name four chemicals which are exchanged between body cells and tissue fluid.

Topic 5

Energy for life

Animals take in energy in the food they eat. This energy has to be transferred into a useful form to power movement, growth, or to keep the body warm. Energy is released from food by a process called **respiration**.

Muscle cells are using large amounts of energy to produce this movement.

Respiration

Respiration is a carefully coordinated series of chemical reactions. It happens in all plant and animal cells. Most living things need oxygen for respiration. When you exercise, respiration happens faster to release more energy. You must get more oxygen into your body, so you breathe faster.

Respiration without oxygen

Many organisms can release energy from food without oxygen. This is called **anaerobic** respiration. Most organisms can only survive in this way for a short time. A few organisms can survive either with or without oxygen, for example, yeast cells. There are a small number of bacteria species which cannot survive in oxygen, for example, *Clostridium tetani*, which causes the disease tetanus.

Key words

respiration
anaerobic

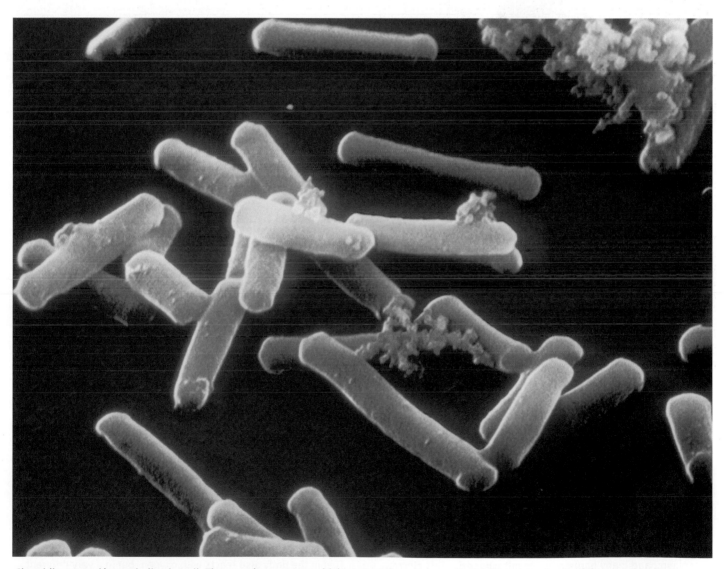

Clostridium tetani bacteria live in soil. They produce spores which protect them from contact with oxygen in air. If the spores enter a human body in a deep cut, the bacteria can grow. (× 13 000)

Find out about:

▷ respiration

5A Energy for life

Your body is a demanding animal. Billions of cells each carry out thousands of chemical reactions every second to keep you alive. These cells need a constant supply of energy to drive these reactions. The food you eat provides you with molecules to make new cells. But it is also a store of chemical energy. This is converted by respiration into energy your cells can use.

Most of your energy comes from **aerobic** respiration. During aerobic respiration glucose from your food reacts with oxygen. The reactions release energy from the glucose. Respiration can be summarized by this equation:

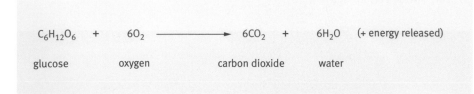

$$C_6H_{12}O_6 \ + \ 6O_2 \longrightarrow 6CO_2 \ + \ 6H_2O \quad \text{(+ energy released)}$$

glucose   oxygen   carbon dioxide   water

Respiration is a long series of reactions. It is summarized by this equation.

This girl is using energy for many different actions – such as processing information in her brain, moving, maintaining a constant internal environment, and growing and repairing her tissues.

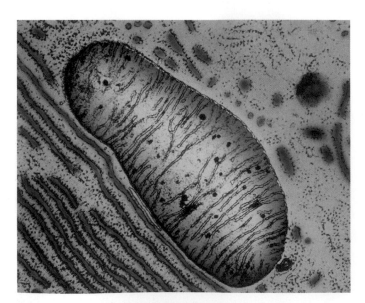

Some of the reactions for respiration take place in the cell cytoplasm, and many happen inside **mitochondria**. This electron micrograph shows a single mitochondrion (magnification × 64 000).

This fuel is combining with oxygen in a violent chemical reaction. Fuel in the body also reacts with oxygen, but in a very different reaction – not at all like combustion.

H Maximizing diffusion

Oxygen moves from the air in your lungs into your blood by diffusion. Carbon dioxide diffuses the opposite way. This is called **gas exchange**. Gas exchange happens at the alveoli in the lungs.

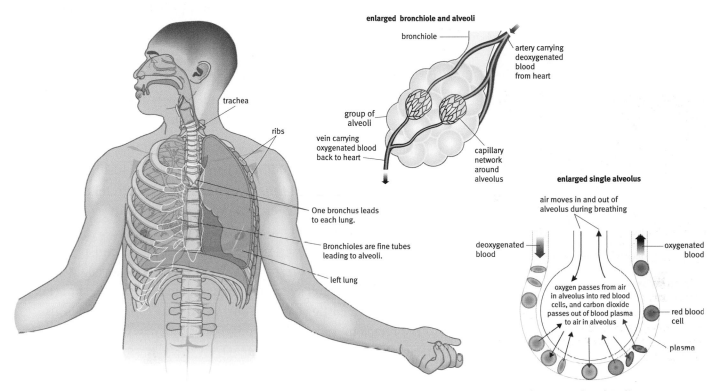

Gas exchange at the alveoli

H Diffusion is the movement of molecules from an area of their high concentration to an area of their lower concentration. The greater the difference in concentration, the faster diffusion happens. (You can remind yourself about diffusion on page 108.)

Faster and deeper breathing refreshes the air in your lungs more often. A faster blood flow also carries oxygen away from the lungs as quickly as possible. Both of these features keep the biggest possible difference between the oxygen concentration in the alveoli and that in your blood. So gas exchange in the lungs happens at its fastest rate.

Key words

aerobic
mitochondria
gas exchange

Questions

1 Write down three processes your body needs energy for.

2 a Write down the word equation for aerobic respiration.
  b Annotate the equation to show where the reactants come from, and what happens to the products.

3 Describe what happens during gas exchange in the lungs.

4 Explain how a large concentration gradient for oxygen is maintained between the lungs and the blood.

Find out about:

▶ your body's response to exercise

This athlete is having a fitness test. The equipment measures the maximum volume of oxygen she consumes in one minute as she cycles harder and harder. High volumes of oxygen consumption show high levels of endurance.

5B The effect of exercise

Responding to exercise

Working muscles need more energy than relaxed muscles. When you exercise, aerobic respiration in muscle cells must happen faster to provide this extra energy. To do this the muscle cells need more oxygen and glucose. The cells also need to get rid of more waste carbon dioxide made during respiration.

Like other chemicals, oxygen, glucose, and carbon dioxide are transported around the body in your blood. So two things happen when you exercise:

▶ *Your breathing rate increases* – more oxygen is brought into your body, and more carbon dioxide can be got rid of. Just sitting around, you breathe about 12 times a minute. Each breath takes in about 0.5 litres of air. During exercise you can breathe three times faster, and four times deeper.

▶ *Your heart rate increases* – oxygen and glucose are transported to your muscle cells faster, and carbon dioxide is removed faster. A resting heart pumps about 5 litres of blood per minute, but this volume can easily be tripled during exercise. Some blood is also redirected to the muscles, from tissues that can reduce their activity, e.g. from the digestive system.

Anaerobic respiration

When you exercise hard your muscle cells need large amounts of energy. The oxygen demand for aerobic respiration may be greater than the body can provide. If this happens the muscle cells can use anaerobic respiration. This releases energy from glucose without oxygen. This can be an advantage if your muscles need extra energy very quickly.

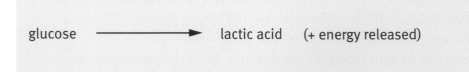

glucose ⟶ lactic acid (+ energy released)

Anaerobic respiration in animals is summarized by this equation.

Anaerobic respiration can only be used by muscles for a short period of time. It releases much less energy from each gram of glucose than aerobic respiration does. Also, the waste product **lactic acid** is toxic if produced in large amounts. It builds up in muscles, making them feel sore and tired.

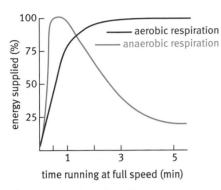

The 100 m sprint takes about 10–11 seconds. The heart and lungs cannot increase the oxygen supply to the muscles fast enough, so most of the energy required during the short race comes from anaerobic respiration.

H Getting rid of lactic acid

Toxic lactic acid cannot be left in muscle cells. After anaerobic respiration it is broken down into carbon dioxide and water. This reaction needs oxygen. So in human beings anaerobic respiration only provides energy without oxygen for a short period of time. The oxygen must be 'paid back' eventually. The amount of oxygen needed to get rid of the lactic acid is called the **oxygen debt**.

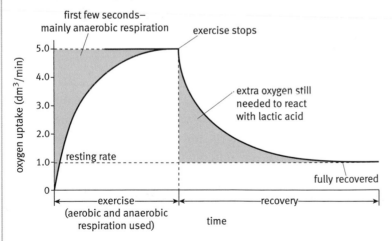

During exercise the heart rate increases, and so does the amount of blood pumped per beat. Both these factors combine to pump more blood per minute. Once exercise has finished you carry on breathing deeply. Your breathing rate returns to normal when all the lactic acid has been broken down.

Questions

1 Write down the word equation for anaerobic respiration in human cells.

2 Explain why human cells cannot use anaerobic respiration for more than a short period of time.

3 Write a flow chart to explain why your heart and breathing rates increase when you exercise.

4 Explain what is meant by the term 'oxygen debt'.

Find out about:

▶ anaerobic respiration in plants and microorganisms
▶ ATP as an energy store

5C Anaerobic respiration and ATP

Anaerobic respiration in other organisms

Many animals use anaerobic respiration for short bursts of energy. For example, both a predator running after prey, and the prey running for its life, will use anaerobic respiration. Other organisms can also use anaerobic respiration, for example:

▶ parts of plants, e.g. roots in waterlogged soils, germinating seeds
▶ some microorganisms, e.g. yeast, lactobacilli (used in cheese and yogurt production)

In these organisms the product of anaerobic respiration is **ethanol** instead of lactic acid:

glucose ⟶ ethanol + carbon dioxide (+ energy released)

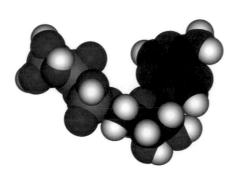

Model of ATP

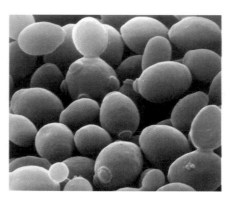

Yeast cells can respire anaerobically until the ethanol builds up and becomes too toxic.

Germinating seeds respire anaerobically.

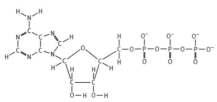

Diagram of an ATP molecule. ATP stands for adenosine triphosphate.

H What happens to the energy from respiration?

All respiration releases energy from glucose. This energy will be needed by many processes in the cell. There must be a way of storing the energy temporarily, so that it can be moved to the part of the cell that needs it. This is achieved by a very important chemical – **ATP**.

ATP is made by the cell using energy released during respiration. ATP molecules move freely around the cell. When energy is needed for reactions in the cell, some ATP is broken down, releasing energy. So ATP can be described as the 'energy currency' of the cell.

H ATP in muscle cells

Skeletal muscles may make up to 40% of a person's body weight. They are used for holding the body upright, breathing, and moving. A whole muscle is made up of hundreds of muscle fibres. Each muscle fibre is full of fine protein filaments. These can slide past each other, shortening the whole muscle. This happens when a muscle contracts to move part of the body.

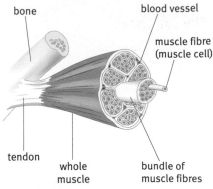

The structure of a whole muscle.

Muscle tissue is packed with thin protein filaments. ATP allows the filaments to slide past each other, contracting the muscle.

Muscle contraction needs a large supply of ATP. At any moment each of your muscle cells has about a million molecules of ATP. This is enough to keep your skeletal muscles going for just 10 seconds. So when ATP is broken down to release energy, it must be remade immediately. Even if you did no exercise, you'd need to break down and rebuild each ATP molecule about 800 times a day.

Questions

1 Describe conditions where anaerobic respiration is an advantage to:

   a human beings

   b another organism

2 Give an example of anaerobic respiration which is used by human beings to make a useful product.

3 Describe how the chemical ATP is produced.

4 Why is ATP sometimes called the 'energy currency' of the cell?

5 Describe how the structure of muscles enables them to contract.

Key words

ethanol

ATP

Topic 6   Get moving

You have an internal skeleton to support your body. This makes you a **vertebrate**. Around your skeleton is a complex system of different tissues which hold your bones together and move them. Altogether they form your **skeletal-muscular system**.

The skeletal-muscular system in action.

Muscles

Muscles pull on your bones to move your skeleton. Different tissues join muscles to bones, and strap bones together. Each of these tissues is designed for the particular job it has to do.

Joints

Sports can be tough on your joints. The ends of the bones are under great force when you run or land from a jump. The tissues that hold bones together can be twisted by a sudden change of direction, or loss of balance. A really bad twist can even pull a muscle away from its bone. Physiotherapists can speed recovery from injury but it is better to be aware of the risks and take steps to avoid them.

Getting fit

Your muscles and joints need to be worked to keep them healthy. This applies to your skeletal-muscular system and your heart muscle. People are different and one way of keeping fit does not suit everyone. Some people prefer to play team sports, others go for a brisk walk every day, and some people like to visit a gym. If you join a gym your fitness is assessed before you begin training. It is useful if the gym keeps a record of your data so that anyone on the team can monitor your progress, and change your training plan if this is needed.

> **Key words**
>
> vertebrate
> skeletal-muscular system

Warming up before a game can help avoid injury.

Find out about:

▶ the skeletal system

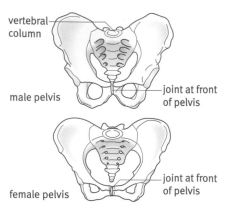

vertebral column

male pelvis

joint at front of pelvis

female pelvis

joint at front of pelvis

One function of the skeleton is to provide protection for internal organs. The pelvis protects the reproductive organs. The female pelvis is shallower and wider for childbearing.

6A The skeleton

Your **skeleton** provides a tough, flexible framework for the rest of your body. It supports the soft tissues of the body. Without your skeleton you would be a jellyfish-like mass. Even when you are standing still, muscles pull on your bones to maintain your posture.

As well as supporting your body your skeleton:

▶ stores minerals such as calcium and phosphorus
▶ makes red blood cells, platelets, and some white blood cells in bone marrow
▶ forms a system of levers with muscles attached, which allows the body to move
▶ protects internal organs

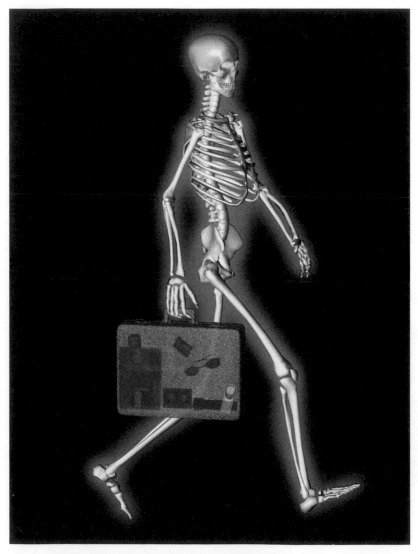

The human skeleton has over 200 bones. Most will move, but some are fixed in position, e.g. those in the skull. Skull bones are flexible during early development, but fuse together soon after birth.

Living bone

The skeleton is not just dry bone. Its tissues, such as bone and cartilage, are made of living cells. Blood brings nutrients and oxygen to the cells.

Bone is continually broke down and rebuilt. Even an adult's skeleton is continually changing. Weight-bearing exercises such as jogging stimulate bone growth, increasing its density. Inactivity makes bone less dense and weaker.

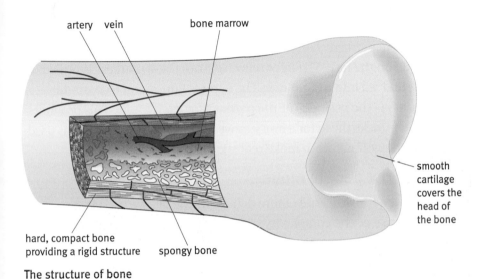

artery   vein   bone marrow

smooth cartilage covers the head of the bone

hard, compact bone providing a rigid structure   spongy bone

The structure of bone

Questions

1 List four functions of the skeleton.

2 Give features from the photographs on this page which show that bone is a living tissue.

3 Describe how exercise changes bones.

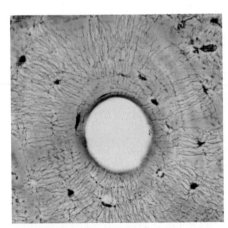

Light micrograph of bone (×600). You can see the central canal surrounded by circular bands. The dark dots are cavities containing bone cells.

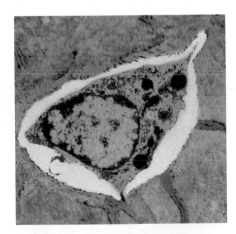

An electron micrograph showing a section through one cavity and its bone cell (×4000)

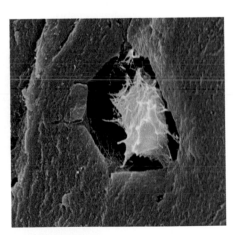

A scanning electron micrograph showing the surface of a single bone cell in its cavity (×4000)

How films can help fractures

You might be surprised to find an engineer working with an anatomy book by his side. But that is what Alessio Murgia does in the Department of Cybernetics at Reading University. Alessio has been using the technology that makes virtual characters in films to help people with mobility problems. This is called kinematics.

Creating virtual characters

To make characters like Gollum in *Lord of the Rings* an actor is covered in special reflective markers. Large reflectors are put onto the body, and smaller ones are used on the face. The light reflected from these markers is picked up by cameras and fed into a computer. The actor is filmed and a computer programme plots the positions of the markers for each frame. This produces a video which tracks the actor's every move and expression. The film is used as a base for the animators to make realistic virtual characters.

Studying how people move

Alessio explains the process in more detail. 'In the lab we used twelve cameras because of the complexity of human movement. Each reflective marker must be picked up by at least two cameras to pinpoint its position.

'This technology can be used to study gait – that's the way people walk – and upper limb movements, for example, how people who have fractured their wrists change the way they use their arms to cope with everyday tasks.' Alessio's work focuses on the human arm, but other scientists have also studied gait to help young people with restricted mobility. These photographs show a patient with celebral palsy filmed using this technology.

Kinematic technology can be used to help people with cerebral palsy. The environment in which these experiments are done is important. Here the lab is painted to look like an underwater world, so the wires and backpack seem like part of the adventure for the child.

If the patient keeps walking in this way he might develop bone deformities as his bones are still growing. On his back, the patient has a box that collects the electrical signals from the muscles – this shows when each muscle contracts during the gait pattern as the subject walks. People involved in this kind of study can compare this with a control pattern from someone with normal gait.'

The computer simulates the child's gait pattern.

Alessio does not treat patients himself. His work is used by a physiotherapist or surgeon to make decisions about the best treatment for a patient. 'In cases like this it might be possible for the surgeon to lengthen or shorten tendons to correct the gait.'

Fractured wrists

Alessio's own research involves the study of shoulder, elbow, and hand kinematics to help people that are recovering from wrist fractures. 'The way we move our limbs is actually very complex – take the arm for example, it's more than just triceps and biceps contracting. There are muscles attached by tendons to sites on the shoulders. If someone has fractured their wrist they will use these muscles to turn their hands instead of the muscles round the wrist. There are two important wrist movements: *pronation* when you rotate your palm downwards, and *supination* when the palm is rotated upwards. These movements are very important in daily living, for example, every time you turn a key, put a cup to your lips, pick something up, or stroke a cat. If you have fractured your wrist you compensate by using other muscles in the elbow and shoulder.

'Because of the many degrees of freedom in the human body there are many ways of achieving a particular movement. In the past physiotherapists have relied on test movements in clinics to monitor how fracture patients are coping with moving, but that is not the same as real tasks at home. Using the movement information extracted from this film, the physiotherapist knows where to intervene to restore the right combination of muscle movement.'

Find out about:

▶ how movement is produced at your joints

6B Joints and movement
Holding the bones together

Two or more bones meet at a **joint**. Different types of joint allow different sorts of movement. Ball-and-socket joints, at your hip and shoulder, are the most versatile. These joints move in every direction, like a computer joystick. Hinge joints, such as the knee and elbow, move in just two directions – back and forwards.

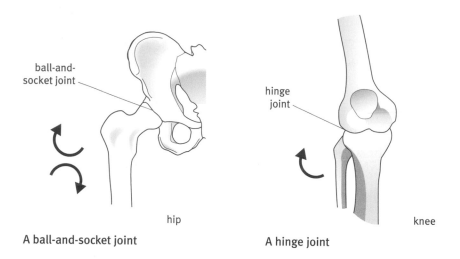

A ball-and-socket joint   A hinge joint

Tough, fibrous bands called **ligaments** hold the bones in place, and limit how far the bones can move. **Cartilage** stops bones from knocking against each other as they move. It forms a rubbery shock-absorbing coat over the end of each bone. This stops the bones from damaging each other. Cartilage is smooth, but friction could still wear it down. To reduce this, as far as possible, the joint is lubricated with oily **synovial fluid**.

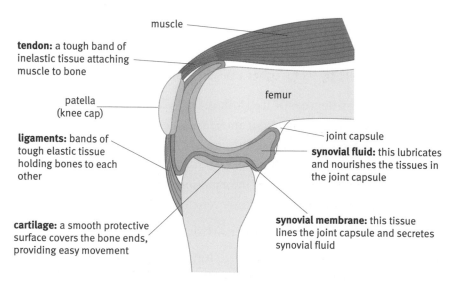

The knee joint. Like most joints in the body, this is a synovial joint.

How muscles move bones

Muscles can only pull a bone for movement. They cannot push it. A muscle contracts to pull on a bone and move it at a joint. After contracting the muscle is only stretched again when the bone is pulled back by another muscle. So at least two muscles must act at every joint:

- One contracts to bend the joint.
- The other contracts to straighten it.

Muscles which work opposite each other are called an **antagonistic pair**.

There are over 600 muscles attached to the human skeleton. They make up almost half the total body weight.

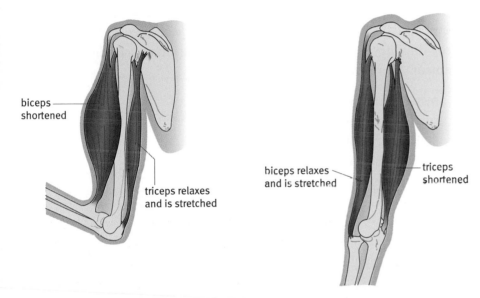

biceps shortened

triceps relaxes and is stretched

biceps relaxes and is stretched

triceps shortened

The biceps and triceps muscles contract to move the elbow joint.

Questions

1 Describe the difference between a tendon and a ligament.

2 Explain why this difference is important.

3 Name the parts of a synovial joint and explain their function.

4 Name the muscle which:

  a bends the arm

  b straightens the arm

5 Explain what is meant by an antagonistic pair of muscles.

6 Professional dancers and gymnasts often develop osteoarthritis in their knee joints in later life. The surface of their cartilage becomes rough and wears away. Suggest what symptoms this will cause.

Key words

joint
ligament
cartilage
tendon
synovial fluid
antagonistic pair

Find out about:

▶ injuries caused by excessive exercise

Joint injuries are common in football players.

6C Sports injuries

Joint injuries

If you follow a sports team you will know how often players may get injured. It is an occupational hazard. Joints are tough and well designed, but there is a limit to the force they can withstand. Common injuries include **sprains**, **dislocations**, torn ligaments, and torn tendons.

Football is particularly hazardous. There are lots of stops, starts, and changes of direction, and perhaps some bad tackles. It is not just professional footballers who suffer – 40% of knee injuries happen to under-15 footballers.

Sprains

The most common sporting injury is a sprain. This usually happens when you overstretch a ligament by twisting your ankle or knee. Often people will say that they have 'torn a muscle', when they have actually sprained a ligament. There are several symptoms:

▶ redness and swelling
▶ surface bruising
▶ difficulty walking
▶ dull, throbbing ache or sharp, cramping pain

The usual treatment for sprains is **RICE** – rest, ice, compress, elevate.

REST means immobilizing the injured part (e.g. keeping the weight off a torn muscle).

ICE acts as an anaesthetic, reduces swelling, and slows the flow of blood to the injured area. To avoid damaging the tissue, the ice is applied indirectly (e.g. in a tea towel or plastic bag) for up to 20 minutes at a time with 30 minutes between applications.

COMPRESSION usually involves wrapping a bandage round the injured part to reduce swelling. The bandage should be snug but not too tight.

AEROBIC EXERCISING of the injured part is not restarted until it has regained at least 75% of the previous level of strength, and then only moderately. This exercise helps build muscle and return the athlete to peak fitness.

SIMPLE STRETCHING ROUTINES help to regain mobility, but only when swelling stops.

ELEVATION means raising the injured limb. This reduces swelling by helping to keep excess fluid away from the damaged area.

Recovery from a sports injury often involves RICE followed by stretching and strengthening exercises. RICE stands for rest, ice, compression, and elevation.

After 72 hours of RICE treatment, heat and gentle massage can be used to loosen the surrounding muscles. If the injury keeps occurring, physiotherapy can be used to strengthen the surrounding muscles. The diagram shows a set of exercises which a physiotherapist might suggest for this type of injury.

 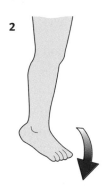 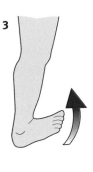

Physiotherapist treating a patient's ankle joint.

Physiotherapists prescribe different exercises for different injuries. If you suffer a joint injury, your GP may refer you to a physiotherapist for treatment.

Dislocations

Gymnasts also suffer from joint injuries, often at the knee joint. Cartilage in the knee is an excellent shock absorber, but floor routines put a lot of force on the joints. If a gymnast lands off balance, their kneecap can become dislocated. This happens when the bone slips out of the joint. In contact sports such as rugby, dislocations of the shoulder are extremely common. Dislocations are very painful.

Gymnasts land with great force. It can be equivalent to carrying ten times their body weight.

Questions

1 Describe
   a the symptoms and   b RICE treatment for a sprain.
2 Describe two other types of common joint injury.
3 Describe a set of exercises which a physiotherapist might give someone to treat a particular joint injury.

Key words

sprain
dislocation
RICE

Find out about:

▶ fitness training

6D Following a training programme

Health and fitness

Regular exercise is very important for a healthy lifestyle. Simple brisk walking is a very effective way to exercise. Before someone begins a fitness training programme, it is important to have a health check. This can be with a GP or fitness trainer. They check factors such as:

▶ general health checks, e.g. blood pressure
▶ whether they take any medicines
▶ whether they smoke
▶ if they drink alcohol, how much?
▶ the amount of exercise they normally do
▶ family medical history
▶ previous treatments for injury or illness

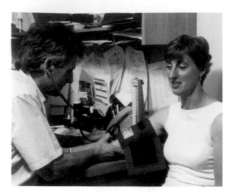

Blood pressure is the force of blood as it flows through the blood vessels.

What is 'normal' blood pressure?

Factors such as your blood pressure and heart rate vary during the day. They are lowest when you are at rest, and higher when you are moving quickly. Two people both sitting at rest will have different heart rates and blood pressure. So there is not a single 'normal' value for heart rate or blood pressure. Doctors use a range to describe the value for blood pressure which most people are within.

How is this information used?

The background information on a person's general health is used to decide on the best fitness programme. There are different types and levels of exercise. Information about a person's current health and fitness levels helps a trainer decide on the best programme for them.

These same checks will also be made by a doctor before they prescribe a patient any medical treatment. All medical treatments can cause unwanted harmful effects. Before prescribing any treatment a doctor weighs up the potential side effects against the benefits they expect the treatment will bring. The patient's current condition is important information when making this decision.

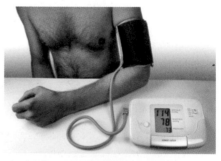

The higher number measures the **systolic** pressure. This is the pressure when the left ventricle contracts to push blood into the arteries. The lower number is the **diastolic** pressure. This is the pressure in the arteries between pumps, when the heart is relaxed and refilling with blood.

Making progress

If you are following a fitness programme your trainer will check your progress regularly. If your fitness improves faster than they had expected, they may increase the intensity of your exercise programme. If you get an injury, they will suggest that you cut out exercises which use the injured joint or muscle until you have recovered.

It is also very important to monitor patients on a course of medical treatment. If they do not respond to a particular treatment, doctors may wish to adjust the dosage of a medicine, or try a different treatment.

Key words

systolic
diastolic

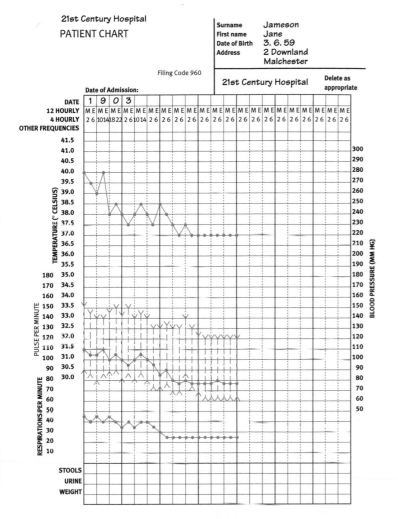

A patient's hospital chart monitors temperature, blood pressure, pulse, and breathing rates.

Keeping records

Information is stored in a person's medical or fitness records. These records must always be available. If the person does not make as much progress as expected, the records will help decisions about changing the treatment or training programme to be made quickly. The information must be stored carefully so that anyone on the medical or fitness team can access them easily. For example, if a patient in hospital needs treatment during the night, staff on duty must have access to records made during the previous day.

You can read more about an athlete's training programme on the next two pages.

Questions

1 List four pieces of medical or lifestyle history that should be checked before a person begins medical treatment or a fitness programme.

2 Explain why this information must be checked.

3 What are the two readings given for blood pressure? Explain the difference between them.

4 Explain why record-keeping is important during a fitness or treatment programme.

5 When a GP prescribes a course of treatment for a patient, they often book regular follow-up appointments. Explain why these appointments are important.

6 Suggest two reasons why a course of medical treatment or a fitness training programme might be changed before it has been completed.

7 Write a short paragraph to describe the stages a physiotherapist would work through to treat someone with a sporting injury.

Anna Bevan winning the 800 metres

Sports training

A new athlete hits the headlines

In 2003 Anna Bevan was an average runner. In 2005, she stormed to victory in the 800 metres. Her coach, Dan Forde, describes how Anna's training programme was developed.

'I coach the athletics team at the university. Anna was studying sports science. During a physiology practical her maximal oxygen consumption (VO$_2$ max) was measured. She gave excellent results, so her lecturer asked me to do a bleep test and step test on Anna.

The tests confirmed that Anna was aerobically very fit. She had been an all-round sportsperson at school, playing tennis, netball, hockey, and rugby. However, her first love was athletics. She had tried sprinting but wasn't very successful. I offered to train Anna and she accepted.'

Before training begins

'It's important for a coach and athlete to relate well and trust each other. Before training began we spent some time talking and got to know each other. Also, I checked Anna's health, because health and fitness are not the same thing. Although Anna performed well in fitness tests, she might have had a medical condition that made it dangerous for her to train seriously.'

Health check

'Anna completed a physical activity readiness questionnaire. I also asked our athletics team doctor to carry out a more detailed health screening.

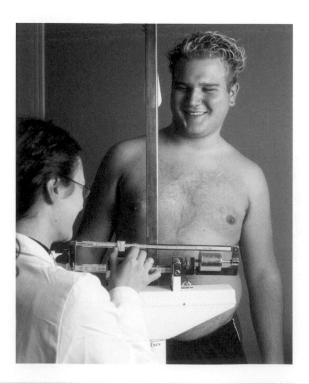

This man is being weighed and measured so that his body mass index can be calculated.

If Anna was aiming to be an elite athlete, she would have to put her body under extreme physical stress. The doctor asked questions about Anna's lifestyle and medical history. Then he took blood and urine samples, and measured her body temperature, resting heart rate, and blood pressure. Anna had an ECG to make sure that her heart was healthy.

'The doctor also measured Anna's weight and height to make a rough calculation of her body mass index. He took skinfold measurements to estimate her body fat content.'

Choosing the right event

'Before Anna started training I wanted to find out why she had not done well in school athletics competitions. I suspected that she might be trying the wrong distance, so I asked for a muscle biopsy. The results showed that Anna's proportion of fast-twitch to slow-twitch fibres suited her better to middle-distance events rather than sprinting. Anna agreed to give this a try, and we designed a training programme for her.'

Starting the programme

'Anna did several sprints with rest, walking, or light jogging in between. She also did one long, slow run each week. Before Anna trained each day her resting heart rate and body temperature were measured. She also weighed herself to make sure she was well hydrated. Water is lost during intensive exercise, and must be replaced before another intensive session.

'Half-way through the first season Anna strained her hamstring muscle. The start of a race was delayed too long and she got cold. When she sprinted out of the blocks part of her muscle snapped, like an overstretched elastic band. A physiotherapist was on hand to perform the **RICE** routine almost immediately. He also gave Anna a rehabilitation programme. We monitored her progress over a number of weeks to ensure she did not push herself too hard too soon. Fortunately she could run at full fitness again before the end of the season.'

B7 Biology across the ecosystem

Summary

Interdependence

▶ Life depends on solar energy absorbed during photosynthesis and stored in chemicals like starch.

▶ Autotrophs make food from minerals, carbon dioxide, and water but heterotrophs need ready-made food.

▶ Chlorophyll absorbs light for photosynthesis. The equation is:

carbon dioxide + water → glucose + oxygen

▶ Some glucose is used for respiration and to make cellulose, protein, starch, and chlorophyll.

▶ Nitrates are absorbed and added to glucose to make proteins.

▶ They are absorbed by active transport in the roots. H

▶ Starch has little effect on the osmotic balance of the cell, so it is used for energy storage. H

▶ Photosynthesis may be limited by low temperatures and low carbon dioxide or light levels.

▶ Human activity is increasing atmospheric carbon dioxide levels.

▶ Compensation points occur when respiration makes as much carbon dioxide as photosynthesis uses.

▶ Energy is transferred when living things are eaten or broken down by decomposers.

▶ Pyramids of biomass show the food available to the herbivores and carnivores in an ecosystem.

▶ Only about 10% of the energy in biomass is passed on at each stage in a food chain. The rest is lost to decomposers or as waste heat.

▶ Soil contains living organisms, decaying material, sand, clay, air, water, and dissolved minerals.

Further up the food chain

▶ Mutualistic relationships benefit partner species; commensalism benefits one without harming the other; and parasitism harms the host.

▶ Parasites cause human disease and reduce farmers' yields.

▶ Parasites evolved with their hosts, so they can evade the host's immune system. For example, malaria parasites hide in red blood cells. They produce large numbers of offspring to ensure transfer to new hosts.

▶ Sickle-cell anaemia is caused by a faulty recessive allele. It makes red cells jam in small capillaries, causing pain, organ damage, and early death. H

▶ Natural selection has increased the allele's frequency where malaria exists because having one copy of the allele protects you. H

New technologies

▶ Bacteria have a cell wall, cell membrane, circular DNA chromosome, and plasmids.

▶ Bacteria and fungi are grown in fermenters to produce antibiotics, single-cell protein, and enzymes like rennin.

▶ Genetic modification involves isolating and copying genes and putting them in new cells.

▶ This is done by adding a virus or plasmid as vector. H

▶ GM bacteria make drugs, and hormones such as insulin. GM plants have added characteristics like disease resistance which lead to higher yields.

▶ Economic, social, and ethical implications have to be considered before genetically modified organisms are released.

▶ Genetic tests are carried out by isolating DNA, adding gene probes, and using UV or autoradiography to locate them.

Circulation

- Blood contains red cells to carry oxygen, white cells to fight infection, and platelets to seal cuts.

- A gene with three alleles, decides your blood type.

- Of the three alleles, I^A, I^B, I^O, two – I^A and I^B – are codominant.

- The chance of inheriting each blood group can be predicted using genetic diagrams. H

- The recipient of a blood transfusion must not have antibodies to the donor's red cells.

- The heart has an atrium on each side, to collect blood from veins, and a ventricle on each side to pump it into the arteries.

- We have a double circulatory system. The right ventricle sends blood to the lungs for gas exchange, and the left ventricle sends it around the body.

- Valves in the heart and veins keep blood flowing in the right direction.

- Tissue fluid bathes cells and aids diffusion of oxygen, carbon dioxide, glucose, and urea between capillaries and tissues.

Respiration

- Aerobic respiration releases large amounts of energy.

- This energy is used to synthesize ATP, the cell's energy currency. H

- The equation for aerobic respiration is:

glucose + oxygen → carbon dioxide + water

- During exercise, respiration increases to provide more energy (ATP) for muscle contraction.

- Heart and breathing rates increase to supply oxygen and glucose faster, and remove carbon dioxide faster, during exercise.

- 'Normal' measurements for factors such as heart rate and blood pressure vary.

- Anaerobic respiration releases less energy. The equation is:

glucose → lactic acid

- Anaerobic respiration is used to provide short bursts of energy when aerobic respiration cannot meet the demand. H

- The 'oxygen debt' is the amount of oxygen used to break down lactic acid after anaerobic exercise. H

Skeletal system

- Vertebrate skeletons support the body and allow movement.

- Bones are held together by slightly elastic ligaments.

- Tough inelastic tendons attach muscles to bone.

- Layers of cartilage and synovial fluid reduce friction at joints.

- Muscles operate in antagonistic pairs because they can only contract.

- Health information is needed before medical treatment or an exercise regime starts.

- Regular contact with health or fitness practitioners and accurate records are essential.

- These records may be needed by other practitioners. H

- The benefits of treatments need to be weighed against their side effects and there can be more than one way to achieve targets.

- Training can be monitored by measuring changes in the heart rate's response to exercise.

- Assessments of progress need to take the accuracy of the monitoring technique, and the reliability of the data, into account. H

- A fitness programme can be modified in response to injury or to promote further improvement.

- Excessive exercise can dislocate a bone from its socket, tear a ligament or tendon, or sprain a ligament.

- Sprains are treated by rest, ice, compression, and elevation (RICE). When the swelling has gone down, stretching routines can be used to regain mobility.

- Physiotherapists prescribe exercises to build muscles and counteract joint problems.

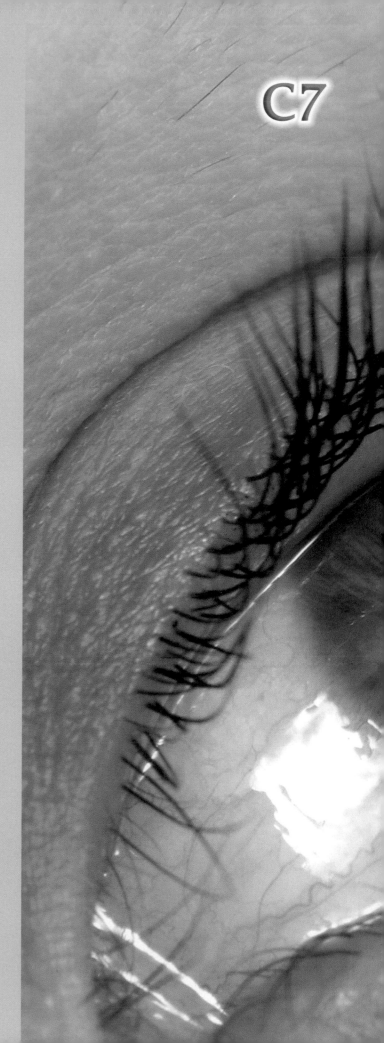

Why study chemistry?

Chemistry is the science which helps us to understand matter on an atomic scale. It is the central science. Knowledge of chemistry informs materials science and engineering as well as biochemistry, genetics, and environmental sciences.

The science

Understanding carbon chemistry helps to explain the chemistry of life. There are so many carbon compounds that chemists have had to find ways to organize their knowledge to study the compounds in families such as the alcohols, carboxylic acids, and esters.

Chemists have theories to help answer key questions about chemical reactions: How much?, How fast?, and How far?

Chemistry in action

Analytical chemists help to protect us by checking that food and water are safe. Analysis of blood helps to diagnose disease. Forensic scientists use analysis to solve crimes.

Chemists synthesize new chemicals to meet our needs. Medicinal chemists synthesize thousands of new compounds in the search for new drugs to treat or cure disease. The chemical industry synthesizes products on a large scale. The industry is changing so that it can be more sustainable.

Chemistry for a sustainable world

Find out about:

- the chemistry of carbon compounds (organic chemistry)
- energy changes in chemistry
- catalysts and the rates of chemical change
- reversible reactions and equilibria
- chemical analysis by chromatography and titrations
- the 'greening' of the chemical industry

Topic 1

The chemistry of carbon compounds

There are more carbon compounds than there are compounds of all the other elements put together. The chemistry of carbon is so important that it forms a separate branch of the subject called **organic chemistry**.

Synthetic polymers make good nets to catch fish for food.

Spiders spin a web with a natural organic polymer to catch food.

Organic chemistry

The word 'organic' means 'living'. At first, organic chemistry was the study of compounds from plants and animals. Now we know that all the complex variety of compounds can be made artificially. Organic chemistry includes the study of synthetic compounds, including polymers, drugs, and dyes.

Chains and rings

It helps to think of organic compounds being made up of a skeleton of carbon atoms supporting other atoms. Some of the other atoms may be reactive, while others are less so. In organic compounds, carbon is often linked to hydrogen, oxygen, nitrogen, and halogen atoms.

Carbon forms so many compounds because carbon atoms can join up in many ways, forming chains, branched chains, and rings. The chains can be very long, as in the polymer polythene. A typical polythene molecule may have 10 000 or more carbon atoms linked together (see Module C2 *Material choices*, Section E). A polythene molecule is still very tiny, but much bigger than a methane molecule.

To make sense of the huge variety of carbon compounds, chemists think in terms of families, or series, of organic compounds.

Bonding in carbon compounds

The bonding in organic compounds is covalent (see Module C4 *Chemical patterns*, Section B). The structures are molecular. The structures can be worked out from knowing how many covalent bonds each type of atom can form. Carbon atoms form 4 bonds, hydrogen atoms form 1 bond, while oxygen atoms form 2 bonds.

> **Key words**
> organic chemistry

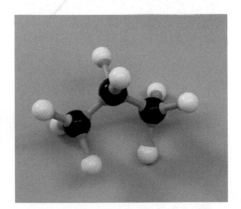

Propane: a hydrocarbon with three carbon atoms in a chain.

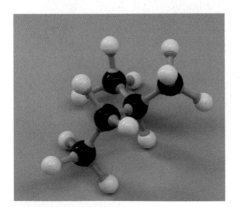

Methylbutane: a hydrocarbon with a branched chain.

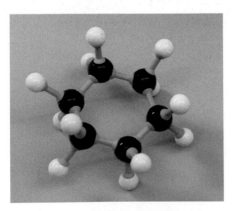

Cyclohexane: a hydrocarbon with a ring of carbon atoms.

Find out about:
▶ the alkane series of hydrocarbons
▶ physical properties of alkanes
▶ chemical reactions of alkanes

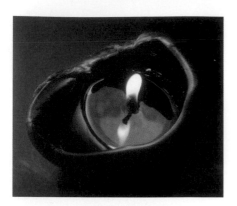

At room temperature the alkanes in candle wax are solid. The flame first melts them and then turns them to gas in the hot wick. The hot gases burn in air.

CH_4 — the molecular formula

H—C—H (with H above and below) — the structural formula showing the chemical bonds

— the tetrahedral shape of the molecule

— the space filled by the molecule

Ways of representing a molecule of methane

1A The alkanes

The **alkanes** make up an important series of **hydrocarbons**. They are well known because they are the compounds in fuels such as natural gas, liquid petroleum gas (LPG), and petrol. The simplest alkane is methane. This is the main gas in natural gas.

The table belowshows five alkanes.

Name	Molecular formula	Structural formula
methane	CH_4	H—C—H (with H above and below the C)
ethane	C_2H_6	H—C—C—H (with H above and below each C)
propane	C_3H_8	H—C—C—C—H (with H above and below each C)
butane	C_4H_{10}	H—C—C—C—C—H (with H above and below each C)
pentane	C_5H_{12}	H—C—C—C—C—C—H (with H above and below each C)

Physical properties of alkanes

The alkanes are oily. They do not dissolve in water or mix with it.

The alkanes with small molecules (up to four carbon atoms) are gases at room temperature. Those with 4–17 carbon atoms are liquids. The alkanes in candle wax have molecules with more than 17 carbon atoms, and these are solid at room temperature.

Liquid alkanes with longer molecules are sticky liquids. Their viscosity makes them suitable as ingredients of lubricants.

Chemical properties of alkanes

Burning

All alkanes burn. Many common fuels consist mainly of alkanes. The hydrocarbons burn in air, forming carbon dioxide and water.

If the air is in short supply, the products may include particles of soot (carbon) and the toxic gas carbon monoxide.

Reactions with aqueous acids and alkalis

Alkanes do not react with common laboratory reagents such as acids or alkalis. The hydrocarbons do not react because the C—C and C—H bonds in the molecules are unreactive.

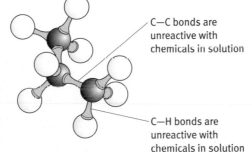

C—C bonds are unreactive with chemicals in solution

Alkanes are generally unreactive because the C—C and C—H bonds do not react with common aqueous reagents

C—H bonds are unreactive with chemicals in solution

Key words

alkane

hydrocarbon

Alkanes do not mix with water. They are less dense than water, so they form a layer on top of it. Here a blue dye colours the upper alkane layer.

Questions

1 a In which group of the periodic table does carbon belong?

b How many electrons are there in the outer shell of a carbon atom?

c Which groups in the periodic table include elements that form simple ions?

d Is carbon likely to form simple ions?

2 Give two examples which show that alkanes, or mixtures of alkanes, do not mix with water?

3 Are the alkanes in petrol more or less dense than water?

4 Write a balanced equation for propane burning in plenty of air.

5 Write a balanced equation for methane burning in a limited supply of air to form carbon monoxide and steam.

97

Find out about:
- physical properties of alcohols
- chemical reactions of alcohols

1B The alcohols

Uses of alcohols

Ethanol is the best-known member of the series of **alcohols**. It is the alcohol in beer, wine, and spirits. Ethanol is also a very useful solvent. It is a liquid which evaporates quickly, and for this reason it is used in cosmetic lotions and perfumes. Ethanol easily catches fire and burns with a clean flame, so it can be used as a fuel.

The simplest alcohol, methanol, can be made in two steps from methane (natural gas) and steam. This alcohol is important as a chemical feedstock. The chemical industry converts methanol to a wide range of chemical products needed to manufacture products such as adhesives, foams, solvents, and windscreen washer fluid.

Structures of alcohols

The first three members of the alcohol series are methanol, ethanol, and propanol.

There are two ways of looking at alcohol molecules that can help to understand their properties. On the one hand, an alcohol can be seen as an alkane with one of its hydrogen atoms replaced by an —OH group. On the other hand, the same molecule can be regarded as a water molecule with one of its hydrogen atoms replaced by a hydrocarbon chain.

Physical properties

Methanol and ethanol are liquids at room temperature. Alkanes with comparable relative molecular masses are gases. This shows that the attractive forces between molecules of alcohols are stronger than they are in alkanes. The presence of an —OH group of atoms gives the molecules this greater tendency to cling together like water.

Even so, the boiling point of ethanol at 78 °C is below that of water (100 °C). Ethanol molecules have a greater mass than water molecules, but the attractions between the hydrocarbon parts are very weak, as in alkanes.

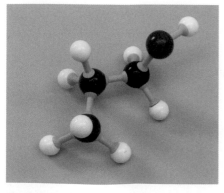

Ethanol: a simple alcohol. Chemists name alcohols by changing the name of the corresponding alkane to '-ol'. Ethanol is the two-carbon alcohol related to ethane.

Propanol: a three-carbon alcohol related to propane.

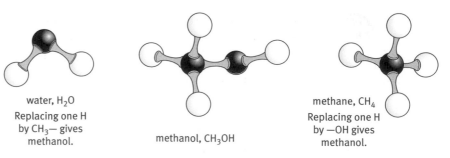

water, H_2O
Replacing one H by CH_3— gives methanol.

methanol, CH_3OH

methane, CH_4
Replacing one H by —OH gives methanol.

Two ways of looking at an alcohol molecule

Overall, ethanol molecules have less tendency to stick together than water molecules.

Similarly the —OH in the molecules of methanol and ethanol freely mix with water, unlike alkanes. However, alcohols with longer hydrocarbon chains, such as hexanol ($C_6H_{13}OH$), do not mix with water because the oiliness of the hydrocarbon part of the molecules dominates.

Chemical properties

The —OH group is the reactive part of an alcohol molecule. Chemists call it the **functional group** for alcohols.

Burning

All alcohols burn. Methanol and ethanol are highly flammable and are used as fuels. These compounds can burn because of the hydrocarbon parts of their molecules.

Reaction with sodium

Alcohols react with sodium in a similar way to water. This is because both water molecules and alcohol molecules include the —OH group of atoms. With water, the products are sodium hydroxide and hydrogen. With ethanol, the products are sodium ethoxide and hydrogen.

$$2\ H-\underset{\substack{|\\H}}{\overset{\substack{H\\|}}{C}}-\underset{\substack{|\\H}}{\overset{\substack{H\\|}}{C}}-O-H\ +\ 2Na\ \longrightarrow\ 2\ H-\underset{\substack{|\\H}}{\overset{\substack{H\\|}}{C}}-\underset{\substack{|\\H}}{\overset{\substack{H\\|}}{C}}-O^-Na^+\ +\ H_2$$

sodium ethoxide

Only the hydrogen atom attached to the oxygen atom is involved in this reaction. The hydrogen atoms linked to carbon are inert.

The product has an ionic bond between the oxygen and sodium atoms. Sodium ethoxide, like sodium hydroxide, is an ionic compound and a solid at room temperature.

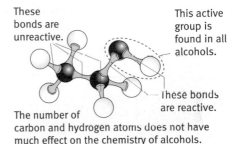

These bonds are unreactive.

This active group is found in all alcohols.

These bonds are reactive.

The number of carbon and hydrogen atoms does not have much effect on the chemistry of alcohols.

Some bonds in ethanol are more reactive than others. Alcohols are more reactive than alkanes because C—O and O—H bonds are more reactive than C—C and C—H bonds. The alcohols share similar chemical properties because they all have the —OH group in their molecules.

Questions

1 Produce a table for three alcohols similar to the table of alkanes on page 180.

2 **a** Use values of relative atomic masses from the periodic table in Module C4, page 95, to show that propane and ethanol have the same relative mass.

  b Propane boils at −42 °C, but ethanol boils at 78 °C. Suggest an explanation for the difference.

3 Write a balanced equation for propanol burning.

4 Write balanced equations for the reactions of sodium with

  a water

  b methanol

Find out about

▶ structures and properties of organic acids
▶ acids in vinegar and other foods
▶ carboxylic acids as weak acids

1C Carboxylic acids

Acids from animals and plants

Many acids are part of life itself. These are the organic acids, many of which appear in lists of ingredients on food labels (see Module C3 *Food matters*, page 217).

Acetic acid (which chemists call ethanoic acid) is the main acid in vinegar. Acetic acid helps to preserve and flavour a range of foods, including pickles and chutneys as well as vinegars.

Citric acid gives oranges and lemons their sharp taste. Lactic acid forms in muscle cells during exercise and in milk as it turns sour.

Some of the acids with more carbon atoms have unpleasant smells. The horrible odour of rancid butter is caused by the breakdown of fats to produce butyric acid. Butyric acid gets this, its traditional name, from its origins in butter. It is also the main cause of the revolting smell of vomit. The modern systematic name is butanoic acid.

Human sweat includes a wide range of chemicals, including fats. Enzymes in bacteria on the surface of skin can quickly break down these compounds into a mixture of organic acids, including butyric, caproic, and caprylic acids (among others). These compounds are largely responsible for the unpleasant, rancid smell of sweaty socks.

Goats' milk contains fats with more caproic acid and caprylic acid than cows' milk. These acids get their names from the Latin word for goat. When the fats break down to the free acids, the result is a strong goaty smell.

The sting of a red ant contains methanoic acid. The traditional name for this acid is formic acid, from the Latin word for ant, *formica*.

Structures and names of organic acids

The functional group in the molecules of organic acids is

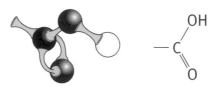

The series of compounds with this reactive group are the **carboxylic acids**. The chemical names of the compounds are related to the alkane with the same number of carbon atoms. The ending 'ane' becomes 'anoic acid'. So the systematic name for acetic acid, the two-carbon acid, is ethanoic acid.

Questions

1 Write the formula of butanoic acid. (Use the table of alkane names on page 180 to help you.)

2 The formula of caproic acid is $CH_3CH_2CH_2CH_2CH_2COOH$. What is the formula of caprylic acid, which has 8 carbon atoms in its molecules?

Formation of vinegar

Oxidation of ethanol produces ethanoic acid. Vinegar is manufactured by allowing solutions of alcohol to oxidize. Bacteria in the solutions help this process.

Oxidation converts beer to malt vinegar. Cider oxidizes to cider vinegar and wine to wine vinegar.

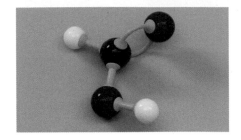

Methanoic acid, HCOOH

Acidity of carboxylic acids

Carboxylic acids ionize to produce hydrogen ions when dissolved in water. They only ionize to a light extent, which means that they are weak acids (see Module C6 *Chemical synthesis*, page 156).

In a molecule of ethanoic acid, there are four hydrogen atoms. Three are attached to a carbon atom and one to an oxygen atom. Only the hydrogen atom attached to oxygen is reactive. This is the hydrogen atom that ionizes in aqueous solution.

Ethanoic acid, CH_3COOH

ethanoic acid → ethanoate ion

Ethanoic acid and the other carboxylic acids show the characteristic reactions of acids with metals, alkalis, and metal carbonates:

- acid + metal ⟶ salt + hydrogen

- acid + soluble hydroxide ⟶ salt + water

- acid + metal carbonate ⟶ salt + carbon dioxide + water

When ethanoic acid reacts with sodium hydroxide, the salt formed is sodium ethanoate.

There is an ionic bond between the sodium ion and the ethanoate ion:

Questions

3 Write word equations and balanced symbol equations for the reactions of methanoic acid with:

  a magnesium

  b potassium hydroxide solution

  c copper(II) carbonate

4 A good way of removing the disgusting smell of butanoic acid from vomit on a carpet or inside a car is to sprinkle it with sodium hydrogencarbonate powder. Write a word equation for the reaction that takes place. Can you explain why the smell might disappear after this reaction?

Organic acids and skin care

The story goes that Cleopatra bathed in asses' milk. This is not as daft as it sounds. All milk, including asses' milk, contains lactic acid. The acid loosens and removes dead skin cells, leaving new, smooth skin underneath.

Dermatologists sometimes use a modern, and more drastic, version of this treatment. They paint the skin with glycolic acid (hydroxyethanoic acid). This peels off the top layer of the skin, removing dead skin cells to reveal the smoother, less wrinkly skin below. But the top layer of the skin is there for a purpose – to act as a barrier to protect what is underneath. So the patient may be left with very red skin that is much more sensitive to UV radiation.

Four steps to smoother skin

Benedicte de Villeneuve is a cosmetic chemist working for L'Oreal. The company makes a milder cosmetic version for people to use at home to help remove fine wrinkles and imperfections.

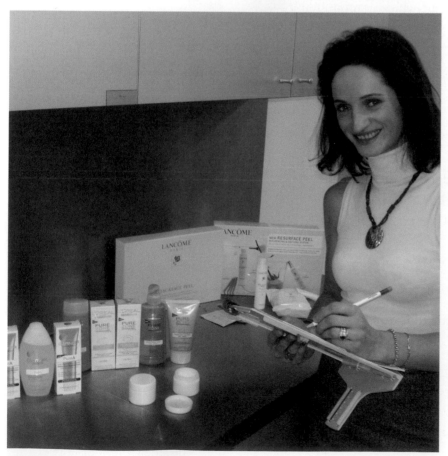

Benedicte de Villeneuve at L'Oréal

'One of our products requires a four-stage process. Users must follow the instructions exactly:

1   'The skin is thoroughly cleansed with a cleansing wipe, which contains mainly ethanol and water.

2   'An emulsion including esters, water, and 4% glycolic acid is applied to the skin for a few minutes only.

3   'The solution is washed off with another wipe that contains an alkaline solution.

4   'A moisturizer containing emollients is applied. Some products have a UV filter too.'

The art of formulation produces products that are attractive, pleasant to use, and effective.

Organic acids can also help people who do not have to worry about wrinkles but have younger, oilier skin prone to spots. Benedicte formulates a range of products containing salicylic acid. 'Salicylic acid is related to aspirin. It is a larger molecule than glycolic acid, so it doesn't penetrate the skin so easily.

'The salicylic acid exfoliates the skin and also acts as an antibacterial. It is added to a whole range of products – cleansers, oil-free moisturizers, and blemish gels.'

The art of formulation

Benedicte originally trained as a pharmacist in Paris, but when a job came up in the labs at L'Oreal, she jumped at the chance. 'Without a knowledge of chemistry, formulating cosmetics would be difficult. Organic chemistry when I was at school could be boring, but now I'm using it every day, and it's great.'

Find out about:

▶ esters from acids and alcohols
▶ synthesis of an ester

1D Esters

Fruity-smelling molecules

When you eat a banana, strawberry, or peach, you taste and smell the powerful odour of a mixture of **esters**. A ripe pineapple contains about 120 mg of the ester ethyl ethanoate in every kilogram of its flesh. There are smaller quantities of other esters together with around 60 mg of ethanol.

Esters are very common. Many sweet-smelling compounds in perfumes and food flavourings are esters. Some drugs used in medicines are esters, including aspirin and paracetamol. The plasticizers used to make polymers such as PVC soft and flexible are also esters (see Module C2 *Material choices*, Section G).

Compounds with more than one ester link include fats and vegetable oils such as butter and sunflower oil (see pages 192–195). The synthetic fibres in many clothes are made of a polyester. The long chains in laminated plastics and surface finishes in kitchen equipment are also held together by ester links.

Ethyl ethanoate (ethyl acetate) is a colourless liquid at room temperature. It has many uses. As well as flavouring food, it is a good solvent. Uses as a solvent include decaffeinating tea and coffee and removing coatings such as nail varnish. It is an ingredient of printing inks and perfumes.

Ester formation

An alcohol can react with a carboxylic acid to make esters. The reaction happens on warming the alcohol and the acid in the presence of a little sulfuric acid to act as catalyst.

The ester with a very strong fruity smell, 3-methylbutyl acetate. It smells strongly of pear drops.

ethanoic acid + methanol ⟶ methyl ethanoate + water

Key words

esters
heat under reflux
drying agent

H Making an ester

The synthesis of ethyl ethanoate on a laboratory scale illustrates techniques used for making a pure liquid product.

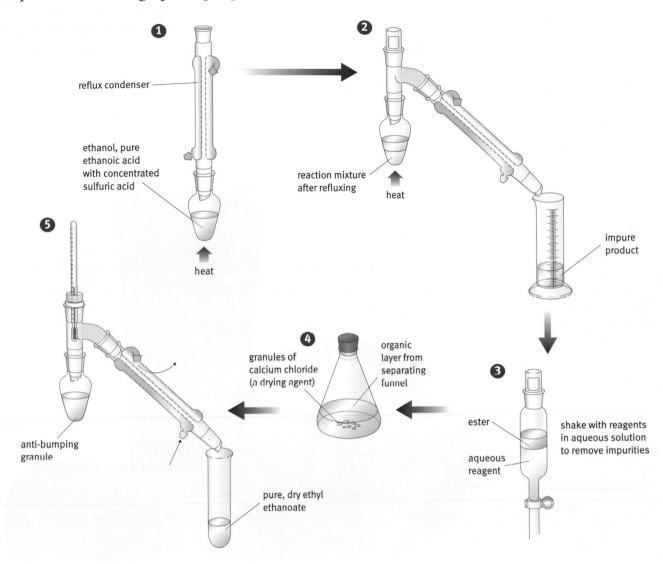

Stages in the laboratory preparation of ethyl ethanoate

Questions

1 a Are the hydrogen atoms bonded to carbon or to oxygen in ethyl ethanoate?

b Would you expect ethyl ethanoate to react with sodium?

c Would you expect ethyl ethanoate to be an acid?

2 Match the steps in the synthesis of ethyl ethanoate with the main stages of a chemical synthesis given in Module C6, Section H.

3 In step A of the synthesis of ethyl ethanoate:

a what is the purpose of the condenser?

b what is the purpose of the sulfuric acid?

4 Calculate the percentage yield if the yield of ethyl ethanoate is 50 g from a preparation starting from 42 g ethanol and 52 g ethanoic acid.

Looking and smelling good

Mimicking nature

Tony Moreton is a chemist working for the Body Shop. Fruit esters crop up all the time in his work: 'We use fruit esters in products that have a fruity smell. They have low molecular masses and low boiling points, which give them the volatility that makes them easy to smell. Their high volatility means they don't linger around for long, and they're referred to as "top notes" in a perfume.

Fruit esters flavour these products.

'As with many organic chemicals, they're flammable, and with their high volatility as well, precautions have to be taken during manufacture.

'The esters used in the industry are "nature identical", which means they are identical to materials found in nature but are made synthetically. Extracting the natural esters would cost about 100 times as much as synthetic ones.'

Esters with a fruity smell

One of the suppliers of ingredients to the Body Shop is a Manchester-based company called Fragrance Oils. One of their products is a blackcurrant perfume concentrate that contains the ester ethyl butanoate. Their perfumery director, Philip Harris, has been familiar with this chemical for a very long time: 'I remember buying strongly flavoured sweets called Pineapple Chunks, which tasted more or less exclusively of ethyl butanoate.

Philip Harris and Farzana Rujidawa working in front of the smelling booths at Fragrance Oils. Philip designed many of the Body Shop's fruit-based fragrances.

'Ethyl butanoate has a strong pineapple aroma, but it's also reminiscent of all sorts of fruity aromas, so we use it in blackcurrant, strawberry, raspberry, apple, mango . . . everything fruity!

'It's quite simply made from ethanol and butanoic acid. The only trouble is that it can hydrolyse back to these starting products, and as butanoic acid is extremely smelly, this isn't so good. We have to avoid using it in alkaline products.

'I've always found it amazing that such an unpleasant smelling material could be used to produce such a delicious fruity smell.'

From fruit esters to soaps

Tony Moreton also uses esters with larger molecules found in various nuts. 'They are formed from glycerol and long-chain fatty acids. They are oily or waxy so are water-resistant, soften the skin, and help retain moisture.

'We can use these fruit esters to produce soap. Synthetic versions of these kinds of esters would be very expensive to make, so in this case we use the natural material.'

Find out about:

▶ structures of fats and oils
▶ saturated and unsaturated
compounds

1E Fats and oils

It is possible to have molecules with more than one ester link between alcohol and acid. Important examples are fats and oils. These compounds release more energy when oxidized than carbohydrates. This makes them important to plants and animals as an energy store.

The structures of fats and oils

The alcohol in fats and oils is **glycerol**. This is a compound with three —OH groups.

The general structure of a compound in which glycerol has formed three ester links with fatty acids. In natural fats and oils the fatty acids may all be the same or they may be a mixture.

The carboxylic acids in fats and oils are often called fatty acids. These are compounds with a long hydrocarbon chain attached to a carboxylic acid group.

Saturated and unsaturated fats

Animal **fats** are generally solids at room temperature. Butter and lard are examples. **Vegetable oils** are usually liquid, as illustrated by corn oil, sunflower oil, and olive oil.

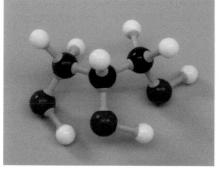

Glycerol, which is also called propan-1,2,3-triol

Chemically the difference between fats and oils arises from the structure of the carboxylic acids. Stearic acid is typical of the acids combined in animal fats. All the bonds in its molecules are single bonds. Chemists use the term **saturated** to describe molecules like this because the molecule has as much hydrogen as it can take. These saturated molecules are straight.

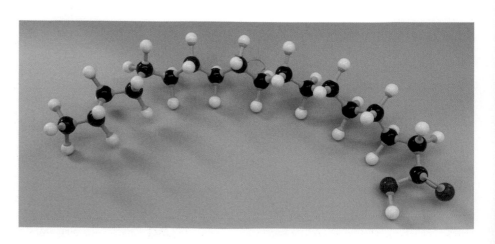

A molecule of stearic acid. It is a saturated compound. The molecule has a very regular shape.

Esters made of glycerol and saturated fats have a regular shape. They pack together easily and are solid at room temperature.

Oleic acid is typical of the acids combined in vegetable oils. There is a double bond in each molecule of this acid. Oleic acid is **unsaturated**. The double bond means that the molecules are not straight. It is more difficult to pack together molecules made of glycerol and unsaturated fats. This means that they are liquid at room temperature.

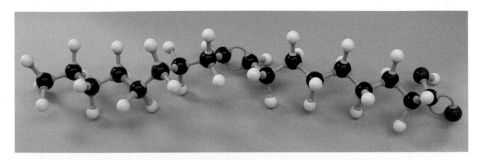

A molecule of oleic acid. The double bond means that there are carbon atoms that do not form four bonds with other atoms. Because there is not as much hydrogen as there would be with all single bonds, these molecules are 'unsaturated'.

Making soap from fats and oils

An ester splits up into an acid and an alcohol when it reacts with water. In the absence of a catalyst this is a very slow change. Chemists call this type of change hydrolysis. 'Hydro-lysis' is derived from two Greek words meaning 'water-splitting'.

$$\text{ester} + \text{water exactly} \longrightarrow \text{acid} + \text{alcohol}$$

A strong alkali, such as sodium hydroxide, is a good catalyst for the hydrolysis of esters. Hydrolysis of fats and oils by heating with alkali produces soaps. Soaps are the sodium or potassium salts of fatty acids.

Questions

1 Chemists sometimes describe fats and oils as 'triglycerides'. Why is this an appropriate name for these compounds?

2 The molecular formula of an acid can be written C_xH_yCOOH. What are the values of x and y in:

  a stearic acid?

  b oleic acid?

3 Manufacturers state that some spreads are high in polyunsaturated fats. Suggest what the term 'polyunsaturated' means.

Key words

glycerol

fats

vegetable oils

saturated

unsaturated

Fats, oils, and our health

The chemistry of fats and oils has triggered food scares. 'Saturated' fats and 'trans' fats are thought to be bad for people, while 'unsaturated' fats (especially polyunsaturated fats) and some 'omega' fatty acids are good. Many people use these terms with little idea of what they mean and limited understanding of the effects of these fats and fatty acids on health.

A range of edible oils from plants

Hydrogenated vegetable oil

Margarine was originally a cheap substitute for butter. It can be made from vegetable oils that have been altered to 'harden' them so that they are solid at room temperature. The easiest way to do this is to turn unsaturated fats into saturated fats by adding hydrogen.

The first margarines were made by bubbling hydrogen through an oil with a nickel catalyst. The hydrogen hardened the oil by adding to the double bonds and turning it into a saturated fat. This is a relatively cheap and easy process. However, research in the 1960s started to show that these saturated fats could contribute to heart disease.

Three types of spread made from vegetable oils

Trans and *cis* fats

Some margarine tubs, and bottles of vegetable oil, give information about *cis*- and *trans*-fatty acids. This refers to how the hydrogen atoms are arranged either side of the double bond.

Trans-fatty acids can form during the hydrogenation process used to make some 'hard' margarines. In the 1990s an American scientist, Walter Willet, found evidence that too much *trans*-fat could aggravate heart disease. Not all scientists agreed with him, and the research continues.

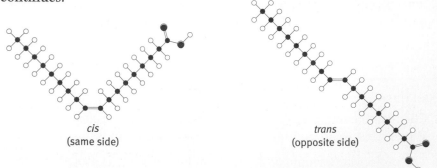

cis
(same side)

trans
(opposite side)

If both parts of the hydrocarbon chain are on the same side of the double bond between carbon atoms, it is *cis*. Nearly all naturally occurring unsaturated fatty acids contain *cis* double bonds. If the two parts of the chain are on the opposite sides of the double bond, it is *trans*. The shape of a *trans*-unsaturated molecule is a bit like a saturated fatty acid. They are not as runny as *cis*-molecules.

Hardening without hydrogen

Food scientists have found ways to turn vegetable oils into solid spreads without adding hydrogen. The fatty acids in vegetable oils are polyunsaturated. The molecules of these fatty acids are not straight because of all the double bonds. So they do not pack together easily.

Imagine what would happen if you could swap the fatty acid chains around so that they all stack together more neatly and make a denser material. This is exactly what modern margarine makers do – using a catalyst, they make the fatty acids rearrange themselves. David Allen works for one of the suppliers to a big supermarket chain: 'It's a bit like musical chairs in that they all change places. Instead of music you have a catalyst, or an enzyme, and the right conditions.'

Omega-3 and omega-6 oils

Omega is the last letter in the Greek alphabet. The letter is used in a naming system which counts from the last carbon atom in the chain of a fatty acid molecule – the carbon atom furthest from the —COOH group. If you count in this way, omega-3 fatty acids have the first double bond between carbon atoms 3 and 4. Omega-6 fatty acids have the first double bond between carbon atoms 6 and 7.

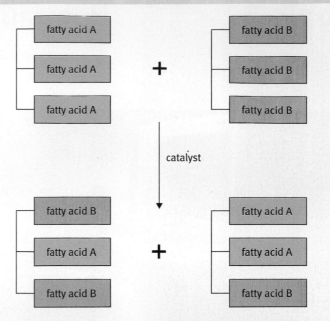

In the presence of a catalyst the fatty acids can swap places between molecules of fats and oils. This results in a mixture. The diagram shows just two of the possible products. This can raise the melting point by several degrees.

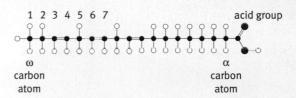

Linolenic acid is a fatty acid with three double bonds. They are all *cis*. This form of linolenic acid is an omega-3 fatty acid. Another form of linolenic acid is an omega-6 fatty acid. If you count from the carbon atom, the omega-6 acid has double bonds between carbon atoms numbered 6 and 7, 9 and 10, and 12 and 13.

Some of these omega compounds are essential fatty acids because our bodies need them but cannot make them. People need to take them in through our diet. According to Professor John Harwood of Cardiff University, it is important to have the right ratio of omega-6 to omega-3: 'You need a ratio of about three times omega-6 to one omega-3. But most people in Western countries take in far too much omega-6 and not enough omega-3 – more like a ratio of 15 to 1.'

Omega-6 fatty acids are found in margarines and most plant oils. Omega-3 acids are found in oily fish and in flax oil. 'Omega-3 can reduce pain in joints,' says Professor Harwood. 'It is also important in the developing brain of the very young and in the brains of the very old, and has implications for cardiovascular disease.'

Topic 2

How much? How fast? How far?

This topic tackles three challenging questions which scientists try to answer when explaining changes to chemicals and materials:

Chemical analysis helps to answer the question 'How much?'.

How much? How fast? How far? These questions matter to the people that control chemical processes. Instruments in the control room help them to monitor the process.

How much?

How much? refers not only to the amounts of reactants and products but also to the quantities of energy given out or taken in during a change.

How fast?

How fast? is important to anyone trying to control changes from cooks in a kitchen to chemical engineers making chemicals on a large scale. Topic 4 on pages 240–251 shows how scientists today are using their understanding of catalysts to make the chemical industry more sustainable.

How far?

How far? is also important to anyone trying to get the maximum yield from a chemical change. The study of carboxylic acids in Topic 1 (pages 184–185) showed that these are weak acids. They do ionize but only to a slight extent. Answering the question 'How far?' helps to explain why some acids, like the organic acids, are weak, while others, such as the mineral acids, are strong.

Molecular theories

Chemists explain their answers to these questions with the help of theories about the behaviour of atoms and molecules. Atoms and molecules are too small to see, so chemists use models to help develop their theories.

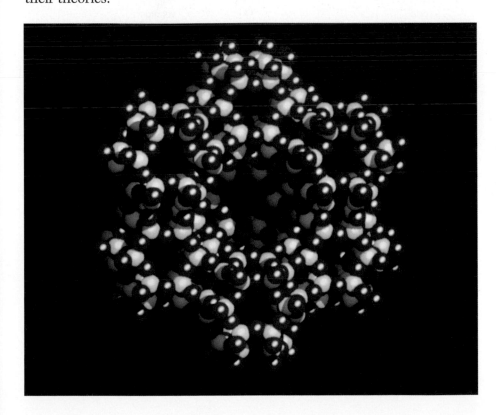

Computer graphic of a model of a zeolite crystal. The yellow atoms are either silicon or aluminium atoms. The red atoms are oxygen. Zeolites are catalysts used to control reactions in the petrochemical industry. Chemists can make synthetic zeolites with crystal structures designed to catalyse particular reactions.

113

A forest fire raging in California, USA

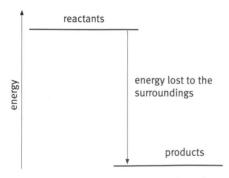

Energy level diagram for an exothermic reaction

2A Energy changes and chemical reactions

All chemical changes give out or take in energy. The study of energy and change is central to the science of explaining the extent and direction of a wide variety of changes. Understanding these energy changes also helps chemists to control reactions.

Changes that give out energy

Many reactions give out energy to their surroundings. This is obvious during burning. Most of the energy we use to keep warm, cook food, and drive machinery comes from fuels reacting with oxygen.

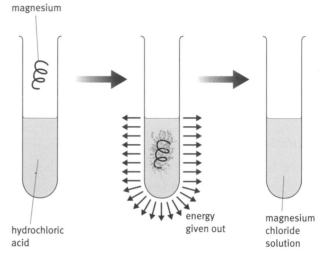

An example of an exothermic reaction

Reactions that give out energy are **exothermic**. Respiration is an example of an exothermic change. During respiration, oxygen and glucose change to carbon dioxide and water in ways that provide the energy for growth, movement, and warmth in living things.

The reaction of magnesium with dilute hydrochloric acid is exothermic. It heats up the test tube and surrounding air.

The change can be described with the help of an **energy level diagram**. Energy is released to the surroundings. So the energy of the product, a solution of magnesium chloride, is less than the energy of the reactants (magnesium and hydrochloric acid).

Changes that take in energy

There are some changes that take in energy from their surroundings. These are **endothermic** reactions. Melting and boiling are endothermic changes of state. Photosynthesis is endothermic: plants take in energy from the Sun to convert carbon dioxide and water to glucose. This is the reverse of respiration.

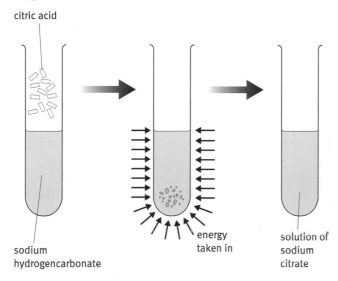

citric acid

sodium hydrogencarbonate

energy taken in

solution of sodium citrate

An example of an endothermic reaction

Traditional sherbet sweets were a mixture of sugar, citric acid, and sodium hydrogencarbonate. The sensation of eating sherbet mixture is a combination of the sweetness of the sugar, the acidity of citric acid, and best of all the fizzing as the acid reacts with the carbonate. This sensation is caused by the chilling effect of an endothermic reaction.

The change can also be described with the help of an energy level diagram. Energy is taken in from the surroundings. So the energy of the product, the solution of sodium citrate, is greater than the energy of the reactants (citric acid and sodium hydrogen carbonate.).

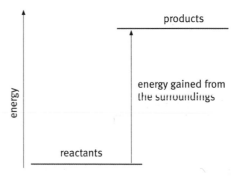

Energy level diagram for an endothermic reaction

Questions

1 Classify these changes as exothermic or endothermic:
   a petrol burning
   b water turning to steam
   c water freezing
   d sodium hydroxide neutralizing hydrochloric acid
2 Turning 18 g ice into water at 0 °C requires 6.0 kJ of energy. Use an energy level diagram to show this change.

How much energy?

There is growing interest in hydrogen as a fuel because water is the only product of its reaction with oxygen. This is a highly exothermic reaction, but even so, a mixture of hydrogen and oxygen has to be coaxed into reacting. At room temperature the two gases do not react. It takes a hot flame or an electric spark to heat up the mixture enough for the reaction to start.

Filling a test car with liquid hydrogen fuel in Germany. In the background is the array of solar cells that generate the electricity to produce the hydrogen at this solar hydrogen filling station.

This is because, in all reactions, regardless of whether they are exothermic or endothermic, some of the chemical bonds in the reactants have to be broken before new chemical bonds in the products can be formed. If the reaction is sufficiently exothermic, then the energy given out keeps the mixture hot enough for the reaction to continue.

The strengths of the chemical bonds that break and form during a reaction determine the size of the overall energy change and whether it is exothermic or endothermic. Think of chemical bonds as tiny springs. In order to get hydrogen to react with oxygen, the tiny springs joining the atoms in the molecules have to be stretched and broken. This takes energy, as you will know if you have ever tried to stretch and break an elastic band.

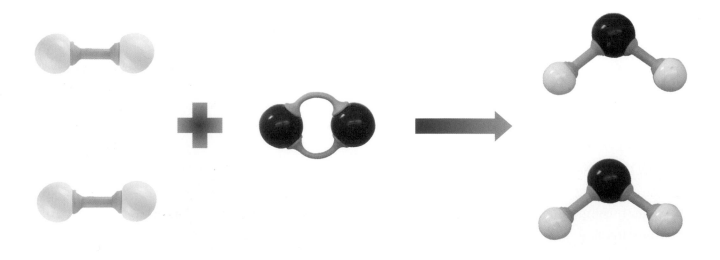

Two H—H bonds and one O=O bond break when hydrogen reacts with oxygen. The atoms recombine to make water as four new O—H bonds form.

The product is water. This is created as new bonds form between oxygen atoms and hydrogen atoms. Bond formation releases energy – just like relaxing a spring. So what decides whether a chemical reaction is exothermic or endothermic is the difference between the energy taken in to break bonds and the energy given out as new bonds form.

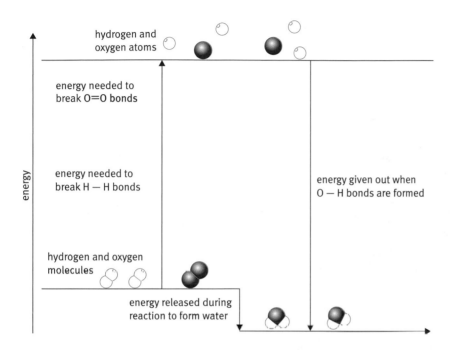

Two H—H bonds and one O=O bond break when hydrogen reacts with oxygen. The atoms recombine to make water as four new O—H bonds form.

Questions

3 Hydrogen burns in chlorine.

$$H_2(g) + Cl_2(g) \longrightarrow 2HCl(g)$$

a Which bonds break during the reaction?

b Which bonds form during the reaction?

c Use the data in the table to calculate the overall energy change for the reacting masses shown in the equation. The energy units are kilojoules (kJ).

Process	Energy change for the formula masses
breaking one H—H bond	434 kJ needed
breaking one Cl—Cl bond	242 kJ needed
forming one H—Cl bond	431 kJ given out

d Is the reaction exothermic or endothermic?

e Draw an energy level diagram for the reaction.

Find out about

▶ collisions between molecules
▶ activation energies

2B How fast?

Molecular collisions

In a mixture of hydrogen gas and oxygen gas the molecules are constantly colliding. Millions upon millions of collisions happen every second. If every collision led to a reaction, there would immediately be an explosive reaction.

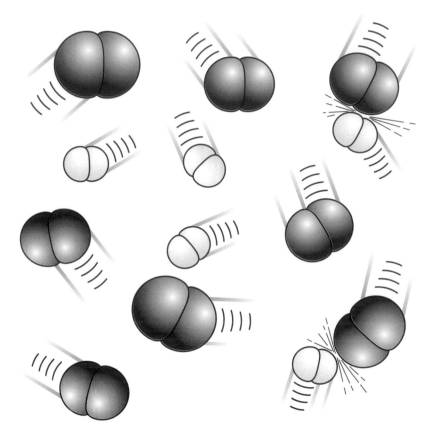

A mixture of hydrogen and oxygen molecules. The molecules that are colliding may react to form new molecules, but only if they have enough energy to start breaking bonds.

Activation energies

It is not enough for the hydrogen and oxygen atoms to collide. Bonds between atoms must break before new molecules can form. This needs energy. For every reaction, there is a certain minimum energy needed before the process can happen. This minimum energy is called the **activation energy**. It is like an energy hill that the reactants have to climb before a reaction will start. The higher the hill, the more difficult it is to get the reaction started.

The collisions between molecules have a range of energies. Head-on collisions between fast-moving particles are the most energetic. If the colliding molecules have enough energy, the collision is 'successful', and a reaction occurs.

Fast and slow reactions

The course of a reaction is like a high-jump competition. The bar is set at a height such that only a few competitors with enough energy can jump it and land safely the other side. The chemical equivalent is shown in the diagram below, where the height of the bar is represented by the activation energy and the landing area by the products of reaction.

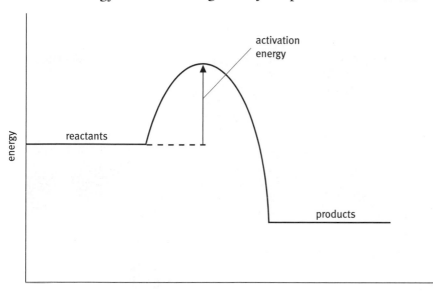

progress of the reaction

The activation energy for a reaction. The size of the activation energy is usually less than the energy needed to break all the bonds in the reactant molecules because new bonds start forming while old bonds are breaking.

If the high-jump bar is low, many competitors are successful. If it is high, the success rate is much less. In chemical reactions, if the activation energy is low, a high proportion of collisions have enough energy to break bonds, and the reaction is fast even at low temperatures.

Reactions in which the activation energy is high are very slow at room temperature, because only a small fraction of collisions have enough energy to cross the activation energy barrier. Heating the mixture to raise the temperature gives the molecules more energy. In the hot mixture more molecules have enough energy to react when they collide.

Questions

1 a Why is a spark or flame needed to light a Bunsen burner?

b Why does the gas keep burning once it has been lit?

2 Adding a catalyst to a reaction mixture means that the activation energy for the change is lower. Suggest why this speeds up the reaction even if the temperature does not change.

Chemistry in action

The explosives expert

All chemists secretly love controlled explosions, even if they do not admit it openly. The word 'control' is important. To be useful, explosions have to be controlled. Designing and understanding that control is part of Jackie Akhavan's job.

Jackie Akhavan works for Cranfield University as an explosives chemist. Her work has applications in quarrying and mining, bomb disposal, demolition, and fireworks.

Two types of explosive

'There are two types of high explosive,' explains Jackie. 'There are primary explosives, which have low activation energies, and secondary explosives, which have higher activation energies.

'Therefore it takes less energy to initiate primary explosives. They are more sensitive to an external stimulus such as friction or impact. This makes them more dangerous to handle than secondary explosives. Secondary explosives are more difficult to initiate.'

Making explosives

The manufacture of old-fashioned primary explosives such as gunpowder and dynamite is very dangerous. Alfred Nobel invented dynamite. He started off by making nitroglycerine from nitric acid, glycerol, and sulfuric acid, but it was fraught with danger. In 1864 his factory blew up, killing several people, including his own younger brother, Emil. After this he combined nitroglycerine with nitrocellulose and silica in solid sticks, which was marginally safer. When Nobel died, he left the money he had made to set up the Nobel prizes.

A fireball from detonating gunpowder

Emulsion explosives are much safer. They are made of an emulsion of ammonium nitrate powder in a mixture of a saturated solution of ammonium nitrate, with oil and air. 'None of these materials are classed as explosives on their own, and it is only when they are mixed together that they become an explosive hazard,' explains Jackie. So the materials can be transported separately to a quarry and mixed on site.

New explosives and detonators

Jackie is a polymer chemist by training, and she has worked on making polymer-bonded explosives. These are secondary explosives and are much easier to control. 'A polymer explosive can be manufactured in a variety of forms, including sheets which resemble plasticine. The explosive can be wrapped around an old bomb or a pipe, and a detonator pushed into the sheet. On initiation, the explosive cuts the metal into two pieces.'

'Some detonators, particularly in mining, still use primary explosives because they are easy to initiate and burn to detonation, resulting in a shock wave which provides the energy to set off the main explosive charge.' Jackie is working on replacements that use a less sensitive secondary explosive.

Jackie has also been involved in new ways of providing the activation energy to make detonators start explosions. This used to be done using an electrical current, but accidents can happen: 'These types of detonator are vulnerable to initiation by unwanted electromagnetic radiation from overhead pylons or thunderstorms. We've recently developed a new detonator that uses secondary explosives and is initiated with a laser pulsed through a fibre optic cable. It is safe to handle and can't be set off by unwanted electromagnetic radiation.'

A controlled explosion in a quarry. There is a puff of smoke, a lot of noise, and a shock wave that loosens the block of rock.

Safety

Safety is always important in chemistry and is essential in Jackie's work: 'I am not allowed to detonate an explosion myself as I don't have the specific training – even though I understand the chemistry.' It is in fact illegal as well as dangerous to carry out unauthorised experiments with explosive chemicals. Jackie is well aware that it is serious business: 'I know the power of explosives and the damage they can do. I still have all my fingers, and I intend to keep it that way!'

Find out about:
- reactions that go both ways
- factors affecting the direction of change

Questions

1 a Write a symbol equation to show water turning into steam.

  b Write another equation to show steam condensing to water.

  c Write a third equation to show the changes in **a** and **b** as a single, reversible change.

2 The pioneering French chemist Lavoisier (1743–1794) heated mercury in air and obtained the red solid mercury oxide.
He also heated mercury oxide to form mercury and oxygen.

  a How can both these statements be true?

  b Why should you not try to repeat the experiment?

3 a Write an equation to show the reversible reaction of carbon monoxide gas with steam to form carbon dioxide and hydrogen.

  b In your equation, what happens in the forward reaction?

  c In your equation, what happens in the backward reaction?

2C Reversible changes

Some changes go only in one direction. For example, the reactions that happen to a raw egg in boiling water cannot be reversed by cooling the egg. To produce a soft-boiled egg, a cook has to check that it stays in the water for just the right amount of time. Other processes in the kitchen are easily reversed. A table jelly sets as it cools but becomes liquid again on warming. Chemists, like cooks, have to understand how to control conditions to get reactions to go far enough and in the right direction.

Burning methane in air is an example of an irreversible change. The gas burns to form carbon dioxide and water. It is then pretty well impossible to turn the products back into methane and oxygen.

Reversible changes of state

In contrast, melting and evaporating are familiar **reversible processes**. Heating turns water into steam, but water re-forms as steam condenses on cooling.

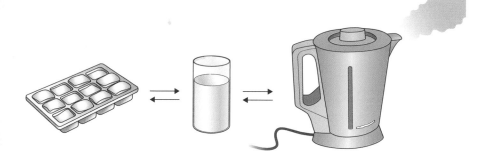

Two familiar reversible processes

Heating turns ice into water:

$$H_2O(s) \longrightarrow H_2O(l)$$

Ice reforms if water cools to 0 °C or below.

$$H_2O(l) \longrightarrow H_2O(s)$$

Combining these two equations gives:

$$H_2O(s) \rightleftharpoons H_2O(l)$$

Many chemical reactions are also reversible. A reversible reaction can go forwards or backwards depending on the conditions. The direction of change may vary with the temperature, pressure, or concentration of the chemicals.

Temperature and the direction of chemical change

Heating decomposes blue copper sulfate crystals to give water and anhydrous copper sulfate, which is white:

$$CuSO_4.5H_2O(s) \longrightarrow CuSO_4(s) + 5H_2O(l)$$

Add water to the white powder after cooling, and it changes back into the hydrated form of the chemical. As it does so it turns blue again and gets very hot:

$$CuSO_4(s) + 5H_2O(l) \longrightarrow CuSO_4.5H_2O(s)$$

Another example of temperature affecting the direction of change is the formation of ammonium chloride. At room temperature ammonia gas and hydrogen chloride gas react to form a white solid, ammonium chloride:

$$NH_3(g) + HCl(g) \longrightarrow NH_4Cl(s)$$

Gentle heating decomposes ammonium chloride back into ammonia and hydrogen chloride:

$$NH_4Cl(s) \longrightarrow NH_3(g) + HCl(g)$$

Concentration and the direction of chemical change

This equation describes the reaction between iron and steam:

$$3Fe(s) + 4H_2O(g) \longrightarrow Fe_3O_4(s) + 4H_2(g)$$

The change from left to right (from reactants to products) is the forward reaction. The change from right to left (from products to reactants) is the backward reaction.

The forward reaction is favoured if the concentration of steam is high and the concentration of hydrogen is low.

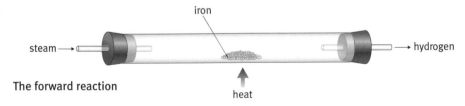

The forward reaction

The backward reaction is favoured if the concentration of hydrogen is high and the concentration of steam is low:

$$Fe_3O_4(s) + 4H_2(g) \longrightarrow 3Fe(s) + 4H_2O(g)$$

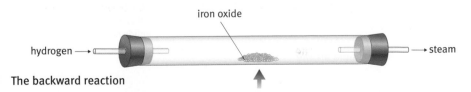

The backward reaction

Ammonium chloride forming where ammonia and hydrogen chloride gases meet above concentrated solutions of the two compounds on glass stoppers.

Find out about

▶ chemical equilibrium
▶ dynamic equilibrium
▶ strong and weak acids

2D How far?

Equilibrium

Reversible changes often reach a state of balance, or **equilibrium**. A solution of litmus in water at pH 7 is purple because it contains a mixture of the red and blue forms of the indicator. Similarly melting ice and water are at equilibrium at 0 °C. At this temperature, the two states of water coexist with no tendency for all the ice to melt or all the water to freeze.

When reversible reactions are at equilibrium, neither the forward nor the backward reaction is complete. Reactants and products are present together and the reaction appears to have stopped. Reactions like this are at equilibrium. Chemists use a special symbol in equations for reactions at equilibrium: $\rightleftharpoons$

So at 0 °C,

$$H_2O(s) \rightleftharpoons H_2O(l)$$

The question 'How far?' asks where the equilibrium point is in a reaction. At equilibrium the reaction may be well to the right (mainly products), well to the left (mainly reactants), or at any point between these extremes.

Reaching an equilibrium state

A mixture of two solutions of iodine helps to explain what happens when a reversible process reaches a state of equilibrium. Iodine is slightly soluble in water but much more soluble in a potassium iodide solution in water. The solution with aqueous potassium iodide is yellow-brown. Iodine is also soluble in organic solvents (such as a liquid alkane), in which it forms a violet solution.

Aqueous potassium iodide and the organic solvent do not mix.

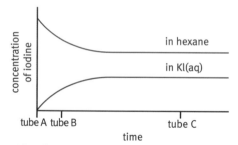

The change of concentration of iodine with time in the mixture shown in the diagram below.

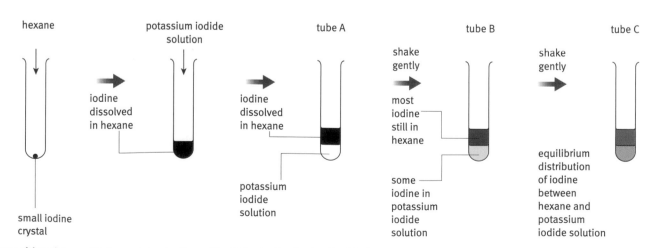

Approaching the equilibrium state starting with all the iodine in the liquid alkane

The graphs show how the iodine concentrations in the two layers change
with shaking. In tube C, the iodine is distributed between the organic
and aqueous layers and there is no more change. In this tube there is
an equilibrium:

Key words
equilibrium

$$I_2(\text{organic}) \rightleftharpoons I_2(\text{aq})$$

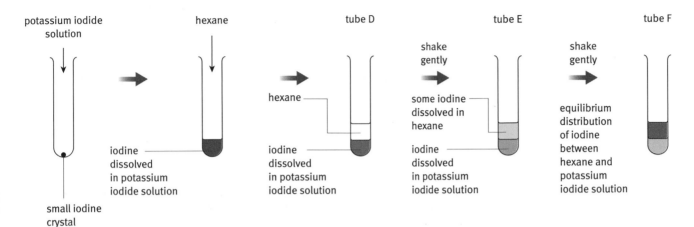

Approaching the equilibrium state starting with all the iodine in the aqueous layer

Tube F looks just like tube C. Tube F is also at equilibrium: equilibrium
mixtures in the two tubes are the same. This illustrates two important
features of equilibrium processes:

▶ At equilibrium, the concentrations of reactants and products do
not change.

▶ An equilibrium state can be approached from either the 'reactant
side' or the 'product side' of a reaction.

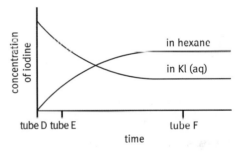

The change of concentration of iodine
with time in the mixture shown in the
diagram above.

Dynamic equilibrium

The diagram below gives a picture of what happens to the iodine molecules if you shake a solution of iodine in an organic solvent with aqueous potassium iodide (see tube A on page 208).

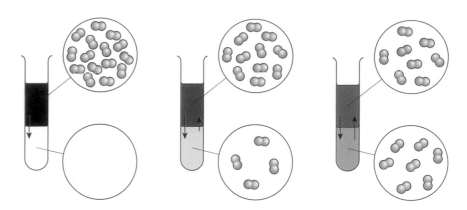

Iodine molecules reaching dynamic equilibrium between two solvents. The solvent molecules are far more numerous. They are not shown.

All the iodine starts in the upper, organic layer. At first, when the solution is shaken, movement is in one direction (the forward reaction) as some molecules move into the aqueous layer. There is nothing to stop some of these molecules moving back into the organic layer. This backward reaction starts slowly because the concentration in the aqueous layer is low. So to begin with, the overall effect is that iodine moves from the organic to the aqueous layer. This is because the forward reaction is faster than the backward reaction.

As the concentration in the organic layer falls, the rate of the forward reaction goes down. As the iodine concentration in the aqueous layer rises, the rate of the backward reaction goes up. There comes a point at which the two rates are equal. At this point both forward and backward reactions continue, but there is no overall change because each layer is gaining and losing iodine at the same rate. This is **dynamic equilibrium**.

Questions

1 Under what conditions are these in equilibrium:

   a water and ice?

   b water and steam?

   c salt crystals and a solution of salt in water?

2 **a** Why do iron and steam not reach an equilibrium state when they react as shown in the upper diagram on page 207?

   b Suggest conditions in which a mixture of iron and steam would react to reach an equilibrium state.

   c What chemicals would be present in an equilibrium mixture formed from iron and steam?

Theories of acidity

Understanding chemical equilibrium allows chemists to control the pH in medicines and to formulate 'pH-balanced' shampoos.

Theories of acidity have come a long way since Robert Boyle (1661) gave the name 'acid' to chemicals with a sharp taste. He explained their properties by imagining spikes on the atoms.

In 1816 Humphry Davy suggested that acids all behave the same way because they contain hydrogen. Later in the same century, Svante Arrhenius took this a step further by thinking of acids as compounds which form hydrogen ions when they dissolve in water.

The Arrhenius explanation still provides a useful working definition of an acid, even though ideas about acidity moved on during the twentieth century, as you will learn if you go on to study chemistry at a more advanced level.

Strong acids

Hydrogen chloride gas dissolves in water to give a solution of hydrochloric acid.

$$HCl(g) + water \longrightarrow H^+(aq) + Cl^-(aq)$$

All the molecules of hydrogen chloride ionize when the gas dissolves in water (see Module C6 *Chemical synthesis*, Section C). Hydrogen chloride is a **strong acid**.

Other examples of strong acids are sulfuric and nitric acids.

Weak acids

Carboxylic acids are **weak acids**. In a dilute solution of ethanoic acid only about one molecule in a hundred ionizes. In solution there is a dynamic equilibrium:

$$CH_3COOH(aq) + H_2O(l) \rightleftharpoons CH_3COO^-(aq) + H^+(aq)$$

Key words
strong acid
weak acids
dynamic equilibrium

As well as his ideas about acidity, Humphry Davy (1778–1829) used electrolysis to discover several new elements, including sodium, potassium, magnesium, and calcium. He showed that chlorine and iodine are elements. He also invented the **safety lamp** for miners.

Questions

3 a How are the reactions of magnesium with hydrochloric acid and nitric acid:
  i similar? **ii** different?

  b How can the Arrhenius theory explain why solutions of hydrochloric acid and nitric acid react in a similar way with magnesium?

4 Explain what it means to say that there is a dynamic equilibrium in a solution of ethanoic acid in water.

Equilibrium at work

pH-balanced

Shampoos and other toiletries are often labelled as being 'pH-balanced', and you might have wondered what that means. Well, it is not just marketing hype; it is about the science of equilibrium.

Controlling the pH in shampoos, bath bubbles, and shower gels helps to protect the skin and eyes.

The pH of something is a measure of how acid or alkaline it is. The nearer 0 it is, the more acid, and the nearer 14, the more alkaline (see Module C6 *Chemical synthesis*, Section B). A pH of 7 means it is neutral. Some products need to be a particular pH to work effectively, and chemists have to make sure that pH does not change. This might happen, for example, if a product sits on a shop shelf for months.

pH control

Stewart Long works for Boots the Chemists as a formulations manager: 'Particular products do have to be made at specific pH values. Skin care products need to be slightly acid at around 5.5. Shampoos tend to be more alkaline.

'Hair colouring products need to be alkaline too. This makes the scales on the hair shaft open up so the colour can penetrate more easily. Conditioners are acidic and this makes the scales flatten down again making the hair shaft smooth and shiny.'

But how does Stewart formulate a particular pH and make sure the product stays that way? 'Well, we have to control what is essentially a reversible reaction, making sure there's the right concentration of H^+ ions in the solution.'

Buffer solutions

Stewart's formulations include buffer solutions. These are mixtures of molecules and ions in solution that help to keep the pH more or less constant. A buffer solution cannot prevent pH changes, but it can even out the large swings in pH that can happen without a buffer. A typical buffer solution consists of a weak acid mixed with one of its salts.

Topic 3

Chemical analysis

The business of analysis

Analytical measurement is important. It is essential to ensure that the things we use in our everyday lives do us good and not harm. Over £7 billion is spent each year on chemical analysis in the UK.

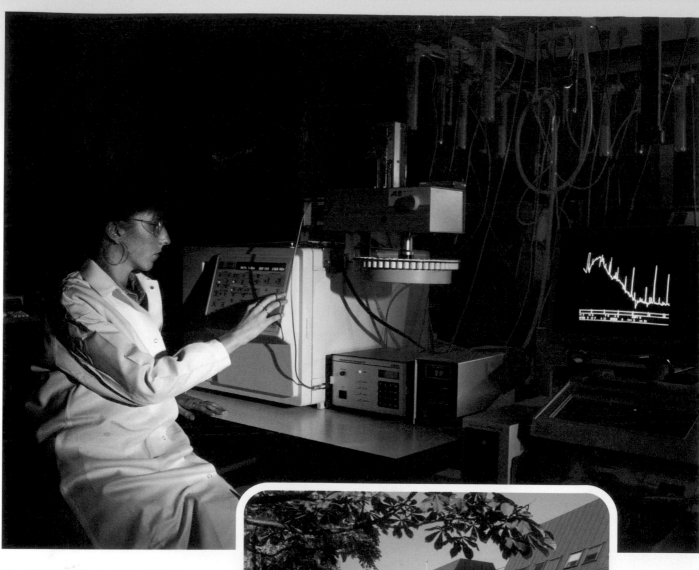

The LGC in Teddington is the UK's largest independent analytical laboratory. Its work covers food and agriculture, oil and chemicals, the environment, health care, life sciences, and law enforcement. It organizes proficiency tests to check the performance of analytical laboratories.

Health and safety

The responsibility for health and safety in a laboratory is shared by
everybody. Observing these regulations helps to keep accidents down
to a minimum and the risk of injury low. Laboratories have their own
health and safety regulations and codes of practice. Many have health and
safety officers.

Looking after equipment

Equipment must be kept in good working condition. It has to be serviced
regularly. Measuring instruments are checked at regular intervals.

Equipment should be cleaned properly after use and stored correctly.
This is particularly important for fragile pieces of equipment such
as glassware.

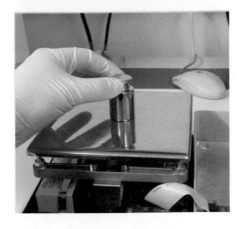

This electronic balance, like all
equipment, must be maintained
correctly and tested.

Accreditation

Analytical laboratories must show that they can do the job. Like the things
tested in them, all laboratories must meet standards. Their standards are
checked by the United Kingdom Accreditation Service (UKAS).

Analysts use proficiency tests to assess their work. Each laboratory receives
identical samples to analyse. They send their results back to the organizers,
who evaluate them. The laboratories are not named in the report, but
results are coded so that a laboratory can recognize its results and see how
well it has done.

International standards

There are international standards too. The International Olympic
Committee (IOC), for example, accredits 27 laboratories to test blood and
urine samples from athletes. The laboratories are all over the world and
analyse 100 000 samples each year.

An analyst testing for stimulants in one of the laboratories accredited by the IOC

Find out about:
- qualitative and quantitative methods
- steps in analysis
- sampling

3A Stages in an analysis

Choosing an analytical method

The first step is to pick a suitable method of analysis. A **qualitative** method can be used if the aim is simply to find out the chemical composition of the specimen. However, if the aim is to find out how much of each component is present, then a **quantitative** approach is essential.

Analysts study samples of blood and urine to look for the presence of banned substances in athletes and other sports people. This can include qualitative analysis to identify drugs and quantitative analysis to find out how much of a banned substance there is in a sample.

Taking a sample

The analysis must be carried out on a **sample** that represents the bulk of the material under test. This can be hard to achieve with an uneven mixture of solids, such as a soil, but much easier when the chemicals are evenly mixed in solution, as in urine.

Measuring out laboratory specimens for analysis

Analysts take a sample and measure out accurately known masses or volumes of the material for analysis. It is common to carry through the analysis with two or more samples in parallel to check on the reliability of the final result. These are **replicate samples**.

Dissolving the samples

Many analytical methods are based on a solution of the specimens. With the analysis of acids or alkalis that are soluble in water, this is not a problem. It can be much more difficult to prepare a solution when analysts are working with minerals, biological specimens, or polymers.

Measuring a property of the samples in solution

When determining quantities, analysts look for a property to measure that is proportional to the amount of chemical in the sample. With an acid, for example, the approach is to find the volume of alkali needed to neutralize it. The more acid present, the greater the volume of alkali needed to neutralize it.

Calculating a value from the measurements

An understanding of chemical theory allows analysts to convert their measurements to chemical quantities. Given the equation for the reaction, and the concentration of the acid, it is possible to calculate the concentration of the acid from the volume of alkali needed to neutralize it.

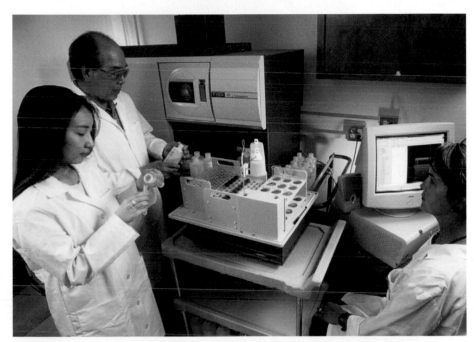

Analysts preparing blood and urine samples for analysis. They are using a type of spectrometer to measure the concentrations of iron and zinc in the samples.

Estimating the reliability of the results

Analysts have to state how much confidence they have in the accuracy of their results. Comparing the values obtained from two or three replicate samples helps.

Questions

1 Who might be interested in the results of the following analyses and why?

  a The potassium ion concentration in soil.

  b The concentration of sulfur dioxide in the air.

  c The concentration of alcohol in blood.

  d The percentage by mass of haematite in a rock sample.

  e The concentration of a steroid hormone in urine.

  f The concentration of nitrates in drinking water.

133

3B Sampling

Analysts work with samples of materials. Rarely do they analyse the whole thing. How big the samples need to be depends on the analyses to be carried out.

Representative samples

The samples the analyst chooses must be **representative**. In other words, the samples should give an accurate picture of the material as a whole.

The composition of a homogeneous material is uniform throughout, like a dairy milk chocolate bar.

The composition of a heterogeneous material varies throughout it, like a chocolate bar made in layers.

Scientists have to decide:

> how many samples, and how much of each, must be collected to ensure they are representative of the material

> how many times an analysis should be repeated on a sample to ensure results are reliable

> where, when, and how to collect the samples of the material

> how to store samples and transport them to the laboratory to prevent the samples from 'going off', becoming contaminated, or being tampered with

Analysing water

Think about analysing water from two different sources. One is bottled water bought at a local supermarket. The other is from a local stream.

The bottled water is clear. There are no solids in suspension. It is likely to be tested for dissolved metal salts. The water is homogeneous, so only a single sample is needed. However, to check a batch of bottles, the analyst would take samples from a number of bottles. How much is needed depends on the test. There are no storage or transport problems. The bottle can be opened in the laboratory. This is a straightforward sampling problem.

Water from the stream may be cloudy. It may contain small creatures. It may be tested for a range of things, from the concentrations of dissolved chemicals to the number and variety of living organisms. Samples may vary from one part of the stream to another. They are likely to be heterogeneous. The time of year when samples are collected will have an effect on the water's composition. Also, samples need to be stored and taken back to the laboratory for analysis. This is a complex sampling problem that needs careful planning.

Questions

1 Suggest how an analyst should go about sampling when faced with the following problems? In each case, identify the difficulties of taking representative samples. Suggest ways of overcoming the difficulties.

   a Measuring the concentration of chlorine disinfectant in a swimming pool.

   b Checking the purity of citric acid supplied to a food processor.

   c Detecting banned drugs in the urine of athletes.

   d Monitoring the quality of aspirin tablets made by a pharmaceutical company.

   e Determining the level of nitrates in a farmer's field.

2 Why is the way that samples are stored important?

Collecting samples

A life of grime

All local authorities have Environmental Health Officers. Most of their work involves checking restaurants, cafes, and food shops, but they do many other things as well, including checking pollution levels. The photograph shows Ralph Haynes of Camden Council in London taking soil samples.

Ralph Haynes taking a soil sample in Camden

Ralph says: 'There is concern that chromium salts from an old metal plating factory nearby may have contaminated the soil. I am taking 1 kg samples and putting them in plastic containers. I am taking care to label it properly. There is a British Standard on labelling, you know: it's called BS5969.

'I'm taking care to take a sample from where I can actually see the change in the soil. I'm also going to take a sample from where I can't see it. Then I'm going to take samples from anywhere where I think people could be at risk – such as gardens where children play.

'Soil samples will keep for a while, but I'm also going to take water samples, and these must get to the lab within a couple of days.'

Sporting samples

Sports men and women are often asked to provide urine samples to check if they have been taking drugs. Sometimes these cases hit the headlines, and allegations have been made in the past that urine samples have been tampered with.

The scientists who carry out the analysis at Kings College, London, have to be sure that they have the right sample and that it has been correctly stored and labelled.

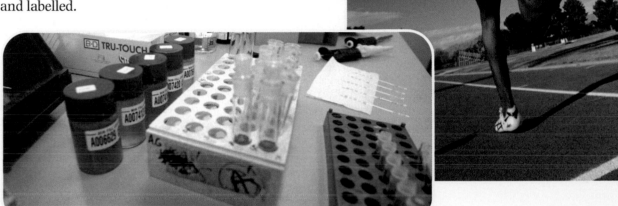

Labelled urine samples from athletes ready for testing

- First, the athlete has to produce the sample in front of a testing officer, who has to actually see the urine leaving the athlete's body and ensure there has been no cheating.

- With the testing officer watching, the athlete is allowed to pour the sample into two bottles. They seal the bottles themselves so that they feel assured no one else has tampered with them.

- The bottles are labelled with a unique code rather than the athlete's name, so the lab does not know the identity of the athlete. The bottles are sent to the lab by courier in secure polystyrene packaging.

- At the lab, one bottle is analysed immediately and the other stored in the freezer in case there is a query at a later date.

'We send the results to the Sports Council,' says Richard Caldwell, one of the analysts. 'It is someone at the Council who tallies up which bottle was collected from which person. It's quite interesting when we have a positive result and we find out from the press a few months later who it was!'

Find out about:

▶ principles of chromatography
▶ paper chromatography
▶ thin-layer chromatography

3C Chromatography

There are several types of **chromatography**. At the cheap-and-simple end is paper chromatography, which can be done with some blotting paper and a solvent. At the expensive end is gas chromatography, which involves high-precision instruments. All types of chromatography, however, work on similar principles.

Chromatography can be used to:

▶ separate and identify the chemicals in a mixture

▶ check the purity of a chemical

▶ purify small samples of a chemical

Principles of chromatography

In chromatography a **mobile phase** moves through a medium called the **stationary phase**. The analyst adds a small sample of the mixture to the stationary phase. As the mobile phase flows along, the chemicals in the sample move through the stationary phase. Different chemicals move at different speeds, so they separate.

▶ The chemical moves quickly if the position of equilibrium favours the mobile phase.

▶ The chemical moves slowly if the position of equilibrium favours the stationary phase.

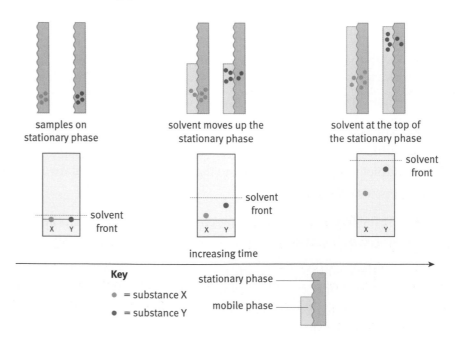

For each chemical there is a dynamic equilibrium for the molecules as they distribute themselves between the two phases. How quickly substances move through the stationary phase depends on the position of equilibrium.

Paper and thin-layer chromatography

Paper chromatography and thin-layer chromatography (TLC) are used to separate and identify substances in mixtures. The two techniques are very similar.

These techniques do not require expensive instrumentation but are limited in their use. Paper chromatography is very rarely used. Thin-layer chromatography (TLC) is 'low technology', but it can be useful before moving on to more complex techniques. TLC is quick, cheap, and only requires small volumes of solution. A large number of samples can be run at once.

TLC is simple and quick, so it is often used to monitor the progress of organic reactions and to check the purity of products.

Forensic laboratories may use TLC to analyse dyes extracted from fibres and when testing for controlled drugs, cannabis in particular.

Stationary and mobile phases

In paper chromatography the stationary phase is the paper, which does not move. In TLC the stationary phase is an absorbent solid supported on a glass plate or stiff plastic sheet.

In both paper chromatography and TLC the mobile phase is a solvent, which may be one liquid or a mixture of liquids. Substances are more soluble in some solvents than others. For example, some substances dissolve well in water, while others are more soluble in petrol-like, hydrocarbon solvents. With the right choice of solvent it becomes possible to separate complex mixtures.

Chemists call solutions in water **aqueous** solutions. The term **non-aqueous** describes solvents with no water in them.

Questions

1 Name two substances that dissolve better in water than in hydrocarbon (or other non-aqueous) solvents.

2 Name two substances that dissolve better in non-aqueous solvents than in water.

Chromatography plates must be spotted carefully. Small, concentrated spots are needed. Their starting position should be marked.

Preparing the paper or plate

The sample is dissolved in a solvent. This solvent is not usually the same as the mobile phase.

A small drop of the solution is put on the paper, or TLC plate, and allowed to dry, leaving a small 'spot' of the mixture.

If the solution is dilute, further drops are put in the same place. Each is left to dry before the next is added. This produces a small spot with enough material to analyse. The separation is likely to be poor if the spot spreads too much.

One way of identifying the chemicals in the sample is to add separate spots of solutions of substances suspected of being present in the unknown mixture. These are called **reference materials**.

Running the chromatogram

The analyst adds the chosen solvent (the mobile phase) to a chromatography tank and covers it with a lid. After the tank has stood for a while, the atmosphere inside becomes saturated with solvent vapour.

The next step is to place the prepared paper or TLC plate in the tank, checking that the spots are above the level of the solvent.

The solvent immediately starts to rise up the paper or plate. As the solvent rises, it carries the dissolved substances through the stationary phase. Covering the tank ensures that the solvent does not evaporate.

The paper, or TLC plate, is taken from the tank when the solvent gets near the top. The analyst then marks the position of the **solvent front**.

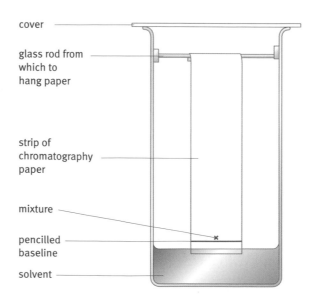

A chromatography tank. The sample spots on the paper or plate must be above the level of the solvent.

Locating substances

There is no difficulty marking the positions of coloured substances. All the analyst has to do is outline the spots in pencil and mark their centres before the colour fades.

There are two ways to locate colourless substances:

◗ Develop the chromatogram by spraying it with **a locating agent** that reacts with the substances to form coloured compounds.

◗ Use an ultraviolet lamp with TLC plates that contain fluorescers, so that the spots appear violet in UV light.

Interpreting chromatograms

Chemicals may be identified by comparing spots with those from standard reference materials.

A chemical may also be identified by its **retardation factor** (R_f). This does not change, provided the same conditions are used. It is calculated using the following formula by measuring the distance travelled by the substance:

$$R_f = \frac{\text{distance moved by chemical}}{\text{distance moved by solvent}} = \frac{y}{x}$$

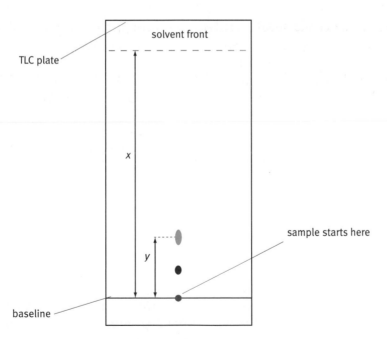

Retardation factors (R_f) can be calculated by measuring the distances travelled by chemicals in the sample and by the solvent.

Key terms

reference materials
solvent front
locating agent
retardation factor

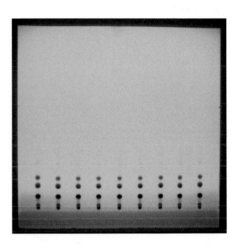

'Invisible' spots can often be seen under a UV lamp.

Questions

3 Why is it sometimes necessary to 'develop' a chromatogram? How can this be done?

4 Why is it sometimes useful to use thin-layer chromatography plates that have been impregnated with fluorescers?

Improving performance

Thin-layer chromatography usually gives better separation than paper chromatography. Improved separation might be achieved by:

◗ using a different solvent for the mobile phase

◗ leaving the chromatogram to develop for longer (though this is limited by how far the solvent front can travel)

An estimate of how much of a substance is present may be made from the intensity of its coloured spot. Sometimes the spot is removed from the chromatogram with a solvent and the intensity of the coloured solution formed matched against reference solutions.

There are instruments that turn TLC into a quantitative technique. The TLC plate is inserted into a spectrophotometer, which measures the intensities of spots. The quantities of each chemical in the mixture can then be calculated.

 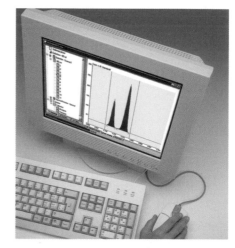

A spectrophotometer can detect and measure the intensities of coloured or colourless spots on a TLC plate.

Questions

5 Paper chromatography is used to separate a mixture of a red and a blue chemical. The blue compound is more soluble in water while the red chemical is more soluble in the non-aqueous chromatography solvent. Sketch a diagram to show the chromatogram you would expect to form.

6 How can quantitative data be obtained from thin-layer chromatograms?

7 Suppose you were testing a white powder that was a mixture of several compounds. Describe how you would set about identifying the compounds using either paper chromatography or thin-layer chromatography.

Faster cheese making

In cheese making, the enzyme rennet coagulates the milk to make solid casein. As the cheese matures, enzymes break up some of the proteins into their amino acids. This gives the cheese its characteristic flavour and texture. The trouble is that the ripening process takes several weeks, and time is money to manufacturers. Asana Nemat Tollahi, a PhD student at London Metropolitan University, is studying the ripening process of Iranian Brined Cheese, which is similar to Greek Feta.

Asana injecting a sample for analysis into her liquid chromatography instrument

Asana takes samples of the cheese at different stages of its ripening. First she has to get the amino acids into solution by pulverizing the cheese, and mixing it with water. Then she injects a sample of this solution into a high-performance liquid chromatography machine. This is a chromatography technique for separating chemicals in solution. It is widely used in the food industry and in food research. The stationary phase is a solid, as in TLC, but instead of being spread on a plate, it is enclosed in a long, thin metal tube called a column. As in TLC, the mobile phase is a liquid. The liquid is pumped at high pressure through the column to separate the chemicals in a mixture.

Asana uses the results to determine which amino acids are present and in what quantities. She is hoping that this will help to find new ways to make the enzymes speed up the reaction.

Asana separating the curds while making cheese

This scientist uses GC to check the quality of water from a river.

3D Gas chromatography

Gas chromatography (GC) is used to separate complex mixtures. The technique separates mixtures much better than paper or thin-layer chromatography.

This technique is also more sensitive than paper or thin-layer chromatography, which means it can detect small quantities of compounds. That is why it is usually preferred to paper or thin-layer chromatography. The technique not only identifies the chemicals in a mixture but can also measure how much of each is present.

Understanding the limits of detection for a technique can be very important, otherwise an analyst can report that a contaminant is absent when it is in fact present but at too low a concentration to be detected. Careful research has been necessary to find out the detection limits for such chemicals as pesticide residues in food.

Stationary and mobile phases

The principles of GC are the same as for paper and thin-layer chromatography. A mobile phase carries a mixture of compounds through a stationary phase. Some compounds are carried through more slowly than others. This is because they have different boiling points or a greater attraction for the stationary phase. Because they travel at different speeds, the compounds can be separated and identified.

The mobile phase is a gas such as helium. This is the **carrier gas**.

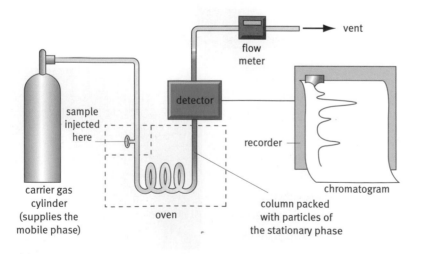

A carrier gas takes the mixture through the column containing the stationary phase. As compounds in the mixture come out the other end, they are detected and recorded.

The stationary phase is a thin film of a liquid on the surface of a powdered solid. The stationary phase is packed into a sealed tube, which is the column. The column is long and thin. Some columns are 25 m long but only 0.25 mm in diameter.

Only very small samples are needed. The analyst uses a syringe to inject a tiny quantity of the sample into the column. Samples are generally gases or liquids.

The column is coiled inside an oven, which controls the temperature of the column. This means that it is possible to analyse solids if they can be injected in solution and then turn to a vapour at the temperature of the column.

Separation and detection

Once the column is at the right temperature, the carrier gas is turned on. Its pressure is adjusted to get the correct flow rate through the column. The analyst injects the sample at the start of the column where it enters the oven. The chemicals in the sample turn to gases and mix with the carrier gas. The gases pass through the column.

In time, the chemicals from the sample emerge from the column and pass into a detector. The chemicals can be identified using mixtures of known composition.

Interpreting chromatograms

The detector sends a signal to a recorder when a compound appears. A series of peaks, one for each compound in the mixture, make up the chromatogram. The position of a peak is a record of how long the compound took to pass through the column. This is its retention time. The height of the peak indicates how much of the compound is present.

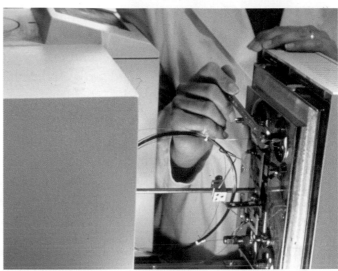

The coiled column inside the oven of a GC instrument. The detector is connected to a computer and the chromatogram appears on the screen.

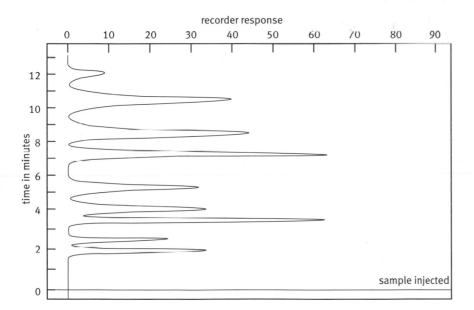

Each compound in the mixture appears as a peak in the chromatogram. The time it takes to get through helps the scientist to identify it. The height of the peak enables the scientists to say how much there is.

Questions

1 Look at the chromatogram on this page.

   a How many components have been separated?

   b Estimate the retention time of each component.

   c Which component was present in the largest quantity and which one was present in the smallest quantity?

Analytical chemist Anna Mukherjee carrying out a GC analysis at the University of Bristol

Chemical archaeology

Richard Evershed is a professor at Bristol University. He has used gas chromatography all his career: 'During my PhD, I used gas chromatography to study the chemical messages insects use to communicate with. After my PhD, I moved to the University of Bristol, where I used gas chromatography and high-performance liquid chromatography to look at the organic chemicals preserved in ancient rocks originating from organisms that lived many millions of years ago.'

Ancient traces

Richard recognized that gas chromatography could also be used to identify the remains of fats, waxes, and resins preserved at archaeological sites. 'We used gas chromatography linked to mass spectrometry for the first time in archaeology to determine the origin of samples of wood tar from King Henry VIII's flagship, the *Mary Rose*.'

Richard has been studying very old cooking pots to find out what people ate in the past. He analyses organic residues trapped in the walls of unglazed vessels. The residues are often mixtures of fats and waxes. He uses gas chromatography to separate the chemicals in the mixtures. By gradually increasing the temperature of the gas chromatography column, he is able to separate compounds with different boiling points. When the temperature reaches the boiling point of a chemical, it turns into gas and is carried by the carrier gas to a flame, where it burns to produce an electrical signal. The separated compounds appear as a series of peaks on the chromatogram.

'We've identified degraded residues of animal fats in pots from Turkey going back 8000 years,' says Richard. 'We've also found plant oils, animal fats, and beeswax in ancient lamps. We made a real breakthrough when we found that we could identify traces of butter in 6000-year-old pottery from prehistoric Britain. This showed us that milking animals is a very ancient practice.'

Analysis of the chemicals absorbed into old pots gives clues to the food that our ancestors cooked.

A whiff of cabbage

Traces of cooked cabbage can survive for a long time. Richard found this to be true when investigating a set of pots dating from late Saxon times. The pots are over a thousand years old. 'I've found traces of cabbage preserved in the pot wall. It's the natural wax you can see on the surface of the cabbage, which is released during boiling. We can extract the same waxes from modern supermarket cabbages, and the gas chromatography traces look pretty much identical.'

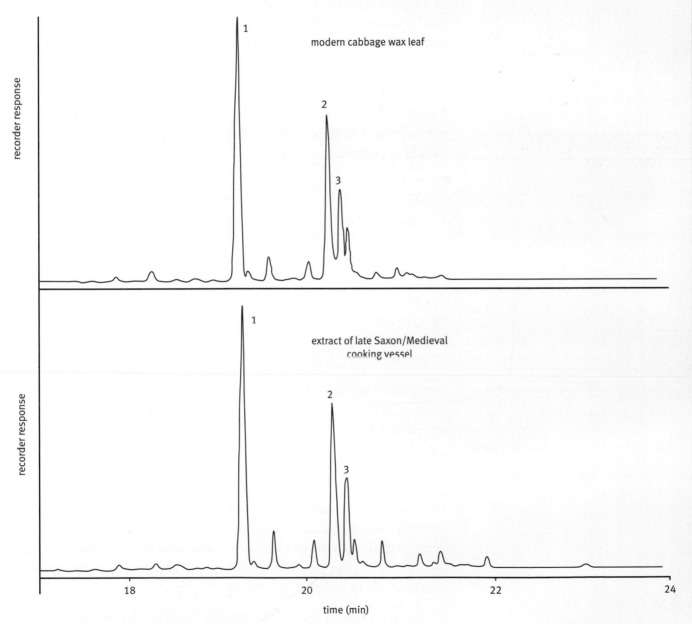

Gas chromatography traces comparing the wax from a modern cabbage leaf with the lipids extracted from a late Saxon cooking pot

Find out about:
- acid–alkali titrations
- standard solutions

3E Titrations

A **titration** is a quantitative technique based on measuring the volumes of solutions that react with each other. Chemists use titrations to measure concentrations and to investigate the quantities of chemicals involved in reactions. Titrations are widely used because they are quick, convenient, accurate, and easy to automate.

Titration procedure

In a typical titration, an analyst uses a **pipette** (or a burette) to transfer a fixed volume of liquid to a flask. In an acid–base titration to find the concentration of an acid, this might be $20 \, cm^3$ of the solution of acid.

Next, the analyst adds one or two drops of a coloured indicator. The indicator is chosen to change colour sharply when exactly the right amount of alkali has been added to react with all the acid. The indicator works because there is a very sharp change of pH at this point, which is called the **end point**.

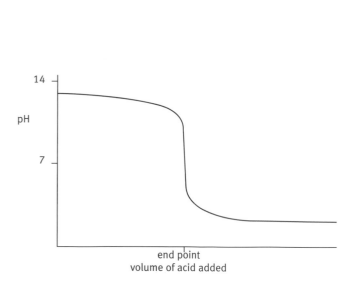

pH change when titrating an alkali with an acid

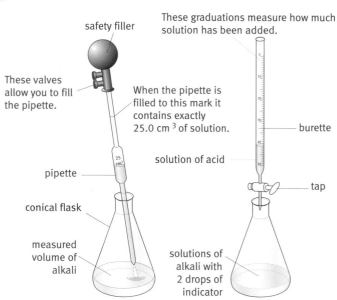

Apparatus for an acid–base titration

The analyst has a **burette** ready containing a solution of acid with a concentration that is known accurately. Then the analyst runs the acid from a burette into the alkali a little at a time until the indicator changes colour. Reading the burette scale before and after the titration shows the volume of alkali added.

It is common to do a rough titration first to get an idea where the end point lies and then to repeat the titration more carefully, adding the acid drop by drop near the end point. The analyst repeats the titration two or three times as necessary to achieve consistent values for the value of alkali added.

Remember

1 litre = 1 dm³ = 1000 cm³

Preparing accurate solutions

The accuracy of a titration can be no better than the accuracy of the solutions used to make the measurements. If chemists know the concentration of a solution accurately, they call it a **standard solution**, because it can be used in analysis to measure the concentrations of other solutions.

Key terms
titration
pipette
end point
burette
standard solution

1 Accurately weigh the sodium carbonate.

2 Dissolve the solute in a small amount of solvent, warming it if necessary.

stirring rod

3 Transfer the sodium carbonate solution **to a graduated flask.**

stirring rod

paper wedge

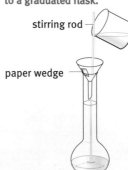

4 Rinse all the solution into the flask with **more solvent.**

wash bottle

5 Add solvent drop by drop to make up the volume to the mark on the flask

6 Stopper and shake the flask

The procedure for making up a standard solution with an accurately known concentration

Questions

1 What is the concentration of these solutions in grams per litre (g/dm^3)?

a A solution of sodium carbonate made by dissolving 4.0 g of the solid in water and making the volume up to 500 cm^3 in a graduated flask.

b A solution of nitric acid made by diluting 6.4 g of the acid and making the volume up to 500 cm^3 in a graduated flask.

c A solution of citric acid made by dissolving 2.25 g of the solid in water and making the volume up to 250 cm^3 in a graduated flask.

2 What is the mass of solute in these samples of solutions?

a A 10 cm^3 sample of a solution of silver nitrate with a concentration of 2.55 g/dm^3.

b A 25 cm^3 sample of a solution of sodium hydroxide with a concentration of 4.40 g/dm^3.

3 Suggest reasons why it is possible to prepare a solution with an accurately known concentration by weighing out anhydrous sodium carbonate and dissolving it in water but not possible to do the same thing with pellets of sodium hydroxide.

4 What volume of a solution of hydrochloric acid containing 18.2 g/dm^3 is needed to remove 5.0 g of limescale (CaCO$_3$)?

Titrating acids in food and drink

Rachel Woods is the quality control manager for Danisco, a company that manufactures ingredients for food and soft drinks. Acids are very important in her work. Some acids occur naturally in the fresh ingredients; others are added to improve flavour and keeping quality.

The quantity of acid in any food or drink is important. Think of a soft drink – too much acid and it tastes sour; too little and it might be insipid. With just the right amount it tastes refreshing and fruity, and just the right amount of acid makes a drink seem more thirst-quenching and satisfying.

Automated titrations

One of the most important acids in Rachel's work is citric acid. She regularly has to test ingredients and finished products to check their citric acid content. She uses a titration machine. Here she is testing a sample of blueberry juice. First, using a dropping pipette, she takes a sample of the juice from the container into a beaker. It is the same beaker in which she will carry out the titration, which makes things so much quicker and simpler. She has weighed exactly 4.30 grams.

Rachel measures the mass of a sample of blueberry juice.

She adds boiled water to the juice to bring it up to the $300 \, cm^3$ mark. She does not use water straight from the tap as it has dissolved calcium hydrogencarbonate in it. Boiling the water removes this. For many titrations distilled water is necessary, but for these food samples ordinary boiled water is fine.

All Rachel has to do is put the pH probe and tube from the burette into the beaker and put in on the stand. It has a magnetic stirrer, so she does not even have to shake the flask. She presses a button, and the burette tube starts to fill from the reservoir bottle. The concentration of her sodium hydroxide, NaOH, solution is $8.0 \, g/dm^3$.

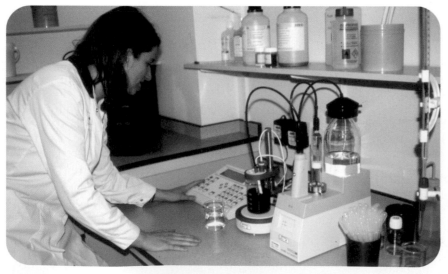

Rachel sets up her automatic titration machine. The burette tube in the middle fills from the reservoir of alkali on the right.

When the burette is full, it slowly pumps the NaOH solution into the beaker. Because blueberry juice contains a natural indicator, you can see a colour change from purply-red to dark blue-grey as it reaches the end point.

The exact point is not easy to see, but that does not matter, as the machine works by measuring the pH of the solution. It measures the quantity of NaOH required to bring the blueberry juice up to a pH of 8.3. Not that Rachel has to measure that volume – far from it: all she has to do is look at the readout on the screen. It shows a little graph and calculates the percentage of citric acid in the juice. No calculation is needed. This sample is 6.08% citric acid, which is exactly what it should be, and using the machine, Rachel can test as many samples as she needs very quickly and simply.

The hands-on method

Not all Rachel's titrations can be done on the machine. Here she is using the traditional method to test the concentration of a sample of butyric acid.

Butyric acid (C_3H_7COOH) is an important part of butter and cheese flavours, so it used in things like cheese-and-onion crisps, and in those 'I-think-it-tastes-like-butter' margarines you see advertised on the TV. Used in this way, butyric acid is great, but unfortunately in large quantities it smells terrible.

It is not Rachel's favourite titration, but she is so used to it she manages to keep smiling. Butyric acid is associated with fats, so it is not soluble in water. Instead it is dissolved in ethanol.

The beaker with the blueberry juice in the titration machine. A magnetic stirrer mixes the juice with the alkali added by the burette. The probe dipping into the solution measures the pH.

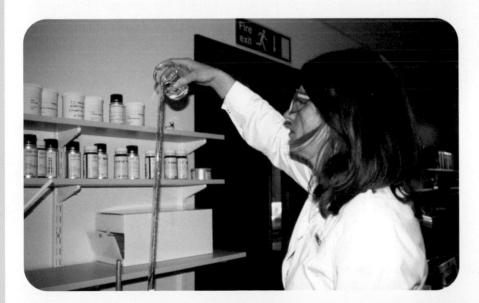

Rachel filling the burette with the acid solution. She keeps her eye level with the zero mark on the burette. She wants the meniscus to sit exactly on the line.

Using a pipette to run a measured volume of the standard potassium hydroxide into a titration flask

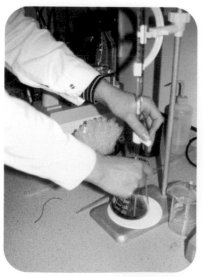

Rachel runs the butyric acid from the burette into the flask during the titration.

The next job is to pipette exactly $20.0 \, \text{cm}^3$ of warm potassium hydroxide, KOH, solution into a clean flask. The concentration of the alkali is accurately known. Again Rachel keeps her eye level with the mark on the pipette as she uses the valve on the filler to adjust the level. A tiny drop of solution is always left in the end of the pipette, but Rachel resists the temptation to blow it out. As she adds a few drops of the indicator, phenolphthalein, the alkaline solution turns a stunning shade of shocking pink.

Now the titration begins. With her right hand she swirls the flask, and with her left hand she gently releases the tap on the burette to let $1 \, \text{cm}^3$ of the acid into the flask at a time. She keeps her eye on the flask all the time. Because she does this titration so regularly, she knows when the end point is coming up. It happens suddenly. First the solution in the centre of the flask goes clear, then the pink colour disappears altogether. At that precise point Rachel closes the tap on the burette and takes a note of the reading: $40.2 \, \text{cm}^3$. She repeats the titration at least once more.

H Interpreting the results

Relative formula masses: $C_3H_7COOH = 88$ and $KOH = 56$

The equation for the reaction in the titration flask is

$$C_3H_7COOH \; + \; KOH \; \longrightarrow \; C_3H_7COOK \; + \; H_2O$$
$$88 \, \text{g} \qquad\quad 56 \, \text{g}$$

Concentration of the potassium hydroxide solution = $11.2 \, \text{g/dm}^3$

In $20.0 \, \text{cm}^3$ of the KOH solution there is

$$\frac{20}{1000} \times 11.2 \, \text{g} = 0.224 \, \text{g}$$

If $56 \, \text{g}$ KOH reacts with $88 \, \text{g}$ of the acid, then $0.224 \, \text{g}$ reacts with

$$\frac{0.224}{56} \times 88 \, \text{g} = 0.352 \, \text{g butyric acid}$$

This amount of acid was present in $40.0 \, \text{cm}^3 = 0.040 \, \text{dm}^3$ of butyric acid solution. So the concentration of the butyric acid solution is

$$\frac{0.352 \, \text{g}}{0.040 \, \text{dm}^3} = 8.80 \, \text{g/dm}^3$$

3F Evaluating results

Scientists need to be able to make sense of analyses and tests. This means that they have to be able to interpret their significance and say what they show. Scientists must also judge how confident they are about the accuracy of results.

Measurement uncertainty

All measurements have an uncertainty. This means that scientists usually give results within a range. For example, they may analyse the purity of a drug and give the answer as $99.1 \pm 0.2\%$. This means that the average value obtained from analyses of several samples was 99.1%. The precise value is uncertain. The scientists are confident that the actual value lies between 98.9% and 99.3%. To show this, they quote the results as 99.1 (the mean) $\pm 0.2\%$.

Errors of measurement are not mistakes. Mistakes are failures by the operator and include such things as forgetting to fill a burette tip with the solution, or taking readings from a sensitive balance in a draught. Mistakes of this kind should be avoided by people doing the practical work.

Types of uncertainty

There are two general sources of **measurement uncertainty**: systematic errors and random errors.

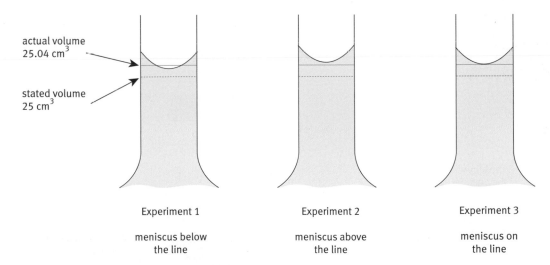

actual volume
25.04 cm³

stated volume
25 cm³

| Experiment 1 | Experiment 2 | Experiment 3 |
| meniscus below the line | meniscus above the line | meniscus on the line |

Systematic and random errors in the use of a pipette. The manufacturing tolerance for a 25 cm³ grade B pipette is ±0.06 cm³. This can give rise to a systematic error. Every time an analyst uses the pipette, the meniscus is aligned slightly differently with the graduation mark. This gives rise to random error.

Random error means that the same measurement repeated several times gives different values. This can happen, for example, from making the judgements about the colour change at an end point or from estimating the reading from a burette scale.

Systematic error means that the same measurement repeated several times gives values that are consistently higher than the true value, or consistently lower. This can result from incorrectly calibrated measuring instruments or from making measurements at a consistent, but wrong, temperature.

It is difficult to determine accurately the volume of liquid in a burette if the meniscus lies between two graduation marks.

The material used to prepare a standard solution may not be 100% pure.

A 250 cm³ volumetric flask may actually contain 250.3 cm³ when filled to the calibration mark owing to permitted variation in the manufacture of the flask.

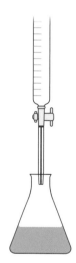

It is difficult to make an exact judgement of the end point of a titration (the exact point at which the colour of the indicator changes).

The burette is calibrated by the manufacturer for use at 20 °C. When it is used in the laboratory the temperature is 23 °C. This difference in temperature will cause a small difference in the actual volume of liquid in the burette when it is filled to a calibration mark.

The display on a laboratory balance will only show the mass to a certain number of decimal places.

Sources of uncertainty in analysis by titration

An analysis or test is often repeated to give a number of measured values, which are then averaged to produce the result.

▶ **Accuracy** describes how close this result is to the true or 'actual' value.

▶ **Precision** is a measure of the spread of measured values. A big spread indicates a greater uncertainty than does a small spread.

precise, not accurate

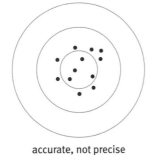
accurate, not precise

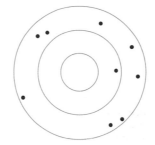
inaccurate and imprecise

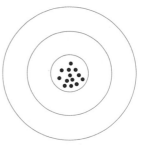
precise and accurate

Accuracy and precision are not the same thing.

Conclusions

The conclusions scientists draw from their work must be valid and justifiable.

▶ Valid means that the techniques and procedures used were suitable for what was being analysed or tested.

▶ Justifiable means that conclusions reached are backed by sound, reliable evidence.

Questions

1 An analyst determined the percentage of potassium in three brands of plant fertilizer for house plants by making five measurements for each brand.

These are the results of measuring the percentage by mass of potassium in three brands:

A   4.93, 4.89, 4.71, 4.81, 4.74

B   6.76, 7.91, 6.94, 6.71, 6.86

C   4.72, 4.76, 4.68, 4.70, 4.69

a Determine the mean and range for each brand.

b What conclusions can you draw about the three brands?

2 Why would the results be inaccurate if an analyst used hot solutions in graduated glassware?

Topic 4

Green chemistry

The chemical industry

The chemical industry converts raw materials into useful products. The products include chemicals for use as drugs, fertilizers, detergents, paints, and dyes.

The chemical industry takes crude oil, air, sea water, and other raw materials and converts them to pure chemicals such as acids, salts, solvents, compressed gases, and organic compounds.

The industry makes **bulk chemicals** on a scale of thousands or even millions of tonne per year. Examples are ammonia, sulfuric acid, sodium hydroxide, chlorine, and ethene.

On a much smaller scale the industry makes **fine chemicals** such as drugs and pesticides. It also makes small quantities of speciality chemicals needed by other manufacturers for particular purposes. These include such things as flame retardants, food additives, and the liquid crystals for flat-screen televisions and computer displays.

Greener industry

The chemical industry is reinventing many of the processes it uses. The industry seeks to become 'greener' by:

▶ turning to renewable resources

▶ devising new processes that convert a high proportion of the atoms in the reactants into the product molecules.

▶ cutting down on the use of hazardous chemicals

▶ making efficient use of energy

▶ reducing waste

▶ preventing pollution of the environment

> **Key words**
> bulk chemicals
> fine chemicals

Harvesting a natural resource. Lavender is distilled to extract chemicals for the perfume industry.

Find out about:
- feedstocks for the chemical industry
- products from the chemical industry

4A The work of the chemical industry

Raw materials

The basic raw materials of the chemical industry are

- crude oil

- air

- water

- vegetable materials

- minerals such as metal ores, salt, limestone, and gypsum

The first step in any process is to take the raw materials and convert them into a chemical, or mixture of chemicals, that can be fed into a process. Crude oil, for example, is a complex mixture of chemicals. An oil refinery distils the oil and then processes chemicals from the distillation column to produce purified **feedstocks** for chemical synthesis.

Chemical plants

At the centre of the plant is the reactor, where reactants are converted into products. The feedstock may have to be heated or compressed before it is fed to the reactor. The reactor often contains a catalyst.

Generally, a mixture of chemicals leaves the reactor. The mixture includes the desired product, but there may also be **by-products** and unchanged starting materials. So the chemical plant has to include equipment to separate the main product and by-products and to recycle unchanged reactants.

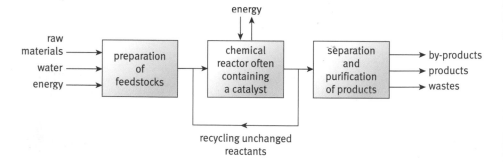

A schematic diagram to summarize a chemical process

Chemical plants need energy. Some of the chemical reactions occur at a high temperature, so energy is often needed for heating. Also, a lot of electric power is needed for pumps to move reactants and products from one part of the plant to another.

Sensors monitor the conditions at all the key points in the plant. The data is fed to computers in the control centre where the technical team controls the plant.

Products from the chemical industry

The chemical industry produces five main types of product. Some of these are made in huge quantities. Other chemicals have high value but are made in much smaller amounts. (See the pie chart in Module C6 *Chemicals of the natural environment*, page 150, which shows the range of products made by the chemical industries in Britain and their relative value.)

Basic inorganics including fertilizers

The industry makes large amounts of these chemicals. Chlorine, sodium hydroxide, sulfuric acid, and fertilizers are all bulk chemicals.

Petrochemicals and polymers

Petrochemical plants use hydrocarbons from crude oil to make a great variety of products, including polymers (see Module C2 *Material choices*, Sections E and G). Among many other chemicals, the industry makes ethene. Ethene, C_2H_4, is then used to make many different products, including polymers such as polythene and PVC, and solvents such as ethanol. The worldwide production of ethene is over 80 million tonnes each year.

Dyes, paints, and pigments

The discovery of a new mauve dye by the young William Perkin in 1856 was the starting point for the development of many new synthetic colours. At that time coal tar was the main source of carbon chemicals for dyes. Modern dyes are made from petrochemicals.

Pharmaceuticals

The pharmaceutical industry grew from the dyestuffs industry. The industry produces drugs and medicines. This is a part of the chemical industry that is changing rapidly to explore the possibilities arising from the growing understanding of the human genome.

Speciality chemicals

Speciality chemicals are used to make other products. They include food flavourings and the liquid crystal chemicals in flat-screen displays.

A maintenance worker inside a large chemical reactor

Key words
feedstocks
by-products

Transport workers bring materials in and out of the chemical plant.

Questions

1 When the tank in the picture on the left is in use, it is filled with a reaction mixture. Suggest the purpose of:

  a the rotating paddle in the centre of the tank

  b the network of pipes round the edge of the tank

Find out about:

▶ new sources of chemicals
▶ measures of efficiency
▶ safer ways to make chemicals
▶ energy efficiency
▶ reducing waste and recycling

4B Innovations in green chemistry

In the second half of the twentieth century the chemical industry found that its reputation with the public was falling. Many people were worried about synthetic chemicals and their impact on health and the environment. Politicians responded by passing laws to regulate the industry. At first, these laws were aimed at dealing with the industry as it was then by treating pollution and minimizing its effects.

Controlling the flow of oil at a refinery. Crude oil is the main source of organic chemicals today.

Crops can be grown to supply feedstocks for the chemical industry rather than for their food value. In Europe this includes growing wheat, maize, sugar beet, and potatoes as sources of sugars or starch.

More recently, legislation has set out to prevent pollution by changing the industry. New laws encourage companies to reduce the formation of pollutants through changes in production and the use of raw materials that are cost effective and renewable.

In the early stages the aim was to cut risks by controlling people's exposure to hazardous chemicals. Now green chemistry attempts to eliminate the hazard altogether. If the industry can avoid using or producing hazardous chemicals, then the risk is avoided.

Green chemistry has the potential to bring benefits both to industry and to society. Innovative green chemistry can increase efficiency, cut costs, and help to avoid the dangers of hazardous chemicals.

Renewable feedstocks

One of the aims of green chemistry is to use renewable raw materials. At the moment, crude oil is the main source of chemical **feedstocks**. Less than 3% of crude oil is used to make chemicals. All the rest is burnt as fuel or used to make lubricants. Even so, reducing the reliance on petrochemicals would help to make the industry more sustainable.

Currently, most polymers are made from petrochemicals. This includes the polyester fibres that are widely used in clothing

DuPont has developed a way of making a new type of polyester by fermenting renewable plant materials. The company calls this polymer Sorona. Manufacturers convert Sorona into fibres for clothing and upholstery.

The chemical starting point for the synthesis of Sorona is malonic acid. DuPont has found that it can produce this acid by fermenting corn starch with bacteria.

Plants can be grown year after year. They are a **renewable resource**. However, growing plants for chemicals takes up land that could be used to grow food. Also energy is needed to make fertilizers and for harvesting crops.

Fabrics made from Sorona are used for clothing and upholstery. It is made using renewable resources, reducing the use of raw materials based on crude oil. Sorona can be recycled. This helps reduce waste.

Key words
renewable resource

Questions

1 Classify these raw materials as 'renewable' or non-renewable':

   a salt (sodium chloride)

   b crude oil

   c wood chippings

   d limestone

   e sugar beet

2 Which of the ways of making industry 'greener' are illustrated by the development of Sorona?

H

Converting more of the reactants to products

Yields

Chemists calculate the **percentage yield** from a production process to measure its efficiency. This compares the quantity of product with the amount predicted by the balanced chemical equation.

A high yield is a good thing, but it is not necessarily an indicator that the process is 'green'. This is illustrated on a small scale by the laboratory process to replace the —OH group in the alcohol butanol with a bromine atom. The product is bromobutane:

$$C_4H_9—OH \ + \ H_2SO_4 \ + \ NaBr \ \longrightarrow \ C_4H_9—Br \ + \ NaHSO_4 \ + \ H_2O$$

Carrying out this reaction in the laboratory uses 35 g sodium bromide and 50 g sulfuric acid to convert 20 g butanol into 30 g of pure bromobutane. The sodium bromide and sulfuric acid are in excess, so the yield is limited by the amount of the alcohol.

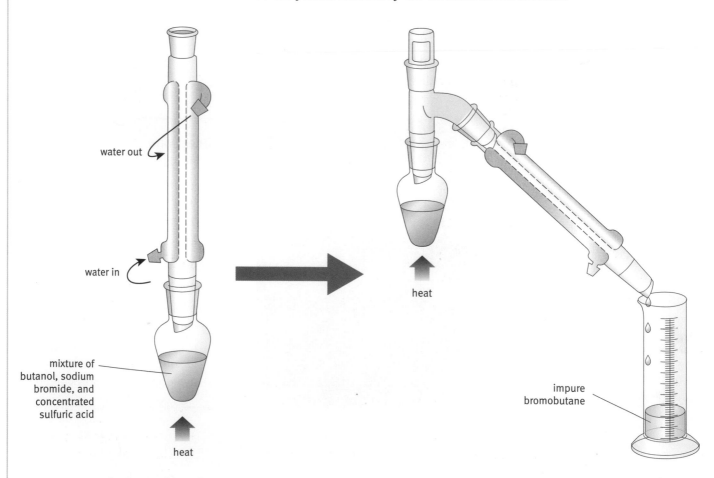

water out

water in

mixture of butanol, sodium bromide, and concentrated sulfuric acid

heat

heat

impure bromobutane

Converting butanol to impure bromobutane

According to the reacting masses in the equation, 74 g of butanol should produce 137 g bromobutane.

So the theoretical yield from 20 g butanol $= \dfrac{20}{74\,g} \times 137\,g = 37\,g$

The percentage yield from the laboratory process $= \dfrac{30}{37\,g} \times 100\% = 81\%$

This is a good yield for a laboratory preparation. However, the result is that only 30 g of product is made from 105 g of the starting chemicals.

Even with an impossible 100% yield the process could at best produce 37 g butanol from a total of 105 g of reactants. There is 68 g of waste.

Atom economy

In 1998, Barry Trost of Stanford University, USA, was awarded a prize for his work in green chemistry. He had introduced the term **atom economy** as a measure of the efficiency with which a reaction uses its reactant atoms.

$$\text{atom economy} = \frac{\text{mass of atoms in the product}}{\text{mass of atoms in reactants}} \times 100\%$$

$C_4H_9{-}OH + H_2SO_4 + NaBr \longrightarrow C_4H_9{-}Br + NaHSO_4 + H_2O$

totals of atoms in the reactants: 4C, 12H, 5O, Br, Na, S
(total relative atomic mass = 275)

totals of green atoms ending in the product: 4C, 9H, Br
(total relative atomic mass = 137)

totals of brown atoms ending as waste: 3H, 5O, Na, S
(total relative atomic mass = 138)

atom economy $= \dfrac{137\,g}{275\,g} \times 100\% = 50\%$

Calculating the atom economy for the laboratory preparation of bromobutane. The atoms in the reactants that end up in the product are shown in green. The atoms that end up as waste are brown.

So, at the very best, only half of the mass of starting materials can end up as product. This is not a green process.

This approach does not take yield into account and does not allow for the fact that many real-world processes use deliberate excess of reactants. It does, however, help in comparing different pathways to a desired product.

Questions

3 Explain the purposes of the condensers used in the apparatus shown for making bromobutane.

4 Heating with a catalyst converts cyclohexanol, $C_6H_{11}OH$, to cyclohexene, C_6H_{10}.

   a What is the percentage yield if 20 g hexanol gives 14.5 g cyclohexene?

   b What is the atom economy, assuming that the catalyst is recovered and reused?

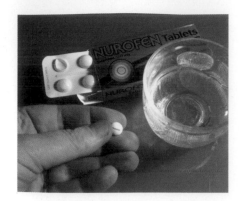

A greener pain reliever

Every year in the UK, people spend around £300 million buying pain killers. One of them is ibuprofen

Boots patented ibuprofen in the 1960s. At that time there were six stages in the complex processes to make the drug.

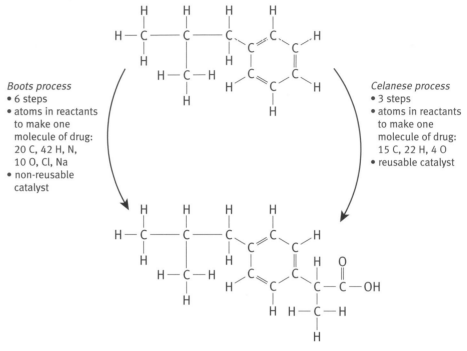

Boots process
- 6 steps
- atoms in reactants
  to make one
  molecule of drug:
  20 C, 42 H, N,
  10 O, Cl, Na
- non-reusable
  catalyst

Celanese process
- 3 steps
- atoms in reactants
  to make one
  molecule of drug:
  15 C, 22 H, 4 O
- reusable catalyst

Two routes for making ibuprofen from the same starting material

There are 33 atoms of all kinds in one ibuprofen molecule. Adding up all the atoms in the chemicals used by Boots shows that the process needed 74 atoms for each ibuprofen molecule formed. So 41 atoms ended up making unwanted chemicals. This was wasteful.

Once the Boots patent for ibuprofen had run out after 20 years, it was possible for other companies to make and sell the drug. A new synthesis was developed by the Celanese Corporation which was more efficient. This new process has only three stages and needs only 41 atoms in the reacting chemicals to make each ibuprofen molecule. It has a much more efficient 'atom economy'. It gives fewer harmful by-products. It is a 'greener' synthesis because it creates less useless waste.

Another feature of the Boots process was that it used aluminium chloride as a catalyst in one key step of the process. Although a catalyst, the aluminium chloride could not be recovered and reused. This added to the waste.

The newer method uses other catalysts: hydrogen fluoride and an alloy of nickel and aluminium. Both of these catalysts can be recovered and reused many times.

Questions

5 What is the molecular formula for ibuprofen?

6 a What is the atom economy for the Boots process for making ibuprofen?

b What is the atom economy for the Celanese process for making ibuprofen?

c Calculate a new value of the atom efficency for the Celanese process, assuming that the ethanoic acid (CH_3COOH) formed as a by-product in one step is recycled in the process and does not go to waste.

Designing new catalysts

Matthew Davidson works at the University of Bath, where he designs new catalysts for the synthesis of polymers. His main strategy is to wrap an organic structure round a metal ion. For example, he has helped a manufacturer to devise a catalyst for making a type of polyester by wrapping citrate ions round titanium ions. This catalyst produces a clear rather than a yellowish polymer, and replaces a catalyst made of antimony, which is a toxic metal.

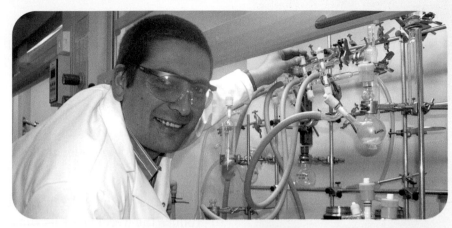

Matthew Davidson in his laboratory

'The main thing about a catalyst is that it has to be highly reactive towards the starting materials but not to the products.'

Matthew enjoys making new complex molecules and then analysing their structure to see what makes them active. 'I have to think about two main things – firstly the size and shape of the catalyst molecules and secondly how they interact with the electrons of other molecules.'

The need for new catalysts

But why do we need new catalysts? Matthew says there are several reasons: 'First, many older catalysts were toxic or contained harmful metals. Greater appreciation of the environment and health means that replacement catalysts need to be made. That is why we wanted to replace the antimony used to make polyesters. It is also the reason why we are researching for catalysts to replace the mercury and tin currently used to make the polyurethane used in training shoe soles.

Matthew Davidson uses physical models and computer models in his work.

'Second, old catalysts may not be as efficient as possible. Our new titanium-citrate catalyst is up to 15% more efficient than the traditional antimony catalyst. This allows more polymer to be made with less catalyst – good for both commercial and environmental reasons.

'Third, there are many useful chemical transformations for which there are no suitable catalysts yet. Catalysts are important for society, in that new ones can help our lives by making new medicines or new polymers.'

This weedkiller can now be made by a method that does not involve the use of toxic cyanide compounds.

Avoiding chemicals that are hazardous to health

The chemical industry produces a large number of synthetic chemicals. Some of these are reactive intermediates which are only used in manufacturing processes.

The aim of green chemistry is to replace reactants that are highly toxic with alternative chemicals that are not a threat to human health or the environment.

The aim is to protect the health of people working in the industry and also people who live near to industrial plants. It is important to avoid chemical accidents, including accidental releases of chemicals through explosions and fires.

Originally the company Monsanto used hydrogen cyanide in the process to produce the weedkiller that the company markets as 'Roundup'. Hydrogen cyanide is extremely toxic. The company has now developed a new route for making the herbicide. The new method has a different starting material and runs under milder conditions because of a copper catalyst.

Similarly, a new process for making polycarbonate plastics has replaced the gas phosgene with safer starting materials: methanol and carbon monoxide. Carbon monoxide is poisonous but it is not as dangerous as phosgene, which is so nasty that it has been used as a poison gas in warfare.

Energy efficiency

All manufacturing processes need energy to convert raw materials into useful products. In the chemical industry, energy is used in several ways, such as:

- to raise the temperature of reactants so a reaction begins or continues
- to heat mixtures of liquids to separate and purify products by distillation
- to dry product material
- to process waste treatment

The energy used in separation, drying, and waste management may be more than that used in the reaction stages.

Burning natural gas or other fossil fuels is the usual source of energy. Often the energy from burning is used to produce super-heated steam, which can then be used for heating around the chemical plant.

The most direct way of reducing the use of energy is to prevent losses of steam from leaking valves on steam-pipes and by installing efficient insulation on reaction vessels or pipes.

A large heat exchanger works like a laboratory condenser. One liquid or gas flows through pipes surrounded by another liquid flowing in the opposite direction. The hotter liquid or gas heats the cooler fluid.

Some of the reactions in the chemical process may be so exothermic that they provide the energy to raise steam and generate electricity which can be 'exported' to other processes nearby. The first step in the manufacture of sulfuric acid is to burn sulfur. This is so exothermic that a sulfuric acid plant has no fuel bills and can raise enough steam to generate sufficient electric power to contribution significantly to the income of the operation.

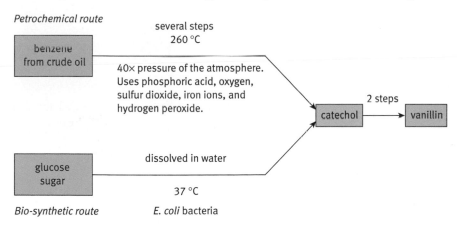

Comparing two routes to the flavouring agent vanillin

Chemical production in general has become much more energy efficient than in the past. The average energy required per tonne of chemical product is less than half that needed 50 years ago.

The aim of green chemistry is not only to make processes more energy efficient but also to lower their energy demand. One of the targets of current research is to develop new processes that run at much lower temperatures. One way of doing this is to use biocatalysts – the enzymes produced by microorganisms. Genetic modification of bacteria can lead to the development of safer processes that run at temperatures only a little above room temperature.

Questions

7   The reaction involving cyanide in the older process for making the active ingredient for Roundup was exothermic. The replacement reaction in the newer process is endothermic. Suggest why this difference contributes to safety.

8   Why can a laboratory condenser be described as a 'heat exchanger'.

9   Write a short paragraph to explain why the biosynthetic route to vanillin is 'greener' than the petrochemical route.

Reducing waste and recycling

One of the principles of green chemistry is that it is better to prevent waste than to treat or clean up waste after it is formed.

One way of cutting down on waste is to develop processes with higher atom economies. Another way is to increase recycling at every possible stage of the life cycle of a chemical product. A third way is to find uses for by-products that were previously dumped as waste.

Recycling

Industries have always tried to recycle waste produced during manufacturing processes. Recycling is easier when the composition of the scrap material is known.

The main UK manufacturer of polypropylene, Basell Polyolefins, used to burn unreacted propene. Much was burnt in an open flame so that not even the energy was recovered. Now the company has installed a distillation unit that makes it possible to separate chemicals from the waste gases. The recovery unit has cut the amount of waste. It collects over 3000 tonnes of propene per year.

A plant for recycling chemicals on a large scale

Open-loop recycling

In some cases, waste from one product is recovered and used in the manufacture of another, lower-quality product. This is open-loop recycling. It cuts down the amount of fresh feedstock needed, and the amount of waste going to landfill.

An example is the use of discarded soft-drinks bottles. The polymer in these bottles is a polyester (PET). Once collected, the PET bottles are fed through grinders that reduce them to flake form. The flake then proceeds through a separation and cleaning process that removes all foreign particles such as paper, metal, and other plastic materials.

The recovered PET is sold to manufacturers that convert it into a variety of useful products such as carpet fibre, moulding compounds, and non-food containers. Carpet companies can often use 100% recycled polymer to make polyester carpets. PET is also spun to make fibre filling for pillows, quilts, and jackets.

Closed-loop recycling

Recycling is better value if the waste material can be used to manufacture the same product with no loss in quality. With plastics this can be done by breaking down the waste into the monomers originally used to make the polymer. Several companies have developed processes for depolymerizing the polyester in soft-drinks bottles. The result is fresh feedstock for making new polymer.

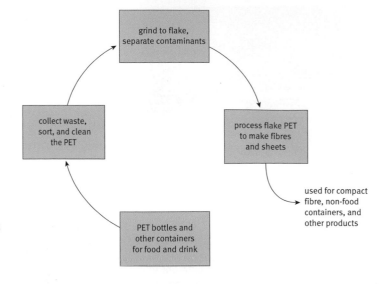

Open-loop recycling

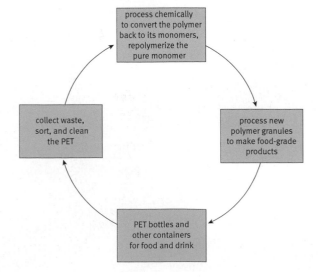

Closed-loop recycling

Questions

10 a Explain in a short paragraph the difference between open-loop and closed-loop recycling.

b Suggest one possible advantage and one possible disadvantage of each of these approaches to recycling.

Titanium dioxide is the white pigment in the paint protecting a railway bridge in Newcastle-upon-Tyne.

New uses for by-products

All chemical processes give a mixture of products: the one that the chemists want to make and others – the by-products. The process is more sustainable if the by-products can be used to make another product, so that less waste has to be dumped.

Huntsman Tioxide has found ways to cut down waste. The company makes titanium dioxide, the world's most important white pigment. Their research and development manager is Tony Jones: 'You'd be amazed at how much titanium dioxide you use in your life. It's mainly used in paint, but also in plastics, paper cosmetics, and toothpaste. It's so safe it's even used in food – when you suck the colour off a Smartie, the white sugar shell you find is coloured with TiO_2.

'The source of the TiO_2 is the mineral ilmenite, which is $FeTiO_3$. We extract the TiO_2 using sulfuric acid. After the process we neutralize the mixture using calcium carbonate to make useful by-products.

'First we get iron sulfate, which we sell to water companies. It is used in the water-purifying process. The iron causes muck in the water to coagulate and settle, leaving clear water for drinking. It can also be used as an additive for cement.

'Then the dirty sulfuric acid is passed over calcium carbonate to form calcium sulfate, also known as gypsum, which is used to make plasterboard. This not only cuts down the waste to landfill sites by 60%, but also reduces the need to mine natural gypsum.

Huntsman Tioxide's plant at Grimsby. The company is the world's third largest producer of titanium dioxide.

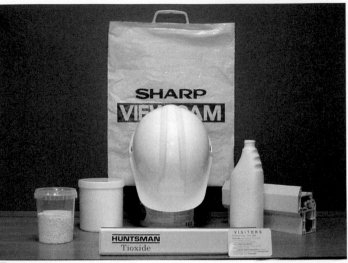

Tony Jones of Huntsman Tioxide with just a few of the many products containing titanium dioxide.

'Then we are left with red gypsum, which is just calcium sulfate stained with iron. That ends up as plaster too – but it's a pink colour. It can also be used by farmers as a conditioner on clay soil.

'The amazing thing is we now sell 500 000 tonnes of titanium dioxide every year, but 1 000 000 tonnes of the co-products. That's nearly twice as much, and remember that the ore has a straight 50/50 Ti/Fe composition!'

In 2001, Huntsman Tioxide installed a new power plant. This is a combined heat and power (CHP) plant that generates electricity and provides steam for heating in the production process. CHP plants are more efficient than conventional power stations.

Cutting pollution by wastes

It is usually impossible to eliminate waste completely. This means that it is important to remove or destroy any harmful chemicals before wastes are released into air, water, or landfills. On many sites, ground water must also be collected and processed, as it may contain traces of the chemicals made and used on the site.

Many manufacturing sites have a single processing plant for dealing with wastes. A wide range of separation techniques may be used, including filtering, centrifuging, and distillation.

Wastes may also be treated chemically to neutralize acids or alkalis, to precipitate toxic metal ions, or to convert chemicals to less harmful materials. Microorganisms or reed beds may be used to break down some chemicals.

Questions

11 What has Huntsman Tioxide done to make the manufacture of titanium dioxide more 'green'?

12 Draw an outline flow diagram to illustrate titanium dioxide production, showing the inputs to the process, the outputs and how they are used.

171

Find out about:

▶ greener ways to make ethanoic acid

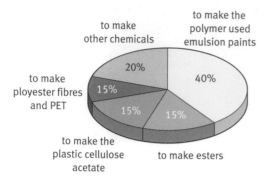

The uses of ethanoic acid

A summary showing the percentages of the products from manufacturing ethanoic acid from hydrocarbons

4C Manufacturing ethanoic acid

The processes that have been developed to manufacture ethanoic acid illustrate the application of the principles of green chemistry.

The industry produces over 8 million tonnes of the acid every year. Such a large amount of the acid is needed because it can be converted to many other useful products.

Oxidation of hydrocarbons

Up to the 1970s, ethanoic acid was produced industrially by the direct oxidation of hydrocarbons from crude oil. There are some countries where this process still operates.

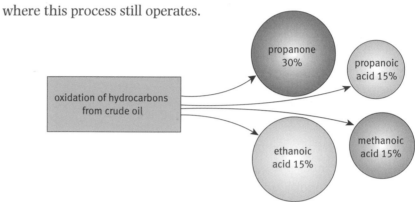

The process operates at 180–200 °C and at 40–50 times the pressure of the atmosphere. The catalyst is cobalt(II) ethanoate. The outcome is a wide range of products, including ethanoic acid, methanoic acid, propanoic acid, and propanone. The atom economy of this process is only about 35%.

This means that there is the cost of separating the products by fractional distillation. There are possible uses for all the products, but the economics of the operation depend on finding a market to sell all the chemicals produced.

Propanoic acid, and its calcium and sodium salts, can be used as mould inhibitors. Propanone is used as a solvent and in the manufacture of plastics. Methanoic acid is used in textile dyeing, in leather tanning, and in the manufacture of latex rubber.

The Monsanto process

From about 1970, ethanoic acid was mainly produced by a new process developed by Monsanto. In this process methanol and carbon monoxide combine to make ethanoic acid in the presence of a catalyst:

$$CH_3OH(l) + CO(g) \longrightarrow CH_3COOH(l)$$

The catalyst is a compound made from rhodium metal and iodide ions.

The Monsanto process is much greener than the earlier process. It has an atom economy of 100%, with all atoms in the reactants going into the product. So there is much less waste, and much less energy is needed to separate and purify the ethanoic acid. The reaction is extremely fast, and the catalyst has a long life.

The yield of ethanoic acid is high. About 98% of the methanol is converted to ethanoic acid.

Methanol is a cheaper feedstock than hydrocarbons from oil. The methanol is usually made from carbon monoxide and hydrogen. However, waste wood can be converted to methanol, so in time the process could be based on renewable biomass instead of on oil.

The Monsanto process for making ethanoic acid

The Cativa process

In 1986, the oil company BP bought all the rights to this process from Monsanto. They now run a variant of the Monsanto process that uses a different catalyst. It is called the Cativa process. The metal iridium replaces rhodium.

The atom economy for the Cativa process is also 100%. The iridium-based catalyst is cheaper. Also there are also green benefits as BP technical manager, Mike Muskett, explains:

▶ 'The process is faster and so we need smaller reactors.

▶ 'The catalyst is even more selective which cuts the energy cost of purifying the product.

▶ 'We don't need as much water in the plant as with the older process, so we need less energy to dry the product.

▶ 'Existing plant can be converted to run the Cativa process: a converted plant can produce 75% more ethanoic acid than was previously possible using the original Monsanto process.'

Questions

1 The catalysts used to make ethanoic acid are based on three metals. Where are these metals in the periodic table? What is the relationship between the three metals?

2 What are the main reasons why the older process based on oxidation of hydrocarbons is so much less 'green' than the newer processes?

3 Why are there fewer distillation and drying steps in the Cativa process than in the Monsanto process?

Summary

Alcohols, carboxylic acids, and esters

▶ Chemists use molecular and structural formulae as well as models to represent organic molecules.

▶ Methane (CH_4), ethane (C_2H_6), propane (C_3H_8) and butane (C_4H_{10}) belong to the alkane series of hydrocarbons.

▶ Alkanes burn but are inert to common aqueous reagents.

▶ Methanol (CH_3OH) and ethanol (C_2H_5OH) are alcohols with important uses.

▶ The —OH functional group gives alcohols their characteristic properties.

▶ The physical and chemical properties of ethanol can be compared to the properties of water and ethane.

▶ Methanoic acid (HCOOH) and ethanoic acid (CH_3COOH) are carboxylic acids.

▶ Ethanoic acid is the acid in vinegar.

▶ The —COOH functional group gives organic acids their characteristic properties.

▶ Aqueous solutions of carboxylic acids show the characteristic reactions of acids with metals, alkalis, and carbonates.

▶ Alcohols react with carboxylic acids, in the presence of a strong acid catalyst, to make esters.

▶ Esters have fruity smells and are used in a variety of products for their odour, taste, inertness, and solvent properties.

▶ Chemists synthesize pure esters using techniques such as heating under reflux, distillation, and purification by treatment with reagents in a tap funnel, as well as drying.

▶ Fats and oils, which are esters of glycerol and fatty acids, act as an energy store in living things.

▶ The acids in fats are mostly saturated compounds (with single C—C bonds in the carbon chains), while the acids in vegetable oils are likely to be unsaturated (with one or more C=C bonds in the carbon chains).

Energy changes in chemistry

▶ Some reaction are exothermic and give out energy; others are endothermic and take in energy.

▶ Chemists use energy level diagrams to represent energy changes during reactions.

▶ Bond breaking is endothermic, while bond forming is exothermic.

▶ The activation energy for a reaction is the energy needed to break bonds to start a reaction.

Reversible reactions and equilibria

▶ Some chemical reactions are reversible.

▶ Reversible reactions can reach a state of dynamic equilibrium.

▶ In a dynamic equilibrium the forward and back reactions are going on at the same rate so that overall there is no change.

▶ In a solution of an acid there is a dynamic equilibrium between the ionized and un-ionized forms of the acid.

▶ Carboxylic acids are weak acids (only slightly ionized) while hydrochloric acid is a strong acid (fully ionized).

Analysis

▶ Qualitative analysis identifies the chemicals present in a sample

- Quantitative analysis measures how much of each chemical there is in a sample.

- Samples for analysis should be representative of the bulk of the material under test.

- Samples are often dissolved in a suitable solvent before analysis.

- Water is an aqueous solvent; organic solvents are non-aqueous.

- Standard procedures for collecting, storing and preparing samples help to ensure that analysis is valid.

- Methods of chromatography involve a mobile liquid or gas moving through a stationary phase which, may be a solid, or a liquid held by a solid.

- Types of chromatography include paper, thin-layer (TLC), and gas chromatography (GC).

- Reference materials can help to identify chemicals separated by chromatography.

- R_f values are a measure of the distance moved by a spot relative to the solvent front in paper or thin-layer chromatography.

- In GC the chemicals in a sample separate because their retention times differ.

- An acid–base titration, using a burette and a pipette, is a procedure for quantitative analysis.

- Concentrations of solutions can be measured in g/dm^3.

- A standard solution is one with a known concentration which can be used in a titration to find the concentration of an unknown solution.

- A standard solution can be prepared by weighing out a specimen of a suitable chemical, dissolving it in water, and then making the volume of solution up to a mark in a graduated flask.

- The mean and range of a set of repeat results for titrations with replicate samples can indicate the degree of uncertainty in the measured value.

Green chemistry

- The chemical industry makes bulk chemicals on a large scale (such as ammonia, sulfuric acid, sodium hydroxide, and phosphoric acid)

- The industry makes fine chemicals on a much smaller scale (such as drugs, food additives, and fragrances).

- Government agencies are responsible for regulating industry to protect the environment as well as the health and safety of workers in the industry, people who live nearby, and users of the products.

- Research by the industry aims to develop new products and processes that are based on renewable resources while being more efficient, in that they use less energy while producing less waste.

- The yield and atom economy of a process are measures of its efficiency.

- A chemical process involves a series of stages, including preparation of the feedstock, synthesis, separation of the products, handling of by-products and wastes, and the monitoring of purity.

- A catalyst provides an alternative route for a reaction with a lower activation energy.

- Ethanol is an example of a chemical which can be made in different ways, some of which are 'greener' than others.

- Ethanol is useful as a solvent, a fuel, and a feedstock for other processes.

- Three methods of making ethanol are: by fermentation of sugar with yeast; use of genetically modified bacteria to act on waste biomass; and by synthesis from petrochemicals.

- In the petrochemical route, ethane is first converted to ethene and then to ethanol.

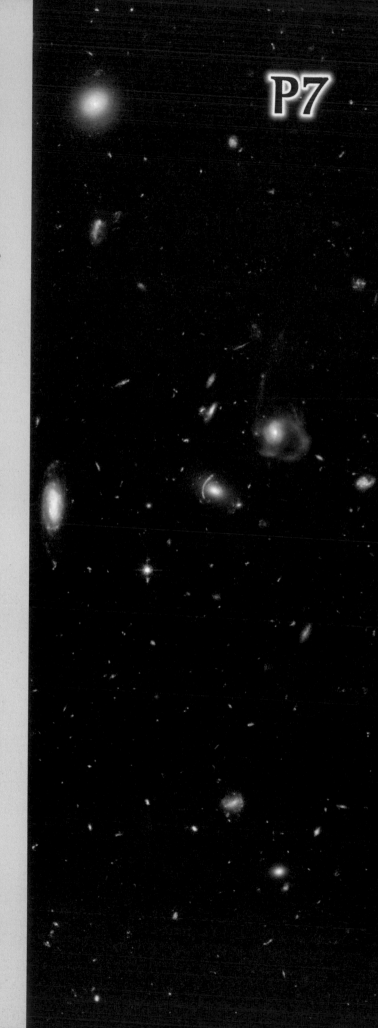

Why study the Universe?

Physics offers an important way of looking at the world. Studying the whole Universe helps us know *where* the Earth is and *when* it is too because, it turns out, the Universe has a history. Though it may seem odd, explaining what happens in stars requires an understanding of matter at the microscopic scale, right down to the smallest sub-atomic particles. Everything in the physical world is made from a few basic building blocks.

The science

In the 1830s, the French philosopher Auguste Comte suggested that there were certain things that we could never know. As an example, he gave the chemical composition of the stars. By 1860, two years after his death, physicists had interpreted the spectrum of starlight and identified the elements present. In this module, you will look at how physicists have gradually extended our understanding of stars and galaxies.

Physics in action

In making their observations, astronomers use many different instruments – think of space probes, new telescopes, computing, and the Internet. Better instruments and new, collaborative observatories have played an essential part in extending astronomers' understanding of what is 'out there'. Physics enables such new technologies. New technologies enable new science.

Observing the Universe

Find out about:

▶ how astronomical instruments are used
▶ how observations of the night sky are interpreted
▶ how a star like the Sun functions
▶ a theory of the life history of stars
▶ how astronomers work together

Topic 1

Observatories and telescopes

Astronomy is the oldest science in the world. Ancient civilizations – for example, the Chinese, Babylonians, Egyptians, Greeks, and Mayans – practised naked-eye astronomy long before the invention of telescopes in the 17th century. They built costly observatories for both practical and religious reasons.

Everything beyond the Earth moves across the sky, from horizon to horizon. Calendars and clocks were based on cycles in these movements: day and night, the phases of the Moon, and seasonal changes in the Sun's path. Long-distance travellers, on sea and on land, navigated using the positions of familiar stars.

Today there are plenty of opportunities to visit astronomical observatories and see some of the great variety of telescopes that have been invented down the years, for a variety of purposes.

The Monument in London was built to commemorate the Great Fire of 1666. It is a cylinder 202 feet (67m) tall – and it is a telescope! It was designed by Christopher Wren and Robert Hooke as an 'azimuthal telescope'. The observer lies down and looks up through the central tube at the sky above. As stars pass directly overhead, they can be timed from night to night, giving accurate measurements of their positions.

The Monument, London

Greenwich Observatory, London

Jodrell Bank, Cheshire

The Royal Observatory Edinburgh

Greenwich Observatory in south-east London was built by the English Navy in the 17th century. They had suffered a number of defeats at the hands of the Dutch, because the enemy were able to navigate better. Dutch astronomy was in advance of the English, giving them more accurate charts of the night sky, which were used to work out a ship's position.

Jodrell Bank in Cheshire is famous for its radio telescopes. At the Visitor Centre, you can see the operators at work, day and night, mapping distant radio sources far beyond our galaxy.

The Royal Observatory Edinburgh is a world-renowned centre for astronomical instrumentation. Here, electronic cameras are designed and built, and images are processed electronically. The staff also work on the systems that control the direction in which a telescope is pointing.

The observatory at Knighton in mid-Wales is part of the Spaceguard Foundation. It keeps an eye out for Near-Earth Objects that might threaten our very existence.

The observatory at Knighton, mid-Wales

Find out about:

▶ the variety of telescopes
▶ the visual images produced by telescopes

1A What is a telescope?

In the autumn of 1609, Galileo made his first observations of the Moon using a **telescope**. He was not the first person to use a telescope to look at the night sky. But the observations Galileo made, and his interpretation of them, had repercussions down the centuries. He changed the way people see the Universe.

Telescopes make things visible which cannot be seen with the naked eye. Galileo's telescope allowed him to see craters on the Moon, and the moons of Jupiter.

The Effelsberg radio telescope in Germany. With a diameter of 100 m, it gathers radio waves from distant objects in the Universe, including galaxies other than our own. The dish is scanned across the sky to generate an image.

This reflecting telescope is at the Calar Alto observatory, over 2000 m above sea-level in southern Spain. Light passes through the ring (diameter 3.5 m) and reflects off the curved, shiny mirror at the back.

This astronomer is using a refracting telescope, which uses lenses to focus light.

An artist's impression of the X-ray Multi-Mirror (XMM) Newton telescope. X-rays enter the telescope at the near end and are reflected by mirrors onto detectors at the far end.

A new golden age of astronomy began in the 1930s, with the accidental discovery of radio waves coming from beyond the Earth. Astronomers realized that objects in space do not only produce visible light. Since then, many new kinds of telescope were invented. Each of them requires a suitable detector and a method of focusing the radiation. Astronomers now gather radiation from across the whole of the electromagnetic spectrum.

These pages show a number of telescopes, some more recognizable than others.

Jocelyn Bell and Anthony Hewish were the discoverers of pulsars. These are distant objects which send out radio waves which vary with an extremely regular pulse. The wires in the field form an aerial which is their 'telescope'. Altogether, there are 1000 posts spaced out over 4.5 acres.

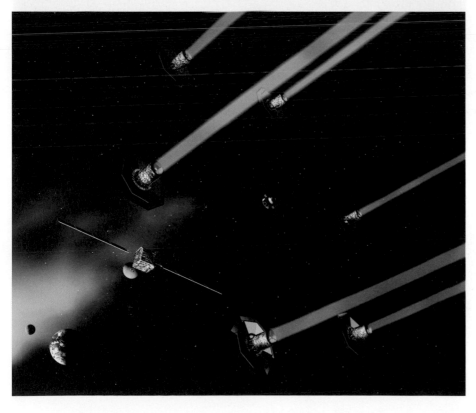

These are the Darwin infrared space telescopes which the European Space Agency proposes to launch in 2014. They will gather infrared radiation from planets orbiting stars other than the Sun.

Questions

1 Different telescopes make use of different types of electromagnetic radiation. List the telescopes shown on these two pages, together with the radiation which each gathers.

2 Telescopes 'make things visible which cannot be seen with the naked eye'. Is that true for all of the telescopes shown here?

This engraving of the Moon, as observed with a telescope, was made by Claude Mellan in 1635, just 25 years after Galileo's first lunar observations.

Seeing is believing

People like to see things with their own eyes. You feel you know something truly exists if you can see it. It is better still if you can touch it, but of course no one can touch most of the objects that astronomers study.

The first telescopes used visible light, so they produced images that people could see. Later, astronomers designed telescopes to gather radio waves, infrared radiation – in fact, every type of electromagnetic radiation, even gamma rays. The human eye cannot detect these, but ways were found to make them into pictures, using computers.

You probably think of the landscape as nearby trees and hills. But the landscape we live in extends well beyond the horizon, and out into space. A leap of human imagination can make that 'cosmic' landscape feel real too.

Radiation from objects in space reaches a telescope after a very long journey. As astronomers look at ever more distant objects, the light they gather set off ever further back in the past. In recent decades, astronomers have collected an enormous number of observations. Interpretation of the raw data is difficult. Yet, by putting together observations from different wavelengths, it is possible for them to build up a picture of the cosmic landscape, and its history.

Some astronomical images are shown on this page.

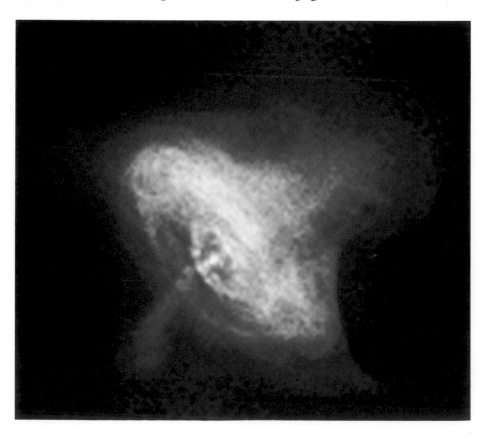

This image was made by an X-ray telescope. Although the human eye cannot detect X-rays, their energies can be measured and converted into an image. This is the Crab Nebula, the remains of a star that exploded in 1054 AD. At its centre is a pulsar.

Hearing pulsars

Jocelyn Bell, an Irish astronomer, was one of the discoverers of pulsars, strange sources of regularly pulsing radio waves. Her telescope was a giant radio aerial, and the 'image' it produced was a long paper chart. In October 1967, she was involved in making a survey of radio sources in the sky.

Six or eight weeks after starting the survey I became aware that on occasions there was a bit of 'scruff' on the records, which did not look exactly like man-made interference. Furthermore, I realized that this scruff had been seen before on the same part of the records – from the same patch of sky.

Whatever the source was, we decided that it deserved closer inspection, and that this would involve making faster chart recordings. As the chart flowed under the pen, I could see that the signal was a series of pulses, and my suspicion that they were equally spaced was confirmed as soon as I got the chart off the recorder. They were 1.3 seconds apart.

Electrical signals from the radio aerial can be played through a loudspeaker, so that the regular pulses can be heard. When first discovered, astronomers considered the possibility that they were a signal from some extraterrestrial civilization. Many other pulsing sources have since been identified, and astronomers now think that these signals come from rapidly spinning neutron stars.

Neutron stars are just one among the amazing variety of extreme and often violent objects that astronomers have discovered 'out there'. Later, you will learn how the classification of stars led to an understanding of how stars work, and how they change.

Jocelyn Bell with part of one of the charts produced by her radio 'telescope', showing the trace produced by a pulsar.

Questions

3 Look at the image of the Moon on the opposite page, and think about how the Moon appears to the naked eye when you see it in the night sky. What extra features has the artist who made this image been able to identify by using a telescope?

4 Look at the image of the Crab Nebula on the opposite page. How can you tell where the X-ray source is strongest?

Find out about:

▶ how converging lenses focus parallel rays
▶ the focal length and power of a lens

1B Describing lenses

The earliest and simplest telescopes used lenses. To understand these telescopes, you need first to understand what lenses do.

The focal length of a converging lens

The picture below shows how you can make a miniature image of a distant object using a single **converging lens**. If you position the screen correctly, you will see a small, inverted image of a distant scene.

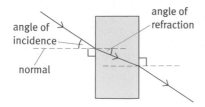

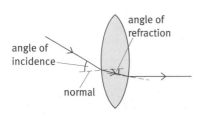

A ray of light bends as it passes at an angle from one material to another. This effect is called **refraction**. Angles are conventionally measured from the **normal**, an imaginary line drawn perpendicular to the boundary at the point where a ray strikes.

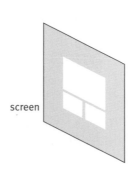

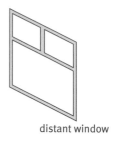

Using a converging lens to make an image.

Rays of light enter the lens. Because of the lens shape, they are refracted (they change direction), first on entering the lens and again on leaving.

A ray diagram shows this. A horizontal line passing through the centre of the lens is called the **principal axis**. Rays of light parallel to the axis are all refracted so that they meet at a point. This is why converging lenses are so called: they cause parallel rays of light to converge.

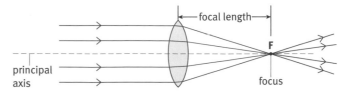

How a converging lens focuses parallel rays of light.

Parallel rays at an angle to the principal axis converge at a different point.

Lenses are cleverly designed. The surface must be curved in just the right way in order for the rays to meet at a point, the **focus**, F. When early astronomers made their own telescopes, they had to grind lenses from blocks of glass. If the glass was uneven, or if the surface was not smooth or was of the wrong shape, the telescope would give a blurred, poorly focused image. It is said that much of Galileo's success was achieved because he made high-quality lenses so that he could see details that other observers could not.

Key words

refraction
converging lens
focus
focal length
principal axis
power
dioptre

The distance from the centre of the lens to the focus is called the **focal length** of the lens. The longer the focal length of a lens, the larger (actual physical size) will be the real image that the lens produces of a distant object.

Estimating the focal length

You can compare lenses simply by looking at them.

◗ A lens with a long focal length is thin; its surfaces are not very strongly curved.

◗ A lens with a short focal length is fatter; its surfaces are more strongly curved.

To estimate the focal length of a converging lens, stand next to the wall on the opposite side of the room to the window. Hold up the lens and use it to focus an image of the window on the wall. Measure the distance from the lens to the wall – this will give you a good estimate of the focal length.

The power of a lens

A fat lens (one with a short focal length) bends the rays of light more. Its **power** is greater. So short focal length equals high power, and long focal length equals low power. As one increases, the other decreases.

Here is the equation used to calculate power when you know the focal length:

$$\text{power (in \textbf{dioptres})} = \frac{1}{\text{focal length (in metres)}}$$

So if a lens has a focal length of 0.5 m, its power is

$$\frac{1}{0.5} = 2 \text{ dioptres}$$

If you look at the reading glasses sold in chemists' shops, or at an optician's prescription, you will see the power of the lens quoted in dioptres.

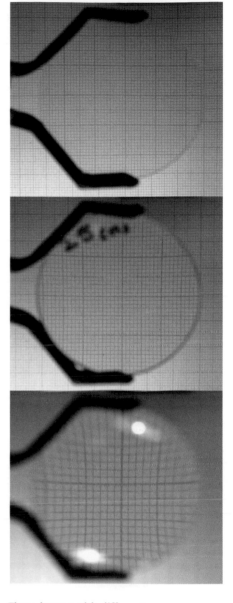

Three lenses with different focal lengths.

Questions

1 a When a ray of light passes from air into glass, which way does it bend: towards the normal or away from the normal?

b Which way does a ray bend when passing from glass into air?

2 Look at the three lenses in the photographs on this page. Put them in order, starting with the one with the shortest focal length. Which one has the greatest power?

3 The focal length of a lens is measured between which two points?

4 A lens has a focal length of 20 cm. What is its power?

5 A pair of reading glasses has lenses labelled +1.5 D (D stands for dioptres). What is their focal length?

Find out about:

▶ the lenses used in telescopes
▶ the magnification produced by a telescope
▶ how bigger apertures give brighter images

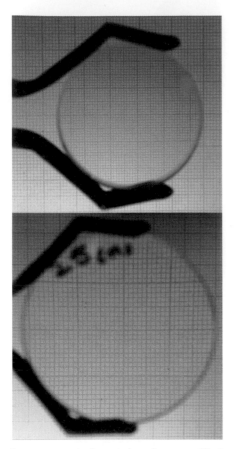

Lenses can produce reduced or magnified images.

Hans Lippershey and his children. Their play with lenses led to the invention of the telescope.

1C Refracting telescopes

Magnifying glass

Any converging lens can act as a magnifying glass. Simply hold it above a small object, look through, and see a magnified view. The image on the retina of your eye is larger than the object itself.

Just two lenses

Telescopes evolved from the lenses used for correcting poor eyesight. These were in use before 1300, though you had to be quite well off to afford a pair of spectacles in those days. The lenses were biconvex; that is, they were convex (bulging outwards) on both sides. The word 'lens' is Latin for 'lentil', which has the same shape.

Such lenses work as magnifying glasses, producing an enlarged image when you look through them at a small object. For medieval scholars, whose eyesight began to fail in middle age, spectacles meant that they could go on working for another 20 or 30 years.

Seeing further

The Dutch inventor Hans Lippershey is credited with putting two converging lenses together to make a telescope. The picture below illustrates the legend that it was in fact his children who, in 1608, held up two lenses and noticed that the weathercock on a distant building looked bigger and closer. Lippershey tested their observation, and went on to offer his invention to the Dutch military.

In fact, Lippershey failed to get a patent on his device. Other 'inventors' challenged his claim, and the Dutch government decided that the principle of the telescope was too easy to copy, so that a patent could not be granted.

Telescopes rapidly became a fashionable item, sold widely across western Europe by travelling salesmen. That is how one came in to Galileo's hands in Padua, near Venice, in 1609.

Refracting telescopes

A telescope that uses lenses to gather and focus light is called a refracting telescope, or **refractor**.

A refractor has two lenses:

▶ The **eyepiece lens** is the one next to your eye.

▶ The **objective lens** is the one closest to the object you are observing.

The same terminology is used for microscopes.

In the sort of telescope that Lippershey invented, the eyepiece lens is fatter than the objective lens. Its surfaces are more strongly curved.

This helps to explain why the telescope was not invented earlier, despite the fact that lenses had been in use in spectacles for three centuries. Spectacle lenses are not very strong, and they tend to be rather similar to each other. In a telescope, to achieve a degree of magnification, you need to have two different lenses, of different powers.

> **Key words**
> refractor
> eyepiece lens
> objective lens

> **Questions**
> 1 Look at the photograph on the opposite page.
>   a Which lens is a converging lens? How can you tell?
>   b What sort of image is produced by a diverging lens?
> 2 Why do you think Lippershey offered his invention to the Dutch military?
> 3 What would you expect to see if you made a telescope using two identical lenses?

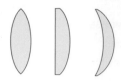

converging lenses

All converging lenses are fatter in the middle than at the edges.

DIY telescope

You can make a telescope using almost any pair of converging lenses. As the illustration on the left shows, this means any lens that is fatter in the middle than at the edges.

Sometimes converging lenses are described as 'convex', but this can be misleading. You can see from the picture that some converging lenses are convex on one side and concave on the other.

Eyepiece and objective

Two converging lenses, mounted in a line, are enough to make a simple telescope.

- The fatter (more curved) lens is the eyepiece lens.

- The thinner lens is the objective lens.

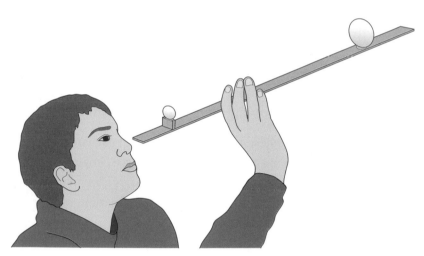

Looking through the eyepiece, you should see an **inverted** (upside-down) **image** of a distant object.

Top: A telescope that uses two converging lenses, like Lippershey's. *Bottom:* This is what you can see through it.

Getting focused

You will only see a clear image if the two lenses are the correct distance apart. That is why optical instruments (such as telescopes, binoculars, and microscopes) are designed so that you can adjust the separation of the lenses. Adjusting the focus means altering the separation of the lenses until you see a clear, unblurred image.

Focusing depends on how far away the object is that you are looking at. Birdwatchers buy binoculars that will focus on a bird just a few metres away, or at a distance of hundreds of metres. Astronomers are only interested in much more distant objects. In fact, astronomical objects are all sufficiently far away that they can be described as being 'at infinity'.

Galileo's telescope was of a different design, with a diverging lens as the eyepiece. This has the advantage that the image seen through the telescope is the right way up. Although telescopes of this type are no longer made, the Galilean telescope is the basis of the opera glasses found in some theatres.

A **diverging lens** makes parallel rays of light diverge. Lenses that are fatter at the edges than in the middle are diverging lenses.

Key words
focusing
inverted image
diverging lens

diverging lenses

Diverging lenses are thinner in the middle than at the edges.

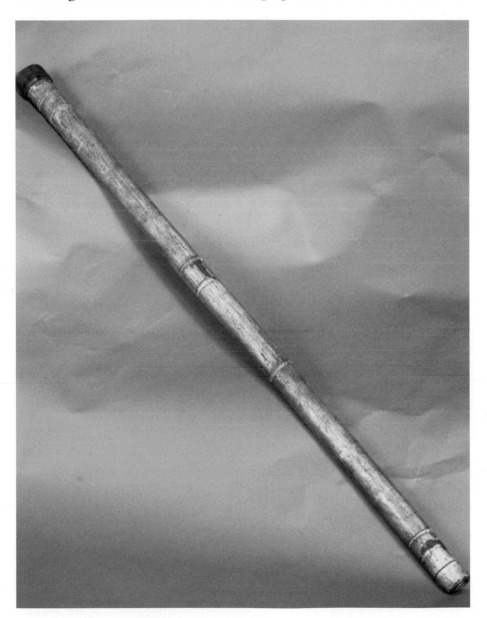

This is a replica of Galileo's telescope. His best telescopes had a magnification of 30 times.

Questions

4 Name four optical instruments mentioned on these pages.

5 What word describes the fact that the image seen through a simple telescope is the wrong way up?

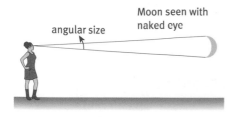

angular size — Moon seen with naked eye

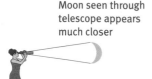

Moon seen through telescope appears much closer

A telescope increases the angular size of the Moon.

Magnification of a telescope

When you look at the Moon, it appears quite small in the sky. Its image on the retina of your eye is quite small. Look at the Moon through a telescope, and it looks enormous. The telescope produces a greatly enlarged image on your retina.

Suppose your telescope is labelled 50×. This says that its **magnification** is 50. There is more than one way of thinking about this:

▶ The telescope makes the Moon appear 50 times as close.

▶ The telescope makes the Moon's angular size seem 50 times as great.

To the naked eye, the Moon has an angular size of about half a degree (0.5°). With the telescope, this is increased to 25°. The telescope has an **angular magnification** of 50.

A telescope does not make a distant star look any bigger – it remains a point of light. However, a telescope spreads out a group of stars, by magnifying the angles between them. This makes it possible to see two stars that are close together as separate objects.

Calculating magnification

The magnification produced by a refracting telescope depends on the lenses from which it is made:

$$\text{magnification} = \frac{\text{focal length of objective lens}}{\text{focal length of eyepiece lens}}$$

Suppose you choose two lenses with focal lengths 50 cm and 5 cm:

$$\text{magnification} = \frac{50\,\text{cm}}{5\,\text{cm}} = 10$$

Aperture and image brightness

A telescope cannot make stars look bigger, because they are too far away. But there is something important the telescope can do – it makes stars look brighter. Dim stars look bright, and stars that are too faint to see come into view.

Without a telescope, you can see up to 3000 individual stars in the night sky; a small telescope can increase this by a factor of at least 10.

So a telescope is better than the naked eye for seeing dim stars. The reason is that the telescope gathers more light than the eye. Think about the objective lens of a telescope. It may be, say, 10 centimetres across. Its aperture is 10 cm. Compare this with the pupil of your eye. On a dark night, the **aperture** of your eye (the 'pupil') might be 5 mm across.

This amateur astronomer has two telescopes with 7- and 11-inch apertures.

Nocturnal creatures such as owls and mice have large pupils to make the most of the available night light (and not for star-gazing). The lenses of a telescope gather light from a star and concentrate the rays before they enter your eye.

The amount of light gathered by a telescope depends on the collecting area of its objective. To see the faintest and most distant objects in the Universe, astronomers require telescopes with very large collecting areas.

Key words
magnification
angular magnification
aperture

Questions

6 Look at the equation for magnification. Use it to explain why a telescope made with two identical converging lenses will be useless.

7 Calculate the magnification provided by a telescope made from lenses with focal lengths 1 m and 5 cm.

8 You are asked to make a telescope with as large a magnification as possible. You have a box full of lenses. How would you choose the two most suitable lenses?

9 Show that four telescopes of diameter 8 m gather as much light as one of diameter 16 m.

Here is one way to gather a lot of light – build four identical telescopes. These quadruplets are part of the European Southern Observatory in Chile. Each has an aperture of 8 m, so when combined they equal a single telescope with an aperture of 16 m.

Find out about:

▶ the advantages of reflecting telescopes over refractors
▶ how mirrors collect light in reflecting telescopes
▶ how reducing diffraction gives better resolution

1D Reflecting telescopes

Mirrors that focus light

The first telescopes used lenses to focus light. But from ancient times people knew that mirrors too could focus light. The mirror must be curved; a curved mirror with the correct shape is described as 'parabolic'.

When parallel rays of light reach a parabolic mirror parallel to its axis, they reflect so that they meet at the focus.

Mirror v. lens

A simple converging lens focuses different colours (frequencies) of light at slightly different points. Used as the objective of a refracting telescope, this lens will produce an unclear image.

The first design for a reflecting telescope, or **reflector**, was proposed in 1636, not long after Galileo's refracting telescope. It used a parabolic mirror as the telescope objective. One advantage of using a mirror is that it reflects rays of all colours in exactly the same way.

Mirrors have other advantages. Astronomers were soon designing optical telescopes with objectives that had larger diameters, to gather more light. You can make very large parabolic mirrors, but you cannot make very large lenses.

▶ The largest objective lens possible has a diameter of about 1 m. Any larger and the lens would sag and change shape under its own weight, making it useless for focusing light.

▶ It is very difficult to ensure that the glass of a large-diameter lens is uniform in composition all the way through.

▶ It is difficult, but perfectly possible to make a mirror 10 m in diameter. Its weight can be supported from the back, as well as the sides.

For these reasons, the largest professional astronomical telescopes use mirrors as their objectives.

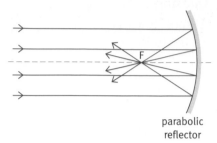

A parabolic reflector is correctly shaped to ensure that every ray parallel to the axis is reflected to the focus.

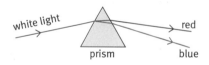

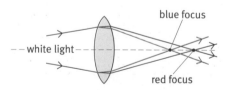

The fact that glass refracts light of different colours by different amounts is useful for prisms but is a problem for simple lenses.

A problem with a reflecting telescope is where to place the observer. In the top diagram, the observer must be inside the telescope. In a different design, a small plane mirror close to the focus of the objective reflects light out of the telescope to an external eyepiece. Many other solutions are in common use.

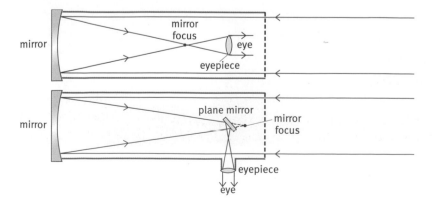

H Diffraction effects

A telescope with a big aperture gathers more light. There is another advantage of a big aperture: it makes it easier to see two stars that are close together. Here's why:

Recall from Module P6 *The wave model of radiation* (page 155) that when light (or any other kind of radiation) passes through an aperture, it tends to spread out. This effect is called **diffraction**. The result is that when you look at a star through a telescope, you see a slightly blurred blob of light rather than a perfect spot.

If you look at two stars that are side-by-side in the sky, their blobs may overlap and you will not be able to resolve (distinguish) them. They will look like a single blob of light.

A large aperture causes less diffraction, so a telescope with a larger aperture has a greater **resolving power**.

Wavelength and diffraction

It is easier to understand how diffraction works by thinking of the radiation passing through an aperture in the form of waves. The effect is greatest when the aperture is similar to the wavelength of the waves.

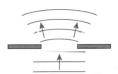
Waves spread out as they pass through the aperture.

A narrower aperture has more effect.

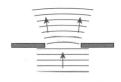
A smaller wavelength gives less diffraction.

To avoid diffraction effects, astronomers design telescopes with apertures much larger than the wavelength of the radiation they want to gather. This explains why radio telescopes, for example, are so large – the wavelength of the radio waves may be several metres (see the photo of a radio telescope on page 180).

Key words
reflector
diffraction
resolving power

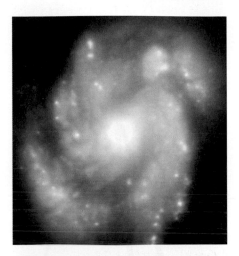

Two views of a region of the night sky, taken with telescopes having different resolving powers.

Questions

1 In a reflecting telescope, is the mirror the objective or the eyepiece?

2 Look at the two photos of the night sky (above). In which are the stars better resolved? Which telescope had the larger aperture?

3 An astronomer finds that she can scarcely resolve (separate) two stars. Which of these will improve the situation?

▸ using a telescope with a smaller aperture

▸ looking at light of shorter wavelength

Find out about:

▶ engineering of telescopes
▶ how data is collected in radio telescopes

The tripod holds this amateur telescope in a fixed position.

1E Bigger and better telescopes

Telescope mountings

Very small telescopes can be hand-held. But with a magnification greater than about 6×, a telescope needs support. Otherwise you see nothing more than a blurred movement.

Telescopes must be moveable, so that they can be pointed to different parts of the night sky. Rotation around two axes at right angles to each other enables a telescope to point in any direction. Telescope supports are called mountings.

Amateur astronomers will use a tripod to support their telescope. The largest of professional telescopes can have masses as big as 100 000 kilograms. Their bearings must have low friction, and the weight of the telescope itself must be balanced carefully, if the telescope is to be easily moved and able to maintain its alignment. This represents an enormous technical challenge.

Temperature changes

Telescope designers have many other interesting problems to solve. Think of the locations of some telescopes – on mountaintops and in deserts. Temperatures fall from day to night, sometimes quite dramatically. The telescope structure will expand as its temperature rises and contract as it cools. Clever engineering gets round these problems too.

Radio reflectors

The 'dish' of a radio telescope is a giant reflector. It is parabolic in shape and needs a wide aperture because the radio waves that it gathers have a much longer wavelength than light. The famous radio telescope at the Jodrell Bank Observatory in Cheshire has a diameter of 76 m.

Radio telescopes at Jodrell Bank. The 76 m dish is on the right.

The radio wave detector is placed at the focus of the dish, where the reflected radio waves are most concentrated. As the dish is steered about, it gathers radio waves from different points in the sky. A picture is gradually built up from the signals received.

The reflecting surface of the dish must be smooth. Any irregularities would reflect radio waves at the wrong angle, and this would contribute to fuzziness of the image.

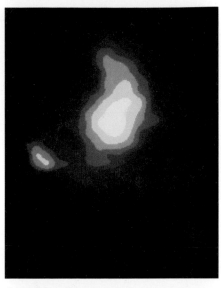

This radio telescope image shows a cluster of galaxies (the M81 cluster). It was made by tuning the Jodrell Bank telescope to the wavelength of radio waves given out by hydrogen gas (21 cm). The most intense waves come from two large galaxies (white areas), but you can also see that the whole cluster of galaxies is embedded in a giant cloud of hydrogen gas.

Here is another way to achieve a large aperture – use several reflectors, then combine their data using sophisticated electronics and fast computing. This is the Hanbury Brown radio telescope in Australia. Six reflectors move along a 6 km track.

Questions

1 Look at the radio telescope image of the M81 cluster of galaxies. What can be seen in this image that would not be seen using an optical (light) telescope?

2 Compare the Hanbury Brown telescope (this page) with the Calar Alto Observatory telescope (page 180). What similarities and differences can you identify?

Find out about:

▶ the parallel nature of light from a distant object
▶ interpreting ray diagrams for mirrors and lenses

1F Ray diagrams for telescopes

To an astronomer, most objects of interest are far off, 'at infinity'. This means that all of the rays of light coming from a distant star can be regarded as being parallel to one another.

Reflectors

The **ray diagram** on the left shows what happens when parallel rays of light reach a parabolic mirror.

This diagram is simple to construct, because each ray has to obey the law of reflection:

$$\text{angle of incidence} = \text{angle of reflection}$$

The photograph below shows the giant radio telescope at Arecibo, in Puerto Rico. Hanging above the dish is the detector, which is moved around to collect reflected waves coming from different directions in space.

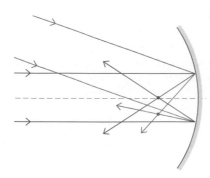

Rays parallel to the axis of the reflector are reflected to the focus. Parallel rays from another direction are focused at a different point.

The Arecibo radio telescope is built into a natural crater. It cannot be steered about.

Refractors

A ray diagram can also be used to represent the way in which a converging lens focuses parallel rays of light. Rays parallel to the axis meet at the focus. Parallel rays from another direction are focused at a point above or below the focus. (See the diagram on the left.)

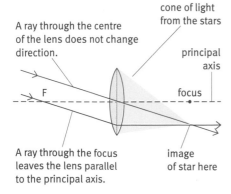

A ray through the centre of the lens does not change direction.

A ray through the focus leaves the lens parallel to the principal axis.

Parallel rays that are not parallel to the principal axis are focused at a point below the focus. All of the light from a star which strikes the lens goes to the same point. The star's image position can be located by drawing just two rays.

Extended object

A distant star is so far away that it appears as a point of light, even through a powerful telescope. But a galaxy looks bigger than this, and is described as being an **extended object**. The Sun, Moon, and planets are extended objects too. The ray diagram on the right shows how a real image is formed of an extended object. It also shows why the image seen in a refracting telescope is inverted.

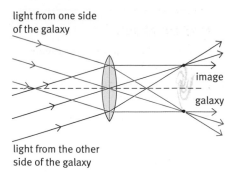

An objective lens is shown gathering light from two sides of a galaxy. Note that the image of the galaxy is inverted.

A refracting telescope

Using what you have learned about lenses can give an explanation of how a telescope made of two converging lenses works. The diagram below shows what happens.

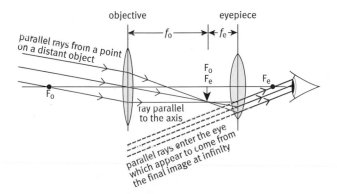

How a telescope made of two converging lenses works.

> Parallel rays of light enter the objective lens from a point on a distant object.

> Each set of parallel rays is focused by the objective lens, so a real image is formed. A weak lens is used for the objective because it produces a larger image of the distant object.

> The eyepiece is a magnifying glass, which you use to look at this real image. A strong lens is used for the eyepiece because it magnifies the image more.

From the diagram, you can see that the angle between the rays from the eyepiece and the principal axis is larger than the angle between the rays from the object and the principal axis. This means that any extended object, for example the Moon, which looks small to the naked eye, will look much larger through the telescope.

The diagram is useful in another way. It shows that, when the telescope is adjusted to focus on a distant object, point F is the focal point of both lenses. So the lenses must be separated by a distance equal to the sum of their focal lengths.

distance between lenses =
  focal length of objective + focal length of eyepiece

Questions

1 Sketch a curved mirror. Draw two rays of light striking the mirror parallel to the axis, and show how the reflected rays cross. Where the rays strike the mirror, draw the normal to the surface of the mirror and mark the angles of incidence and reflection.

2 If you look through a converging lens at a distant scene, you see an inverted image. Explain why this is so, using a diagram to support your explanation.

Key words
ray diagram
extended object

Find out about:

▶ the effects of the atmosphere on light from stars

▶ the need to reduce light pollution

The *Hubble Space Telescope* orbits above the Earth, avoiding the effects of atmospheric absorption and refraction of light. As well as gathering visible light, Hubble also gathers ultraviolet and infrared radiation.

1G Windows in the atmosphere

Some telescopes are built on high mountains. Others are carried on spacecraft in orbit around the Earth. This is partly because some types of electromagnetic radiation are absorbed by the atmosphere (see the diagram on page 173).

▶ Visible light, microwaves, and radio waves can pass through the atmosphere without being significantly absorbed.

▶ Other radiation, including X-rays, gamma rays, and much infrared, is absorbed.

Our eyes, and those of other creatures, have evolved to make use of the wavelengths that reach the surface of the Earth.

Twinkle, twinkle

If you look up at the stars in the night sky, you are looking up through the atmosphere. Even when the sky appears clear, the stars twinkle. This shows an important feature of the atmosphere.

The stars, of course, shine more or less steadily. Their light may travel across space, uninterrupted, for millions of years. It is only on the last few seconds of its journey to your eyes that things go wrong. The twinkling, or scintillation, is caused when starlight passes through the atmosphere.

The atmosphere is not uniform. Some areas are more dense, and some areas are less dense. As a ray of light passes through areas of different densities, it is refracted and changes direction. The atmosphere is in constant motion (because of convection currents and winds) so areas of different density move around. This causes a ray to be refracted in different directions, and is the cause of scintillation.

Some astronomical telescopes record images electronically. Computer software allows them to reduce or remove completely the effects of scintillation from the images they produce.

Dark skies, please

A telescope sees stars against a black background. However, many astronomers find that the sky they are looking at is brightened by light pollution. Much of this is light that shines upwards from street lamps and domestic lighting. Scattered by the atmosphere, the light enters any nearby telescope.

Another consequence is that it has become difficult to see the stars at night from urban locations. People today are less aware of the changing nature of the night sky, something that was common knowledge for our ancestors.

In 2006, the city authorities in Rome decided that enough was enough. To reduce light pollution and to save energy, it was decided to switch off many of its 170 000 street lights, thereby cutting its lighting bill by 40%. Illumination of its ancient monuments has been dimmed, as well as lights in shop and hotel windows.

The Campaign for Dark Skies, supported by amateur and professional astronomers, campaigns to reduce light pollution. But it is not only light radiation that affects astronomers. Radio waves used for broadcasting and mobile phones can interfere with the work of radio telescopes, so certain ranges of frequencies must be left clear for astronomical observations.

These two maps show the amount of light pollution across the United Kingdom in 1993 and 2000. The red areas indicate where most light is emitted, the dark-blue areas where the least is emitted. You can see that the red areas have grown over the seven years between surveys. But the biggest change is in the countryside. Here the light pollution, although at lower levels than in towns and cities, has increased across large areas of England

1993

2000

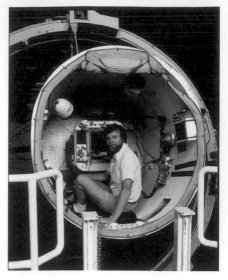

David Malin as a young scientist.

Images of the stars

A large aperture gathers more light, so that fainter stars can be seen. But there is another way to see faint stars – collect their light over a long period of time. There are two ways to do this:

▶ use photographic film or plates, or

▶ use an electronic device to record the light.

David Malin is an astronomer based in Sydney, Australia. He has made a name for himself by producing stunning images of the night sky.

'Light passing down the telescope is passed through three filters in turn – red, green and blue – to produce three separate images on black-and-white photographic plates. These are then used in the enlarger to create a single coloured image.

'The photographs below compare the results of this technique with a photo of the same area of the sky photographed on the standard colour film use by astronomers.'

The photo on the left was produced from three separate colour images. The one on the right used standard colour film.

Going electronic

Photographic images of stars can give great images, but most astronomers today use electronic imaging systems. These are based on charge coupled devices (CCDs), which are the devices used in digital cameras to record images. Electronic imaging has a number of advantages:

▶ Images are stored digitally.

▶ They can be merged and processed by computers.

▶ They can be sent around the world, for use by colleagues working elsewhere.

However, photographic plates can be scanned to turn them into digital images.

A barred spiral galaxy, photographed using a CCD.

Processing digital images

Astronomical images often suffer from unwanted speckles called noise, and from poor contrast. They can be improved using some of these techniques:

▶ adding images together but retaining only the parts, like stars, that are the same in each image

▶ sharpening images to accentuate the edges of astronomical objects

▶ using false colour to highlight information in a single picture

These techniques are based on methods that were developed to improve photographic plates. However, astronomers can now apply them more quickly and with more control using their desktop computers rather than a darkroom.

Topic 2

Mapping the heavens

Telescopes have revealed many unexpected features of the Universe, and they continue to do so today. However, many fundamental ideas about the Solar System and the stars beyond were developed before the invention of the telescope.

Look, no lenses! This sailor is demonstrating the use of an **astrolabe**, an astronomical instrument invented over 2000 years ago. The instrument measures the angle of a star above the horizon. It was used for navigation, astronomy, astrology, and telling the time.

Day-time astronomy

You do not have to stay up all night to make valid astronomical observations. You can see the Sun cross the sky every day from East to West, moving at a steady rate. That is an observation that any scientific theory of the Universe must account for. You may also have noticed that the Moon follows a similar path, sometimes by day and sometimes by night.

Around the pole

The stars also move across the night sky. Their movement is imperceptible, but it is revealed by long-exposure photography. The photo also shows that the stars appear to rotate about a point in the sky directly above one of the Earth's poles.

Eclipses

Sometimes it is rare and unusual events that reveal something important. When the Sun passes behind the Moon in a total eclipse, you can see the Sun's gaseous corona.

The Sun sets – a time-lapse photograph.

This photograph shows the motion of the stars across the sky. The exposure time was 10.5 hours.

A total eclipse of the Sun. The outer atmosphere or corona becomes visible. Its appearance changes from one eclipse to the next.

Key words
astrolabe

203

Find out about:

▶ phases of the Moon
▶ the difference between sidereal and solar days
▶ the motion of the planets against the background of fixed stars

The Moon is shown here at intervals of three days. The Sun is off to the right. Notice that it is the half of the Moon facing the Sun which is lit up.

2A Naked-eye astronomy

The spinning observatory

The Sun and Moon move across the sky in similar but slightly different ways:

▶ The Sun appears to travel across the sky once every 24 h (on average).

▶ The Moon moves very slightly slower, reappearing every 24 h 49 m.

People are, of course, deceived by their senses. The Sun is not moving round the Earth. It is the Earth that is spinning on its axis. That is why the Sun rises and sets every day, and why we experience day and night.

The situation with the Moon is more complex. The spinning of the Earth makes the Moon cross the sky. But the Moon is also slowly orbiting the Earth, from West to East. One complete orbit takes about 28 days.

Even without taking into account the fact that the Earth is orbiting the Sun, you can use these ideas to explain the changing **phases of the Moon**.

The Moon's phases

At any time, half of the Moon is lit up by the Sun's rays, just like the Earth. The view from the Earth depends on where the Moon is around its orbit.

▶ When the Moon is on the opposite side of the Earth to the Sun, an observer on the Earth can see the whole of its illuminated side. This is a full Moon.

▶ When the Moon is in the direction of the Sun, the side that is in darkness faces the Earth. This is a new Moon.

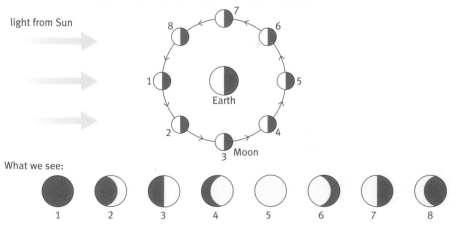

The phase of the Moon changes as it orbits the Earth.

H The spinning, orbiting observatory

Earth-bound observers see the sky from a rotating planet. That is why the stars appear to move across the night sky. Their apparent motion is slightly different from the Sun's:

▶ The stars appear to travel across the sky once every 23 h 56 m.

That is 4 minutes less than the time taken by the Sun. The difference arises from the fact that the Earth orbits the Sun, once every year.

Key words

phases of the Moon
sidereal day
solar day

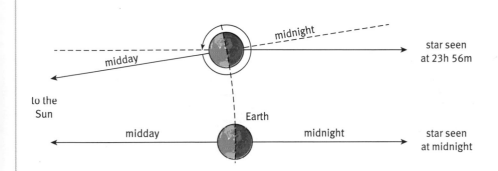

You can think of the Sun and stars as fixed. We view them from a spinning, orbiting planet.

Imagine looking up at a bright star in the sky. 23 h 56 m later, it is back in the same position. This tells you that the Earth must have turned through 360° in this time, and you are facing in the same direction in space.

The Sun not behave like the stars. Repeat the above observation, this time looking at the Sun. After 23 h 56 m, the Earth has turned through 360°, but the Sun has not quite reached the same position in the sky. The diagram shows that, in the course of a day, the Earth has moved a short distance around its orbit. Now it must turn a little more (4 minutes' worth) for the Sun to appear in the same direction as the day before.

Days are measured by the Sun. The average time it takes to cross the sky is 24 h, and this is called a **solar day**. We could choose to set our clocks by the stars (although this would be very inconvenient). Then a day would last 23 h 56 m; this is called a **sidereal day** ('sidereal' means 'related to the stars').

Questions

1 Draw a diagram to show the relative positions of the Earth, Sun, and Moon when the Moon is at first quarter (half-illuminated, as seen from Earth).

2 **a** If the Earth orbited the Sun more quickly – in, say, 30 days – would the difference between sidereal and solar days be greater or less?

b Work out the time difference between sidereal and solar days.

3 Why would it be 'inconvenient' if we set our clocks according to sidereal time?

205

Mapping the heavens

The night sky changes through the year. You may have noticed that some newspapers publish monthly star charts to help you work out what stars are visible, and when. These charts are drawn using knowledge of the positions of the stars and planets in the sky.

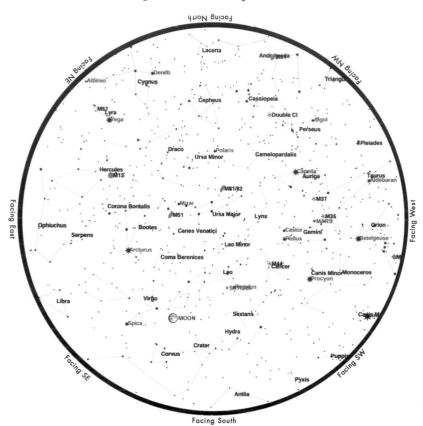

A star chart for March 2008.

Astronomers give the position of astronomical objects in the sky in terms of angles. Imagine standing in a field, looking at a star. Two angles are needed to give its position:

▶ Start by pointing at the horizon, due North of where you are. Turn westwards through an angle until you are pointing at the horizon, directly below the star. That gives you the first angle.

▶ Now move your arm upwards through an angle, until you are pointing directly at the star. That gives you the second angle.

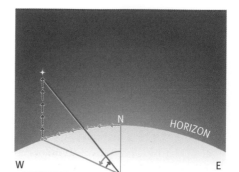

Two angles describe the position of a star.

Constellations

Another way astronomers identify particular stars is to state the **constellation** they are in. A constellation is a group of stars that form a pattern in the sky, and the names people use for them go back a very long time. Some are familiar from the signs of the zodiac. They have no real significance – the stars in a constellation may be vastly separated from each other in space, but it is convenient to use their names to identify areas of the sky.

Some constellations seen on a winter night are different from those of a summer night. This is because the Earth travels half way round its orbit in six months. You see the stars that are in the opposite direction to the Sun and so, after six months, you can see the opposite half of the sky.

Each day, a particular star rises 4 minutes earlier. After 6 months, those extra minutes add up to 12 hours, so that a star which is rising at dusk in June will be setting at dusk in December.

Heavenly wanderers

Five **planets** can be seen with the naked eye from Earth – Mercury, Venus, Mars, Jupiter, and Saturn. These were recognized as different from stars long, long ago, because they appear to move, very slowly, night by night, against the background of 'fixed stars'. The diagram on the right shows the changing positions in the sky of three planets at dawn in late 2007.

The most striking thing is that the planets generally move steadily in one direction across the background of stars, but, at times, they slow down and go into reverse. This is known as **retrograde motion**.

To explain the behaviour of planets, recall that both the Earth and the planets are orbiting the Sun. An observer looking towards Mars sees it against a backdrop of the fixed stars. Its position against this backdrop depends on where the Earth, and Mars, are in their orbits.

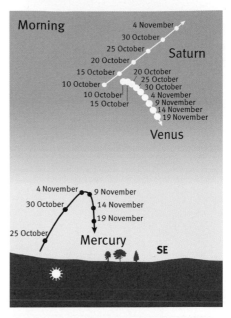

The pattern of movements of planets in the sky is different from that of stars. This diagram shows the pattern of movement of three planets just before sunrise.

Key words
constellation
planet
retrograde motion

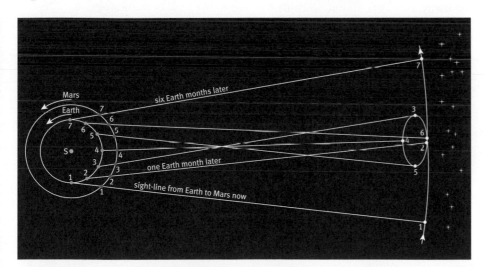

From months 1 to 3, Mars appears to move forwards. Then, for two months, it goes into reverse before moving forwards again.

Questions

4 a Draw a diagram to explain why you see some different constellations in winter and summer. The diagram on page 205 may help you.

b Use your diagram to explain why there are some stars that can never be seen from the UK, but that can be seen from places in the southern hemisphere.

5 Mercury is the closest planet to the Sun. It is only ever seen at dawn or dusk, close to the Sun in the sky. Draw a diagram to explain why.

Find out about:

▶ why solar and lunar eclipses happen

▶ the effect of the Moon's orbital tilt

2B Eclipses

Astronomers can predict when an eclipse of the Sun (a solar eclipse) will occur. A solar eclipse happens just a few times each year. And a total eclipse at any particular point on the Earth is a rare event.

Eclipses involve both the Sun and the Moon.

▶ In a **solar eclipse**, the Moon blocks the Sun's light.

▶ In a **lunar eclipse**, the Moon moves into the Earth's shadow.

The predictability of eclipses shows that they must be related to the regular motions of the Sun and Moon. Their rarity suggests that some special circumstances must arise if one is to occur.

The first way to explain a solar eclipse is to think of the Sun and Moon and their apparent motion across the sky. The Sun moves slightly faster across the sky than the Moon, and its path may take it behind the Moon. For us to see a total eclipse, the Sun must be travelling across the sky at the same height as the Moon. Any higher or lower and it will not be perfectly eclipsed.

The fact that the Moon precisely blocks the Sun is probably a coincidence. The Sun is 400 times the diameter of the Moon, and it is 400 times as far away.

Provided the Sun's path across the sky matches the Moon's, a total eclipse may be seen.

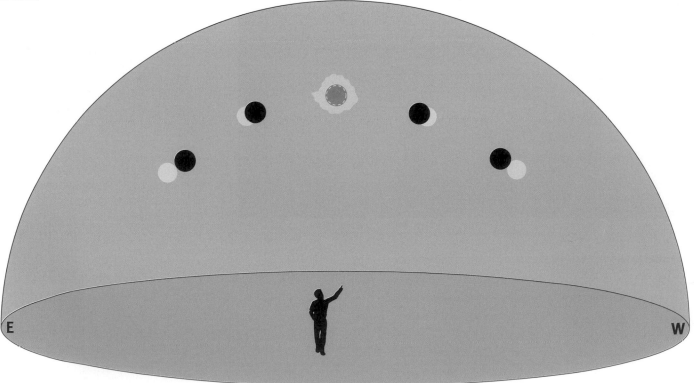

Umbra and penumbra

The diagram below shows a different way of explaining eclipses, both solar and lunar. Both the Earth and the Moon have shadows, areas where they block sunlight. Because the Sun is an extended source of light, these shadows do not have hard edges. There is a region of total darkness (the **umbra**), fringed by a region of partial darkness (the **penumbra**). The Earth's shadow is much bigger than the Moon's.

> **Key words**
> lunar eclipse
> solar eclipse
> umbra
> penumbra

- If the Moon's umbra touches the surface of the Earth, a solar eclipse is seen from inside the area of contact.

- If the Moon passes into the Earth's umbra, a lunar eclipse is seen.

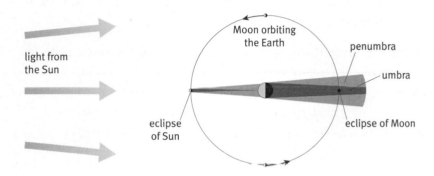

The umbra and penumbra for an eclipse of the Sun and an eclipse of the Moon.

H Why the rarity?

The Moon orbits the Earth once a month, so you might expect to see a lunar eclipse every month, followed by a solar eclipse two weeks later. You do not – eclipses are much rarer than this. The reason is that the Moon's orbit is tilted relative to the plane of the Earth's orbit by about 5°. Usually Earth, Sun and the Moon are not in a line so no eclipse occurs.

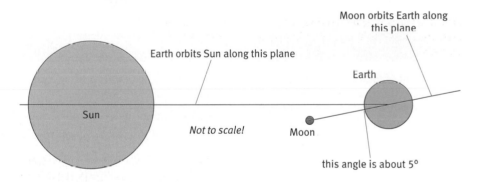

The Moon's orbit is tilted relative to the plane of the Earth's orbit around the Sun. The effect is exaggerated here.

Questions

1 At times, the Moon's orbit takes it further from Earth so that it looks smaller in the sky. Now, if it is in front of the Sun, the result is that we see a ring of bright sunlight around the black disc of the Moon. This is an annular eclipse. Construct a diagram like the one opposite to show why this happens.

2 What is the phase of the Moon at the time of

   a a solar eclipse, and

   b of a lunar eclipse?

3 Explain why a person on Earth is more likely to see a lunar eclipse than a solar eclipse.

Eclipse trips

Today, solar eclipses are big business. Thousands of people select their holiday dates to coincide with an eclipse. Tour operators organize plane-loads of eclipse spotters, and cruise liners sail along the track of the eclipse. Guest astronomers give lectures to interested audiences. And, provided the clouds hold off, hundreds of thousands of satisfied customers will get a view of a spectacular natural phenomenon.

The moment of total eclipse. For a few tens of seconds, the Moon blocks the Sun's bright disc and the solar corona is visible. Photograph by Fred Espenak.

Scientific expeditions

For centuries, astronomers have travelled to watch eclipses for scientific purposes. They have helped us to learn about the dimensions of the Solar System, and about the Sun and Moon. Take the question of the corona. For a long time, scientists had been unable to agree whether the corona was actually part of the Sun, or a halo of gas around the Moon, illuminated by sunlight during an eclipse.

The picture on the left shows a scientific expedition that travelled to India to observe and record the total solar eclipse of 12 December 1871. They took photographs from which it was possible, for the first time, to develop a scientific description of the Sun's corona (outer atmosphere).

A scientific purpose?

But is it worth studying eclipses today? Are there good scientific reasons to take tonnes of scientific equipment off to some distant land? One person who thinks so is Fred Espenak, an astrophysicist at NASA's Goddard Space Flight Centre. His interest is in the atmospheres of planets, moons, and the Sun.

Preparing to observe a solar eclipse in 1871.

Fred uses an infrared spectrometer to examine radiation coming from planetary atmospheres. A spectrometer is a device that splits light (or other radiation) into its different wavelengths, just as a prism or diffraction grating splits white light into the colours of the spectrum. By studying the wavelengths that are present, it is possible to deduce the chemical composition of the source of the radiation. One of Fred's experiments, to measure atmospheric flow, was carried on the Space Shuttle.

A solar eclipse is the only time that an earthbound observer can study the Sun's corona. This is a mysterious part of the Sun, extending far out into space. The mystery is its temperature. We see the surface of the Sun, which is hot, at about 5500 °C, but the corona is far hotter – perhaps 1.5 million degrees. Measurements during eclipses may help to explain how this thin gas become heated to such a high temperature.

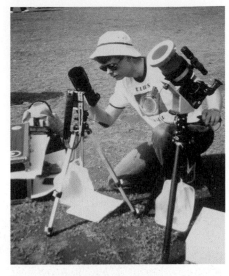

A young Fred Espenak, preparing to observe an eclipse in 1983. He is now a veteran of over 20 eclipse expeditions.

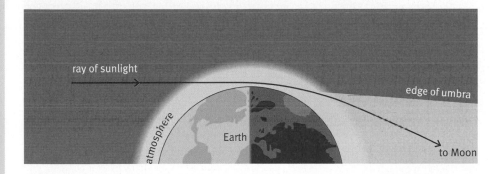

During a lunar eclipse, light from the Sun is refracted as it passes through the Earth's atmosphere, and lights up the Moon.

And lunar eclipses? Fred's main interest is in examining the light that reaches the Moon through the Earth's atmosphere at this time. The quality of the light can be a good guide to the state of the Earth's atmosphere, indicating pollution from such causes as forest fires and volcanoes.

A composite image of the Moon moving in and out of eclipse. The central image shows the Moon lit up by sunlight that has been refracted through the Earth's atmosphere. Another photograph by Fred Espenak.

Find out about:

▶ parallax as an indication of distance

▶ parsecs and light-years as units of distance

▶ the observed and intrinsic brightness of a star

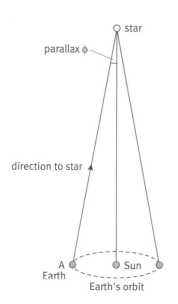

Defining the parallax angle.

These two photos illustrate the effect of parallax. They show the same view, but the photographer moved sideways before taking the second one. The closest object, the person on the bench, has moved furthest across the image.

2C Star distances

Parallax angles

The stars are far off. How can we measure their distances? One way is to use the idea of parallax.

Imagine looking across a city park in which there are a number of trees, scattered about. You take a photograph. Now take two steps to the right and take another photograph. Your photos will look very similar, but the *relative* positions of the trees will have changed slightly. Perhaps one tree that was hidden behind another has now come into view.

Now superimpose the photos one on top of the other and you will see that the closer trees will have shifted their positions in the picture more than those which are more distant. You have observed an effect of **parallax**.

Astronomers can see the same effect. As the Earth travels along its orbit round the Sun, some stars seem to shift their positions slightly against a background of fixed stars. This shifting of position against a fixed background is what astronomers call parallax, and it can be used to work out the distance of the star in question.

The diagram on the left shows how astronomers define the **parallax angle** of a star. They compare the direction of the star at an interval of six months. The parallax angle is *half* the angle moved by the star in this time. Equally, it is half the angle moved by the star on a star map.

From the diagram, you should be able to see that, the closer the star, the greater is its parallax angle.

The scale of things

In the Middle Ages, astronomers imagined that all of the stars were equally distant from the Earth. It was as if they were fixed in a giant crystal sphere, or perhaps pinholes in a black dome, letting through heaven's light. They could only believe this because the patterns of the stars do not change through the year – there is no obvious parallax effect.

They were, of course, wrong. But it is not surprising that they were wrong, because parallax angles are very small. The radius of the Earth's orbit is about 8 light-minutes, but the nearest star is about 4 light-years away – that's over 250 000 times as far.

Parallax angles are usually measured in fractions of a second of arc. There are:

 ▶ 360° in a full circle

 ▶ 60′ (minutes) of arc in 1°

 ▶ 60″ (seconds) of arc in 1′

So a second of arc is $\frac{1}{3600}$ of a degree.

Astronomers use a unit of distance based on this: the **parsec**.

 ▶ An object whose parallax angle is 1 second of arc is at a distance of 1 parsec.

Because a smaller angle means a bigger distance:

 ▶ An object whose parallax angle is 2 seconds of arc is at a distance of 0.5 parsec.

A parsec is about 3.1×10^{13} km. This is of a similar magnitude to a light-year, which is 9.5×10^{12} km. Typically, the distance between neighbouring stars in our galaxy is a few parsecs.

<aside>
Key words
parallax
parallax angle
parsec
</aside>

Questions

1 Draw a diagram to show that a star with a large parallax angle is closer than one with a small parallax angle.

2 Which is bigger, a parsec or a light-year?

3 How many light-years are there in a parsec?

4 If a star has a parallax angle of 0.25 seconds of arc, how far away is it (in parsecs)?

How bright is that star?

Measurements of parallax angles allow astronomers to measure the distance to a star. This only works for relatively nearby stars. But there are other methods of finding how far away a star is.

In the late 17th century, scientists were anxious to know just how big the Universe was. The Dutch physicist Christiaan Huygens devised a technique for measuring the distance of a star from Earth. He realized that, the more distant a star, the fainter its light would be. This is because the light from a star spreads outwards, and so, the more distant the observer, the smaller the amount of light that reaches him or her. So measuring the **observed brightness** of a star would give an indication of its distance.

Here is how Huygens set about putting his idea into practice:

▶ At night, he studied a star called Sirius, the brightest star in the sky and one of the Sun's closest neighbours.

▶ The next day, he placed a screen between himself and the bright disc of the Sun. He made a succession of smaller and smaller holes in the screen until he felt that the speck of light he saw was of the same brightness as Sirius.

▶ Then he calculated the fraction of the Sun's disc that was visible to him. It seemed that roughly 1/30 000 of the Sun's brightness equalled the brightness of Sirius. His calculation showed that Sirius was 27 664 times as distant as the Sun.

How wrong he was! Astronomers now know that Sirius is more than 500 000 times as distant as the Sun. This is where Huygens went wrong:

▶ First, there was subjectivity in his measurements. He had to judge when his two observations through the screen were the same.

▶ Second, his method assumed that Sirius and the Sun are identical stars, radiating energy at the same rate.

▶ Third, he had to assume that no light was absorbed between Sirius and his screen.

Huygens understood these problems with his method, but he was keen to find a method of estimating the distances of the stars.

Luminosity

Scientists now think that stars are not all the same. There are big ones and small ones, hot ones and cooler ones. A big, hot star radiates more energy every second than a small, cool star. To judge the **luminosity** of a star, you could imagine putting it next to the Sun. If you could see all stars at this distance, you would have a fair test of their luminosity.

So luminosity depends on two factors:

 ▶ Its **temperature**: a hotter star radiates more energy every second from each square metre of its surface.

 ▶ Its **size**: a bigger star has more surface that radiates energy.

Observed brightness (what an observer sees from Earth) depends on the star's distance from Earth, as well as the star's luminosity. Also, any dust or gas between Earth and the star may absorb some of its light.

Key words
luminosity
observed brightness

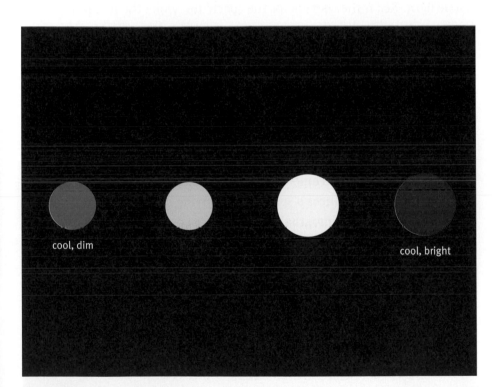

Stars differ in size and temperature, so they radiate different amounts of energy.

Questions

5 Look at the diagram on this page. Which of the stars shown has the greatest luminosity? Which has the least? Explain how you know.

6 Explain how two stars having the same observed brightness may have different luminosity.

Find out about:

▶ how colour is related to temperature
▶ how the spectrum of radiation from a hot object depends on its temperature

Stars come in different colours.

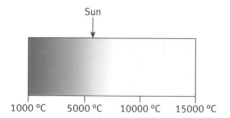

Sun

1000 °C   5000 °C   10000 °C   15000 °C

The colour of a star depends on its surface temperature.

2D   Star temperatures

Colour and temperature

A star produces a continuous range of frequencies across the **electromagnetic spectrum**. Most of its radiation is in the infrared, visible and ultraviolet regions of the spectrum, but stars also produce radio waves and X-rays. If you look out at the stars at night, you may get a hint that they shine with different colours – some reddish, some yellow (like the Sun), others brilliantly white. It is more obvious if you look through binoculars or a telescope.

Colour is linked to temperature. Look back to the diagram on page 164 which compares the radiation from objects at different temperatures. Imagine heating a lump of metal in a flame. At first, it glows dull red. As it gets hotter, it glows orange, then yellow, then bluish white.

You might notice that these colours appear in the order of the spectrum of visible light. Red is the cool end of the spectrum, violet the hot end. For centuries, the pottery industry has measured the temperature inside a kiln by looking at the colour of the light coming from inside.

So the colour of a star gives a clue to its surface temperature.

Analysing starlight

At one time, astronomers judged the colours of stars and classified them accordingly. However, it is better to analyse stars, light using an instrument called a **spectrometer**. A spectrometer can be attached to a telescope so that it produces a spectrum, showing all of the frequencies that are present. The photographs show how a spectrometer turns the light from each star into a spectrum.

The Pleiades is a group of bright stars. With a spectrometer, the light from each star is broken up into a spectrum (above).

Comparing stars

Better still is to turn the spectrum of a star into a graph. This shows the intensity (energy radiated per unit area of a star's surface) for each frequency in the spectrum.

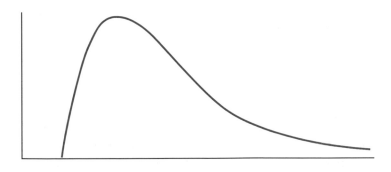

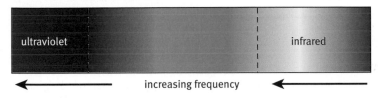

The graph of the spectrum provides information about intensity as well as showing which frequencies are present.

The next diagram, on the right, shows the results of comparing the spectra of hotter and cooler stars.

▶ For a hotter star, the area under the graph is greater; this shows that the luminosity of the star is greater.

▶ For a hotter star, the **peak frequency** is greater; it produces a greater proportion of radiation of higher frequencies.

These are not special rules for stars: they apply to any hot object.

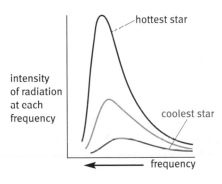

The spectra of hotter and cooler stars

Questions

1 Stars A and B are the same size, but star A is hotter than star B.

a Which star has greater luminosity?

b If you examined the spectra of these stars, which would have the greater peak frequency?

c Sketch graphs to show how these stars' spectra would differ.

Find out about:

▶ the brightness–period relationship for Cepheid variable stars

▶ how this helps to measure astronomical distances

▶ how we know about galaxies beyond our own

2E Galaxies

Cepheid variable stars

Life on Earth relies on the fact that the Sun burns at a steady rate – we would be in trouble if it got brighter and dimmer as the days went by. Most stars burn steadily like this. But, in 1784, a new type of star was discovered by an English astronomer called John Goodricke.

Goodricke noticed that a star called δ Cephei (δ = delta) varied in brightness. It went from bright to dim and back to bright again in an interval of a week or so, and this variation was very regular. The graph below shows modern measurements of the brightness of this star.

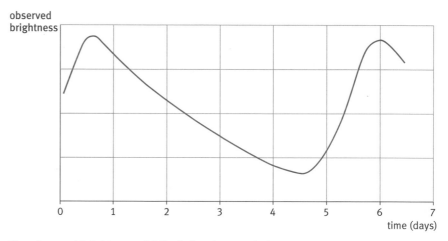

The observed brightness of δ Cephei varies regularly.

Many stars have been found that vary in this way, and they have been named **Cepheid variables**, or simply Cepheids. It is now thought that a star like this is expanding and contracting so that its temperature and luminosity vary. Its diameter may vary by as much as 30%.

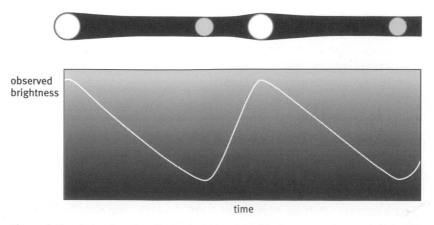

The variation in luminosity of a Cepheid is caused by its expansion and contraction.

Henrietta Leavitt

Henrietta Leavitt, whose work opened up a new method of measuring the Universe.

Key words
Cepheid variable

In the early years of the twentieth century, an American astronomer called Henrietta Leavitt made a very important discovery. She looked at Cepheids in a nearby group of galaxies (the Magellanic Clouds). She noticed that the brightest Cepheids varied with the longest periods, and drew a graph to represent this.

Because the stars she was studying were all at roughly the same distance, Leavitt realized that the stars which appeared brightest were also the ones with the greatest luminosity – they were not brighter simply because they were closer. So, by measuring the period of variation of a Cepheid, she could determine its luminosity.

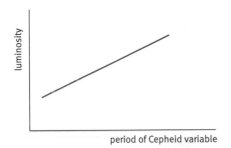

The luminosity of a Cepheid variable star is related to its period.

Measuring the Universe

Henrietta Leavitt had discovered a method of determining the distance to a star in a distant galaxy. This is how to do it:

▶ Look for a Cepheid variable in the galaxy of interest.

▶ Measure its observed brightness and its period of variation.

▶ From the period, determine its luminosity.

▶ Knowing both the luminosity and the intensity of its light at the telescope, calculate the distance of the star (and hence of the galaxy).

The same method can be used to find the distance to a Cepheid variable in our own galaxy.

Questions

1 From the graph on the opposite page, deduce the period of variation of δ Cephei.

2 Why did Henrietta Leavitt assume that the stars she was studying were all at roughly the same distance from Earth?

Galaxies: one or many?

Today, astronomers think that our Sun is just one of many thousands of millions in our galaxy, the Milky Way. They also believe that the Milky Way is just one galaxy among hundreds of billions in the Universe. But it took a long time to develop this picture.

Most of the stars seen with the naked eye are stars of the Milky Way. However, telescopes reveal many more stars, as well as some fuzzy-looking objects that look bigger than individual stars. These were originally called nebulae. ('Nebula' means 'cloud'.)

At the start of the 20th century, scientists generally thought that these nebulae were stars gradually forming from matter thinly scattered through space. If they appeared as fuzzy blobs, it seemed that they could not be very far away.

An American astronomer called Harlow Shapley set out to test this idea. He directed his telescope at a number of nebulae and measured their distances. He found that they seemed to form a spherical cloud whose centre was far from the Solar System. He guessed that each nebula was, in fact, a cluster of stars, and together these formed a sphere around the centre of the Milky Way galaxy.

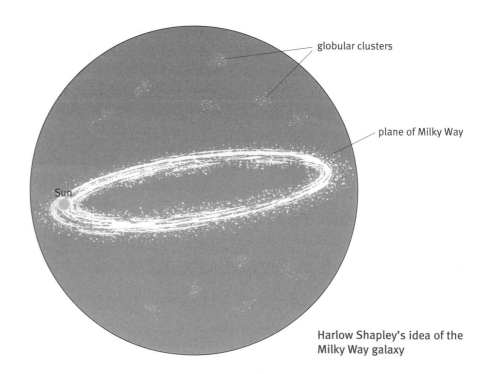

Harlow Shapley's idea of the Milky Way galaxy

Shapley presented his findings in 1920. His idea of our galaxy is a simple version of what is generally accepted today. The star clusters he was looking at are now known as **globular clusters**, and they orbit the centre of the Milky Way.

Is that all there is?

But Harlow Shapley was wrong about one thing. He claimed that the Milky Way galaxy was the entire Universe. This was challenged by another American, Heber Curtis. Curtis had been studying 'spiral nebulae' (rather than the globular clusters). He felt that these objects were very distant from the Milky Way, and possibly even were other objects on a similar scale to the Milky Way. In other words, they were galaxies in their own right.

The matter was decided in 1923, by exciting new results from Edwin Hubble (yet another American). Hubble was studying the Andromeda Nebula when he spotted a dim Cepheid variable star within it. He measured its period and its observed brightness, and deduced its surprising distance. Andromeda was almost one million light-years away, far greater than the dimensions of the Milky Way.

Hubble's striking result convinced astronomers that the Andromeda Nebula, at least, was a giant object outside of our galaxy. Today, the *Hubble Space Telescope* has revealed many more galaxies, scattered through space, at distances of up to 13 or 14 *thousand million* light-years. The distances between galaxies are measured in **megaparsecs** (Mpc). 1 Mpc = 1 million parsecs.

The *Hubble Space Telescope* has given us a striking view of a Universe that contains many billions of galaxies.

Questions

3 What force holds the globular clusters in their orbits around the centre of the galaxy?

4 Edwin Hubble observed a Cepheid in the Andromeda nebula. Why did it appear dim?

5 If there are 100 thousand million galaxies each with 100 thousand million stars, how many stars is that?

Key words

globular cluster
megaparsec

Physics in action

Mapping the Milky Way

In 2005, a brand new image of our Galaxy, the Milky Way, was published. From the image below, you can see that the Milky Way is a spiral galaxy, with several arms emerging from the centre. It is described as a barred spiral, because there appears to be a denser region of stars, a 'stellar bar', crossing the centre of the galaxy.

The Milky Way

Here is part of the press release that accompanied the publication of this image:

With the help of NASA's *Spitzer Space Telescope*, astronomers have conducted the most comprehensive structural analysis of our galaxy and have found tantalizing new evidence that the Milky Way is much different from your ordinary spiral galaxy.

The survey using the orbiting infrared telescope provides the fine details of a long central bar feature that distinguishes the Milky Way from more pedestrian spiral galaxies.

'This is the best evidence ever for this long central bar in our galaxy,' says Ed Churchwell, a UW-Madison professor of astronomy and a senior author of a paper describing the new work in an upcoming edition of *Astrophysical Journal Letters*, a leading astronomy journal.

Using the orbiting infrared telescope, the group of astronomers surveyed some 30 million stars in the plane of the galaxy in an effort to build a detailed portrait of the inner regions of the Milky Way. The task, according to Churchwell, is like trying to describe the boundaries of a forest from a vantage point deep within the woods: 'This is hard to do from within the galaxy.'

Spitzer's capabilities, however, helped the astronomers cut through obscuring clouds of interstellar dust to gather infrared starlight from tens of millions of stars at the center of the galaxy. The new survey gives the most detailed picture to date of the inner regions of the Milky Way.

'We're observing at wavelengths where the galaxy is more transparent, and we're bringing tens of millions of objects into the equation,' says Robert Benjamin, professor of physics at the University of Wisconsin.

It shows a bar, consisting of relatively old and red stars, spanning the center of the galaxy roughly 27 000 light-years in length – 7 000 light years longer than previously believed. It also shows that the bar is oriented at about a 45-degree angle relative to a line joining the Sun and the center of the Galaxy.

The press release mentions a new discovery – that our Galaxy has a bar at the centre – as well as two of the big problems with mapping the Galaxy: it is difficult to make a map from inside the Galaxy, and there are clouds of dust and gas that obscure the view.

An earlier attempt

In 1785, William Herschel attempted to determine the shape of the galaxy. Looking through his telescope, he counted all the stars he could see in a particular direction. Then he moved his telescope round a little and counted again. Once he had completed a complete circle, he could draw out a map of a slice through the Milky Way.

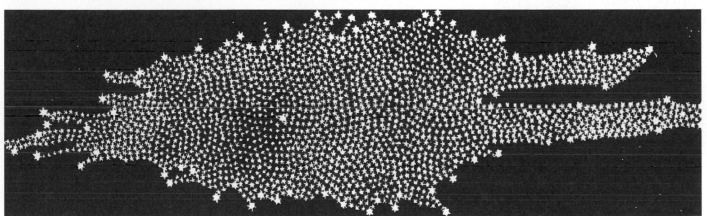

William Herschel's map of a slice through the Milky Way. The Sun is shown near the centre. The more stars seen in a particular direction, the greater the distance to the edge in that direction.

He knew that he was making the following assumptions:

▶ that his telescope could detect all the stars in the direction he was looking, and

▶ that he could see to the far end of the galaxy

Herschel himself discovered his first assumption to be incorrect when he built a bigger telescope. Astronomers now know that his second assumption too was incorrect. Dust in the galaxy makes it difficult to see stars in the packed centre of the galaxy.

Today, astronomers use infrared telescopes because infrared radiation is less affected by dust and so gives a clearer view. And it was William Herschel who, in 1800, discovered the existence of infrared radiation.

Find out about:

▶ the discovery of the recession of galaxies

▶ evidence for the expansion of the Universe

2F   The changing Universe

Moving galaxies

Edwin Hubble was fortunate to be working at a time (the 1920s) when the significance of Cepheid variables had been realized. They could be used as a 'measuring stick' to find the distance to other galaxies. At the same time, he was able to use some of the largest telescopes of his day, reflectors with diameters up to 200 inches (5 metres).

He conducted a survey of galaxies, objects that had not previously been seen, let alone understood, until these powerful instruments became available. In his book *The Realm of the Nebulae,* he described what it was like to see individual stars in other galaxies:

> The observer looks out through the swarm of stars which surrounds him, past the borders and across empty space, to find another stellar system . . . The brightest objects in the nebula can be seen individually, and among them the observer recognizes various types that are well known in his own stellar system. The apparent faintness of these familiar objects indicates the distance of the nebula – a distance so great that light requires seven hundred thousand years to make the journey.

Edwin Hubble using the 48-inch telescope at the Mount Palomar observatory.

Redshift

Hubble used Henrietta Leavitt's discovery to determine the distance of many galaxies. At the same time, he made a dramatic discovery of his own. This was that the galaxies all appeared to be receding (moving away) from us. He deduced this by looking at the spectra of stars in the galaxies. The light was shifted towards the red end of the spectrum, a so-called redshift.

It turned out that, the more distant the galaxy, the greater its **speed of recession** – another linear relationship. Hubble's graph shows that, although his data points are scattered about, the general trend is clear.

The Hubble constant

Hubble's finding can be written in the form of an equation:

$$\text{speed of recession} = \text{Hubble constant} \times \text{distance}$$

The quantity called the **Hubble constant** shows how speed of recession is related to distance. His first value (from the graph) was about 500 km/s per megaparsec. In other words, a galaxy at a distance of 1 Mpc would be moving at a speed of 500 km/s. A galaxy at twice this distance would have twice this speed.

Other astronomers too began measuring the Hubble constant, using many more distant galaxies. Hubble's first value was clearly too high. For decades, the measurement uncertainties remained high and so there were disputes about the correct value. By 2001, the accepted value of the Hubble constant was 72 ± 8 km/s per Mpc.

Back to the big bang

The fact that the galaxies are moving apart led to two important ideas:

▶ The Universe itself may be expanding, and may have been much smaller in the past.

▶ The Universe may have started by exploding outwards from a single point – the big bang.

Edwin Hubble's discovery of the moving galaxies was to lead to one of the most extraordinary scientific ideas ever.

Key words

speed of recession
Hubble constant

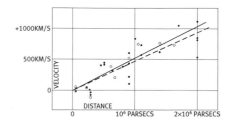

Edwin Hubble's graph, relating the speed of recession of a galaxy to its distance.

Questions

1 Calculate the speed of recession of a galaxy which is at a distance of 100 Mpc, if the Hubble constant is 70 km/s per Mpc.

2 Using the same value of the Hubble constant, calculate the distance of a galaxy whose speed of recession is 2000 km/s.

3 A galaxy lies at a distance of 40 Mpc from Earth. Measurements show its speed of recession is 3000 km/s. What value does this suggest for the Hubble constant?

Topic 3

Inside stars

The Sun is our star. By understanding the Sun better, astronomers hope to be able to make more sense of the variety of stars they see in the night sky.

The Sun is much closer than any other star, so it is the easiest star to gather detailed scientific data on. Scientists study its surface and analyse the radiation coming from it. They turn their telescopes on it, and send spacecraft to make measurements from close up.

The surface of the Sun is quite dramatic when seen from close up. These are sunspots, cooler areas of the surface. They are still very hot, but perhaps 1000 °C cooler than the average surface temperature of about 5500 °C.

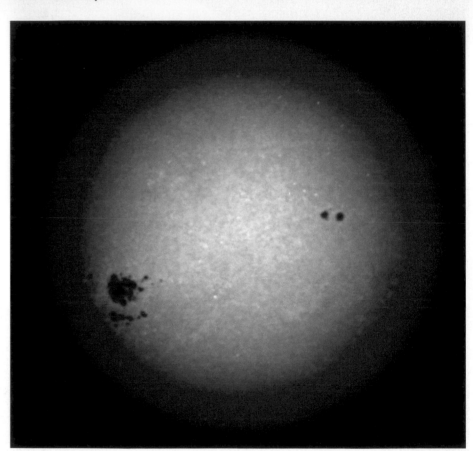

An energy source

What makes the Sun work, how it keeps pouring out energy, day after day, year after year, millennium after millennium – for billions of years, and why it burns so steadily are questions that puzzled scientists for centuries.

Some suggestions were that it was powered by volcanoes, that it was burning coal, that it used the energy of comets that fell into it, or simply the energy of the Sun itself as it collapsed inwards under the pull of its own gravity.

A 17th century view – the Sun as an enormous lump of coal.

Solar telescope

The McMath–Pierce solar telescope stands on a hill-top in Arizona, USA. The astronomers who use it study large images of the Sun and analyse the light gathered by the telescope. In doing this, they are applying some of the latest technology to repeat some historic experiments first performed two centuries ago.

The McMath–Pierce solar telescope. The tower on the right is 30 m high and carries the reflector that sends a beam of sunlight down the sloping shaft to an underground observation chamber.

The image of the Sun produced by the solar telescope is about 80 cm across. Some of the light passes through the hole in the table into a spectrometer for detailed analysis.

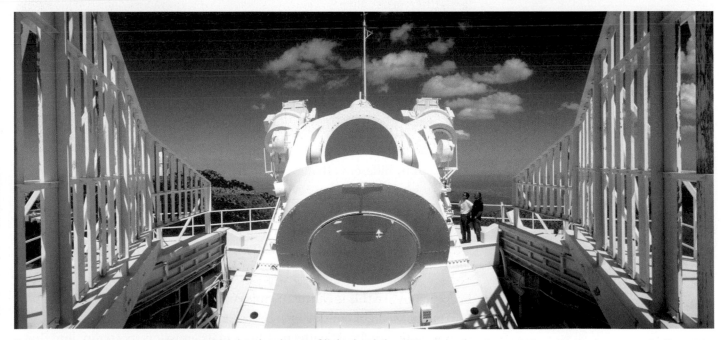

Here you can see the 2.1 m reflector, which sends a beam of light down the 152 m focusing channel. The reflector is automatically rotated to track the movement of the Sun across the sky.

Find out about:

- absorption and emission spectra as 'fingerprints' of elements
- electron energy levels and photons

3A The composition of stars

The mystery of the Sun

It might seem impossible to find out what the Sun is made of. But it turns out you can do this by examining the light it gives out. If sunlight is passed through a prism or diffraction grating, it is split into a spectrum, from red to violet.

In 1802, William Woolaston noticed that the spectrum of sunlight had a strange feature – there were black lines, showing that some wavelengths were missing from the continuous spectrum. These lines are now called Fraunhofer lines, after Joseph von Fraunhofer who made many measurements of their wavelengths. He could not, however, explain their origin.

Here is how you can make a spectrum. Light is passed through a narrow slit, so that you start with a tall, narrow strip of white light. This is then spread out into its different wavelengths by the prism. The photograph below shows a spectrum of sunlight.

The spectrum of sunlight, showing the dark Fraunhofer lines.

The colours of the elements

Before he looked at sunlight, Fraunhofer had been studying the light given out by different chemicals when they burn. He knew that sodium burns with a yellow flame. When he looked at the spectrum of light from a sodium flame, Fraunhofer saw that it consisted of just a few coloured lines, rather than a continuous band from red to violet. He could measure the wavelengths of the different colours that made up the spectrum of sodium.

A spectrum like this is called an **emission spectrum**, because you are looking at the light emitted by a chemical. Today, we know that each element has a different pattern of lines in its emission spectrum, and that this can be used to identify the elements present.

Making sense of sunlight

The dark Fraunhofer lines in the spectrum of sunlight were not explained until 1859. They are caused by the absorption of some colours, rather than emission. To understand what is going on, you have to think of the structure of the Sun.

▶ The interior of the Sun produces white light, with all wavelengths present.

▶ As this light passes through the Sun's atmosphere, some wavelengths are absorbed by atoms of elements (including sodium) that are present there.

As a result, the light that reaches us from the Sun is missing some wavelengths, which correspond to elements in the Sun's atmosphere.

This is an example of an **absorption spectrum**. The wavelengths of the absorption lines reveal which elements have been doing the absorbing. From this, astronomers can identify the elements present in the Sun and in the most distant stars.

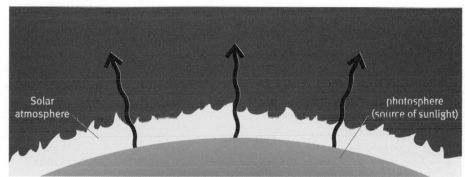

Light from the interior of the Sun must pass through its atmosphere before it reaches us.

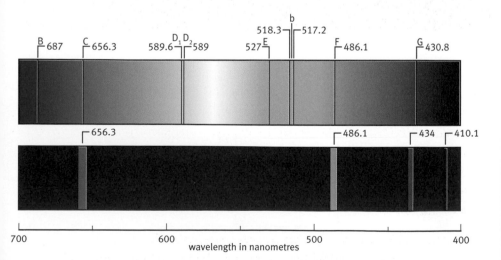

Lines in the emission spectrum of hydrogen (*bottom*) correspond to dark absorption bands in the Sun's spectrum (*top*). The numbers are the wavelengths of lines in the hydrogen spectrum in nanometres.

Questions

1 'Light is a messenger from the stars'. Explain how this statement is true.

2 Look at the emission spectrum of hydrogen. What colours are the main emission lines in this spectrum? Which is the strongest (most intense) line?

Understanding line spectra

The line spectrum of an element is different from that of every other element – it can be thought of as the 'fingerprint' of the element. In 1868, two scientists used this fact to discover a new element: helium. Norman Lockyer (English) and Jules César Janssen (French) took the opportunity of an eclipse of the Sun to look at the spectrum of light coming from the edge of the Sun. Janssen noticed a line in the spectrum that he had not seen before. He sent his observation to Lockyer, who realized that the line did not correspond to any known element. He guessed that some other element was present in the Sun, and he named it 'helium' after the Greek name for the Sun, 'Helios'.

Emitting light

To understand why different elements have different emission spectra, you need to know how atoms emit light. The light is emitted when electrons in atoms lose energy – the energy they lose is carried away by light.

That is a simple version of what happens, and it does not explain why only certain wavelengths appear in the spectrum. Here is a deeper explanation:

▶ The electrons in an atom can only have certain values of energy. Scientists think of them as occupying points on a 'ladder' of **energy levels**.

▶ When an electron drops from one energy level to another, it loses energy.

▶ As it does so, it emits a single **photon** of light – that is, a packet of energy. The energy of the photon is equal to the difference between the two energy levels.

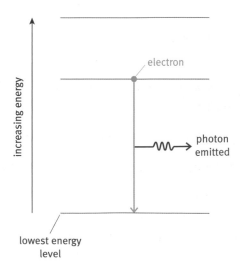

An electron gives out a single photon of light as it drops from one energy level to another.

The greater the energy gap, the greater is the energy of the photon. High-energy photons correspond to high-frequency, short-wavelength light.

In the simplified diagram of energy levels shown here, you can see that only three photon energies are possible. The most energetic photon comes from an electron which has dropped from the top level to the bottom level.

Absorbing light

The same model can explain absorption spectra. The dark lines come about when electrons absorb energy from white light.

▶ White light consists of photons with all possible values of energy.

▶ An electron in a low energy level can only absorb a photon whose energy is just right to lift it up to a higher energy level. When it absorbs such a photon, it jumps to the higher level.

▶ The white light is now missing photons that have been absorbed because their energies corresponded to the spacings in the ladder of energy levels. The 'missing' photons correspond to the dark lines in an absorption spectrum.

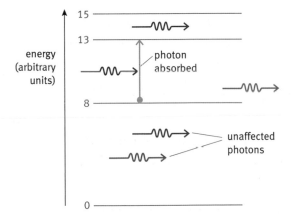

An electron jumps from one energy level to another when the atom absorbs a single photon of light.

The diagram above shows values of energy for each level (in arbitrary units). You can see that:

▶ Photons of energies 2, 7, and 8 would be absorbed.

▶ Photons of energies 1, 6, and 9.3 would not be absorbed.

A photon with sufficient energy can ionize an atom. An electron gains so much energy that it escapes the attractive force of the nucleus, and leaves the atom. As a result, the atom is left with net positive charge.

Questions

3 What sub-atomic particles are associated with the emission and absorption of light?

4 For the energy level diagram on this page:

   a Explain how photons of energies 2, 5, and 8 would be absorbed.

   b Give other energy values that would also be absorbed.

   c Explain how an atom could emit a photon of energy 13 units.

3B Atoms and nuclei

How do scientists know about the structure of atoms? The diagram of an atom as a miniature 'solar system', with the **nucleus** at the centre and electrons whizzing round like miniature planets, has become very familiar. It is often used just to suggest that something is 'scientific'.

The 'solar system' model of the atom dates back to 1910, and an experiment thought up by Ernest Rutherford. Scientists were beginning to understand radioactivity, and were experimenting with radiation. Rutherford realized that alpha and beta particles were smaller than atoms, and so they might be useful tools for probing the structure of atoms. So he designed a suitable experiment, and it was carried out by his assistants, Hans Geiger and Ernest Marsden.

Here is how to do it:

- Start with a metal foil. Use gold, because it can be rolled out very thin, to a thickness of just a few atoms.

- Direct a source of alpha radiation at the foil. Do this in a vacuum chamber, so that the alpha particles are not absorbed by air.

- Watch for flashes of light as the alpha particles strike the detecting material around the outside of the chamber.

- Work all night, counting the flashes at different angles, to see how much the alpha radiation is deflected.

Find out about:

- models of the atom
- how alpha particle scattering reveals the existence of the atomic nucleus

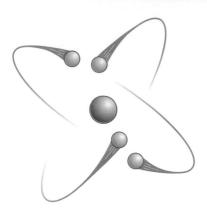

The 'solar system' model of the atom.

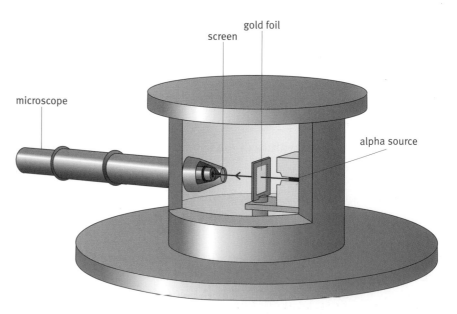

Rutherford's experiment. An alpha particle striking the scintillating material gives a tiny flash of light.

Results and interpretation

This is what Geiger and Marsden observed:

- Most of the alpha particles passed straight through the gold foil, deflected by no more than a few degrees.

- A small fraction of the alpha particles were actually reflected back towards the direction from which they had come.

And here is what Rutherford said:
'It was as if, on firing a bullet at a sheet of tissue paper, the bullet were to bounce back at you!'

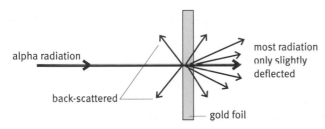

Only alpha particles passing close to a nucleus are significantly deflected.

In fact, less than 1 alpha particle in 8000 was back-scattered (deflected through an angle greater than 90°), but it still needed an explanation.

Rutherford realized that there must be something with positive charge that was repelling the alpha particles (which also have positive charge). And it must also have a lot of mass, or the alpha particles would just push it out of the way.

This 'something' is the nucleus of a gold atom. It contains all of the positive charge within the atom, and most of the mass. Note that, at this time, scientists had no knowledge of protons and neutrons, the particles that make up the nucleus.

Rutherford's analysis of his data showed that the nucleus was very tiny, because most alpha particles flew straight past without being affected by it. The diameter of the nucleus of an atom is roughly a hundred-thousandth of the diameter of the atom.

Questions

1 What charge do the following have:
  a the atomic nucleus?
  b alpha radiation?
  c electrons?

2 Put these in order, from least mass to greatest:
  gold atom, alpha particle, gold nucleus, electron.

3 Make a prediction: Geiger and Marsden repeated their experiment using a thicker gold foil. Would more alpha particles be reflected back towards the source, or fewer? Explain your answer.

Small particles, big science

At the time of Rutherford's experiment, no-one knew about protons and neutrons and the role they played in the atom. But once the neutron had been discovered in 1932, the modern picture of the atom was established. These ideas explained a lot – the pattern of the periodic table, for example – so physicists had been able to explain most of chemistry!

It seemed that all matter was made of just three particles: protons, neutrons, and electrons. It was very satisfying to think that all of matter could be boiled down to just three particles, but that idea did not last long. Physicists studying cosmic radiation from space discovered something that was different, particles with masses in between those of protons and electrons. As so often happens, a new discovery caused an attractive, simple scientific theory to collapse like a pack of cards. But at least that left plenty of scope for new ideas and experiments.

Probing the very small

Rutherford's experiment showed scientists how to investigate something as small as an atomic nucleus. You need a lot of atoms (the gold foil) and something of a similar size to the nucleus (the alpha particle) to act as a probe.

Alpha particles move fast – at about 10 million m/s. That means they have enough momentum to get close to an atomic nucleus and feel its effects. But when scientists began to suspect that protons and neutrons were not fundamental after all, they wanted to look *inside* the particles of the nucleus.

CERN nestles at the foot of the Alps, straddling the border of Switzerland and France. The circle shows the location of the 27 km tunnel containing the LHC.

To look inside protons and neutrons, it takes even more energetic particles than alpha particles, and to get these, large particle accelerators must be built. Big particle accelerators are amongst the biggest and most complex machines ever made, and they are very expensive. An example is the Large Hadron Collider (LHC) at CERN, Geneva.

Today, most physicists think that there are even more fundamental particles called **quarks**. It takes three quarks to make a proton or a neutron, and just two to make some of the other particles that have been discovered from studies of cosmic rays and in other experiments.

An international project

CERN is the European Centre for Nuclear Research. It is funded by 20 countries because, for most, just one accelerator would be too expensive. By cooperating, their scientists get to use all of the facilities at CERN, including the LHC. The LHC is in the form of a circular tunnel, 27 km in circumference.

▶ The accelerator produces two beams of high-energy protons.

▶ The beams travel around the tunnel in opposite directions.

▶ At one point, the paths of the two beams cross and protons collide.

▶ Detectors record the debris from the collision, and scientists analyse these records.

Back to the beginning

The point of all this is that the protons CERN's scientists are using have energies that are millions of times greater than Rutherford's alpha particles, so they hope that the LHC will tell them more about the fundamental nature of matter.

At the same time, there is a link with astronomy. In the early history of the Universe, shortly after the Big Bang, all matter and energy was compressed into a tiny volume so that particles such as protons had very high energies – just like those in the LHC. So the LHC is effectively recreating the conditions that existed at that time.

> **Key words**
> quarks

Just some of the people involved in the LHC project. This team manages and coordinates the experimental areas.

Inside the LHC tunnel. These are some of the giant magnets used by the LHC accelerator.

Find out about:

▶ the processes of fusion and fission
▶ the attractive and repulsive forces between nuclear particles

3C Nuclear fusion

Knowing about the structure of the atom can help us to understand how the Sun releases energy. The Sun is made mostly of hydrogen. Hydrogen burns with oxygen to make water, but there is very little oxygen in the Sun, so that cannot be the source of its energy. To understand how hydrogen on its own can have fuelled the Sun for 4.5 billion years, you need to look inside the atom and inside the nucleus.

Recall from Module P3 *Radioactive materials* that atomic nuclei are made of two particles:

▶ **protons**, which have positive charge, and

▶ **neutrons**, which are electrically neutral

These particles have similar masses and account for most of the mass of an atom (because electrons have very little mass).

A balance of forces

The nucleus of an atom is made up of protons and neutrons. This tells us something important – protons and neutrons are happy to stick together. There must be an **attractive force** that holds protons and neutrons together, and that can even hold two protons together despite the fact that they repel each other because of their positive charges. This force is called the **strong nuclear force**.

The strong nuclear force has a short range. It only acts when two nucleons (protons or neutrons) are very close together. In a nucleus, the particles are separated by just the right distance so that the strong nuclear force is balanced by the electrical (electrostatic) force.

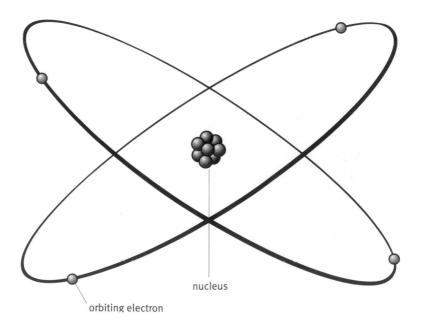

In this diagram, protons are shown as red spheres and neutrons as black.

nucleus

orbiting electron

Joining up

In the process of **nuclear fusion**, the nuclei of two hydrogen atoms join together and energy is released. The diagram below right shows one way in which this happens. Note that the nuclei are of two different isotopes of hydrogen – both are hydrogen, because they have just one proton in the nucleus.

Picture bringing two atoms close together: their nuclei repel each other, because of the electrical (electrostatic) force. They will not fuse together. Push hard enough: they come close enough for the attractive force to take over, and the nuclei fuse. Energy is released.

You would have to do a lot of work to push two nuclei together, but you would get a lot more energy out when they fused.

You can think of fusion as the opposite of nuclear fission, the process used in nuclear power stations.

- ▶ **Fission:** a large nucleus splits, releasing energy and a few neutrons, and forming two medium-sized nuclei.

- ▶ **Fusion:** two small nuclei join together, releasing energy and forming one bigger nucleus.

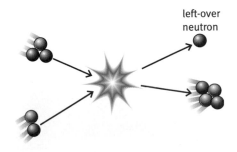

left-over neutron

Fusion

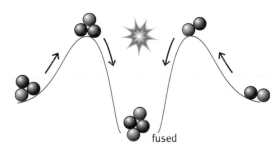

Pushing two hydrogen nuclei together: the 'hills' represent the repulsive force between them. The deep 'valley' represents the stable state they reach when they fuse together.

In the stars

It is tricky to force two nuclei to fuse in a laboratory on Earth, but it happens all of the time in stars. Because the interior of a star is very hot – millions of degrees – the particles within it are very energetic. They are moving very fast. There is a small chance, when any two particles collide, that their momentum will be enough to overcome the repulsion between them, and to bring them within the short range of the strong nuclear force. They will then fuse. Each time this happens, energy is released.

The Sun was almost 100% hydrogen when it formed. Today, it is 71% hydrogen and 27% helium.

Key words

fusion
fission
proton
neutron
strong nuclear force

Questions

1 a What attractive force acts between particles in the nucleus? And what repulsive force?

   b Which of these two forces has the greater range?

2 The Sun contains 1% oxygen nuclei. There are 8 protons in an oxygen nucleus. Explain why these are less likely to fuse together than hydrogen nuclei.

3 Use information on these two pages to make an estimate of the lifespan of the Sun. Explain the assumptions you have made.

Find out about:

▶ how the pressure, volume, and temperature of a gas are related
▶ how to convert between temperature scales

3D How gases behave

Great balls of fire

The Sun is mostly hydrogen and helium – two gases. As you have seen, it releases energy by fusing hydrogen nuclei to make helium nuclei. This goes on in the core of the Sun and most other stars.

So a star is a giant ball of hot gas. To understand better how stars work – how they get hot, the forces that hold them together – you need to learn about gases in general.

Describing a gas

Think of a balloon. You blow it up, so it is filled with air. How can you describe the state of that air? What are its properties?

Volume – the amount of space the gas occupies, in m^3.

Mass – the amount of matter, in kg.

Pressure – the force the gas exerts per unit area on the walls of its container, in Pa ($= N/m^2$).

Temperature – how hot the gas is, in °C (or K – see page 241).

These are all measurable quantities that a physicist would use to describe the gas. Understanding how these properties change is important. For example, the engine of a car relies on the pressure of an expanding gas to provide the motive force that makes the car go.

Pressure and volume

Now picture squashing the balloon. You are trying to decrease its volume. Its pressure resists you. It is easier to understand what is happening by pressing on a gas syringe.

A steam engine works by allowing a gas (steam) to expand so that it pushes a piston.

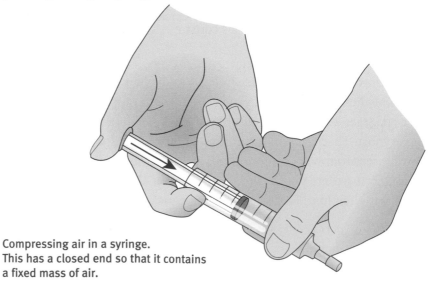

Compressing air in a syringe.
This has a closed end so that it contains a fixed mass of air.

volume

pressure

Increasing the pressure on a gas reduces its volume.

> It is easy to push the plunger in a little.

> The more you push on the plunger, the harder it gets to move it further.

This shows that the pressure of the air is increasing as you reduce its volume. If you reduce the force with which you press on the plunger, the air will push back and expand. The graph on the previous page shows this relationship:

> When the volume of a gas is reduced, its pressure increases.

Explaining pressure

The connection between the pressure and the volume of a gas was worked out before anyone was sure that gases were made of particles. Yet you can use the **kinetic model of matter** to explain these findings. In this model, a gas consists of particles (atoms or molecules) that move around freely, and most of the volume of the gas is empty space.

> The particles of a gas move around freely. At room temperature, they have speeds around 450 m/s.

> As they move around, they bump into the walls of their container – see the first diagram on the right. (They also bump into each other.)

> Each collision with the walls causes a tiny force. Together, billions of collisions produce gas pressure.

Now think about what happens if the same gas is compressed into a smaller volume – see the diagram on the right. The collisions with the walls will be more frequent, and so the pressure will be greater.

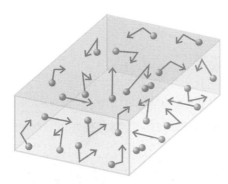

Particles of a gas collide with the walls of its container. This causes pressure.

Questions

1 Imagine that a fixed mass of gas is compressed into half its original volume. The temperature remains constant. Which of the following statements are correct?

   A The pressure of the gas will increase.

   B The average separation of the particles of the gas will decrease.

   C A particle of the gas will strike the walls of the container with greater force.

   D A particle of the gas will strike the walls more frequently.

As cold as it gets

Now think about what happens when a gas gets cold. Blow up a balloon and put it in the freezer – it starts to shrink. Its pressure and volume have both decreased.

In an experiment to investigate this, it is best not to change one factor (temperature) and then to allow two others (pressure and volume) to change. So experiments are designed to control one factor while the other is allowed to change. The picture below shows how a fixed volume of air (in a rigid flask) can be heated to change its temperature. The gauge shows how the pressure of the gas changes.

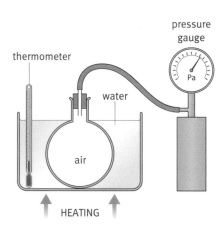

Because the flask is rigid, the volume of the air inside does not change as it is heated or cooled.

Heating up, cooling down

The graphs on the left show the results of experiments like this. Think about the effects of cooling down a fixed mass of gas.

- Fixed volume of gas: as the gas is cooled, its pressure decreases steadily.

- Fixed pressure of gas: as the gas is cooled, its volume decreases steadily.

Both of these graphs show the same pattern: the pressure and volume of the gas decrease as the temperature decreases, and both seem to be heading for a value of zero at a temperature well below $0\,°C$. Whatever gas is used, the graph heads for roughly the same temperature.

The point where a graph like this reaches zero is known as the **absolute zero** of temperature. In practice, all gases condense to form a liquid before they reach this point.

$$\text{absolute zero} = -273\,°C$$

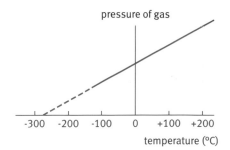

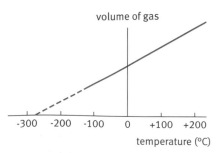

As a gas is cooled, its pressure and volume decrease.

Temperature scales

In everyday life, we use the Celsius scale of temperature. This has its zero, 0 °C, at the temperature of pure melting ice. You can also define a scale that has its zero at absolute zero, the **Kelvin scale**. The individual divisions on the scale (degrees) are the same as on the Celsius scale, but the starting point is much lower. Because nothing can be colder than absolute zero, there are no negative temperatures on the Kelvin Scale.

Temperatures on this scale are given in kelvin (K).

Here is how to convert from one scale to the other:

▶ temperature in K = temperature in °C + 273

▶ temperature in °C = temperature in K − 273

So, for example, suppose your body temperature is 37 °C. What is this in K?

▶ temperature in K = 37 °C + 273 = 310 K

A kinetic explanation

When a gas is cooled down, the particles of the gas lose energy, so they move more slowly.

▶ If the volume of the gas is fixed, each particle takes longer to reach a wall. So particles strike the walls less frequently. They also strike with less force. So the pressure decreases for these two reasons.

▶ If the pressure is to remain constant, the volume of the gas must decrease to compensate for the fact that the collisions are weaker and less frequent.

Eventually, you can picture the particles of the gas losing all of their kinetic energy, so that they do not collide with the walls at all. There is no pressure. This is absolute zero.

Key words

absolute zero
Kelvin scale

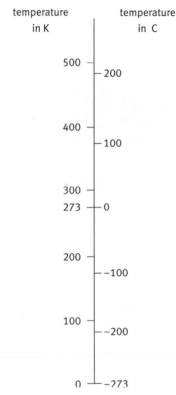

Comparing the Celsius and Kelvin scales of temperature.

Questions

2 What are the values of the following temperatures on the Kelvin scale?

 a 0 °C

 b 100 °C

 c −100 °C

3 What are the values of the following temperatures on the Celsius Scale?

 a 0 K

 b 200 K

 c 300 K.

4 The surface temperature of the Sun is roughly 5800 K. What is this in °C, equally roughly?

Weather from the Sun

▶ January 1997, USA. Millions of satellite TV viewers lose their picture as their satellite is destroyed.

▶ March 1989, eastern Canada. Six million people shiver as their power grid trips out.

What links these two events? Could they happen again?

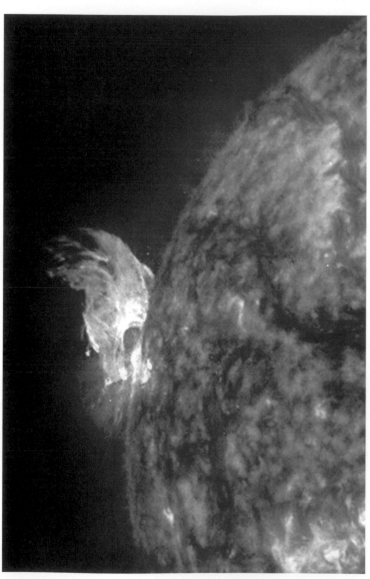

A coronal mass ejection bursting out from the surface of the Sun. (Photograph taken using ultraviolet light.)

Both these dramatic events were caused by the Sun. From Earth, the Sun appears to burn brightly and steadily, day by day. When astronauts first travelled above the atmosphere, they took photographs that revealed a different side to it. The photos showed giant bubbles of gas bursting out of the Sun and flying out into space. These are now known as coronal mass ejections (CMEs) and may weigh as much as 100 billion tonnes.

Heading this way

A coronal mass ejection can travel through space at speeds of around 1.5 million km/h, so they take about 4 days to travel the 150 million km to Earth. This is fast, but much slower than light, which takes just 500 seconds to reach us from the Sun.

CMEs consist of electrically charged particles. When one reaches Earth, it can produce dramatic aurora effects in the night sky (the aurora borealis). It can also have some more drastic effects:

▶ Satellites' electrical systems may be destroyed and radio communications disrupted.

▶ Power systems may be damaged by the associated magnetic field.

The realization that events on the Sun could have such serious impacts on the technologies people depend on here on Earth led scientists and engineers to wonder whether it is possible to forecast the 'weather' coming our way from the Sun.

Scopes in space

The answer was the *SOHO* space observatory, launched in December 1995. (*SOHO* stands for Solar and Heliospheric Observatory.) This carried an instrument called a coronagraph, designed and built by Professor George Simnett and colleagues at Birmingham University. The corona is the Sun's outer atmosphere; monitoring the corona with the coronagraph allows us to see when a CME bursts out of the Sun, and to track it. If it is heading our way, a warning forecast is issued.

You cannot usually see the Sun's corona, except when there is a total eclipse of the Sun. Then the Moon blocks the Sun's bright disc and the glowing corona becomes visible. A coronagraph is a telescope inside which a circular disc is fixed. Like a permanent eclipse, this blocks the Sun and allows a camera at the back of the telescope to photograph the corona.

The coronagraph has other uses. Because it blocks out the disc of the Sun, it has made it possible to spot over 1000 previously unobserved comets, mostly as they plunged into the Sun. (Even in the early 20th century, many scientists believed that the Sun gained its energy from the kinetic energy of comets that fell into it.)

Warning on the web

Websites today carry space 'weather forecasts' so that precautions can be taken where necessary. For example, astronauts on the *International Space Station* may need to turn their craft so that they are shielded from incoming particles from the Sun. Other spacecraft may fold up their solar panels to avoid them being damaged.

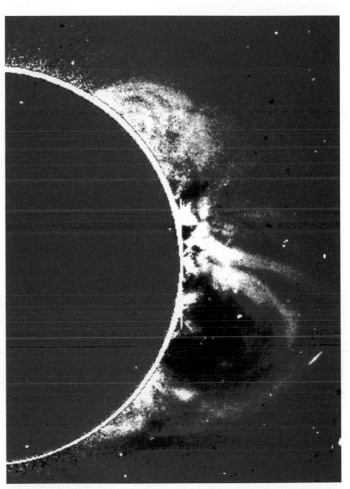

A CME photographed by the *SOHO* coronagraph. You can see the eclipsing disc clearly on the left.

Topic 4

The lives of stars

The photograph at bottom left shows a set of prominent stars in the southern sky, forming the shape of a cross. This is the Southern Cross, which Catholic sailors regarded as very significant when the Spanish and Portuguese Empires expanded in the 15th and 16th centuries. It now appears on the Australian flag. Once this particular group of stars has been pointed out to you, it is hard *not* to recognize it whenever it is above the horizon.

Humans seem to impose a sense of order whenever they can. In the night sky, the signs of the zodiac provide an example of this. The picture at bottom right shows the pattern of stars that make up the constellation of Leo (the Lion). To see the lion, you need to be told which stars form its legs, tail, head, and so on. From the picture, you can see that this is not at all obvious.

The picture came from a book published in Italy in the 13th century. It was a new Latin translation of a book called *The Pattern of Fixed Stars*, written in Arabic in 964 AD. But these patterns go back much further in history, to at least 2500 years ago. And they are still in use today. Astronomers name stars according to the constellation they are in. Astrologers use the movements of planets across constellations to tell fortunes.

The Southern Cross, photographed from Cuba.

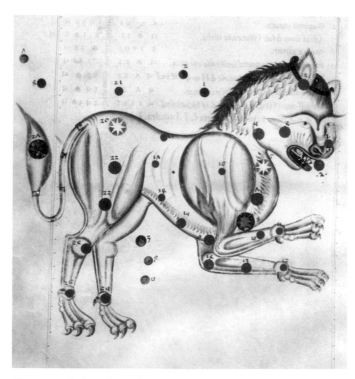

The constellation of Leo the Lion.

Unchanging Universe?

The human history of constellations tells us something striking: the pattern of stars in the night sky has changed very little over thousands of years. In the Middle Ages, astronomers generally thought that the heavens were unchanging. In that way, the sky was quite different from our everyday, Earth-bound experience. Different laws applied 'up there' from 'down here'.

Then, in 1572, a Danish astronomer called Tycho Brahe made a surprising discovery – what he took to be a new star, or 'nova'. It appeared in the constellation of Cassiopeia, almost overhead. It was visible for 18 months or so, after which it gradually faded away. Now we know that what Tycho saw was not a new star, but an old one, exploding towards the end of its life. It was what is called a supernova, and it showed that stars really can change.

Today, astronomers keep a watch for supernovas. They are rare events in our galaxy, but they can also be spotted in other galaxies. They are useful, because one type (Type 1a) seems to explode with a standard brightness. This means that they can be used for measuring distances – the dimmer the supernova, the more distant it is. Combining this with measurements of redshift provides a way of gathering more data for estimates of the expansion of the Universe.

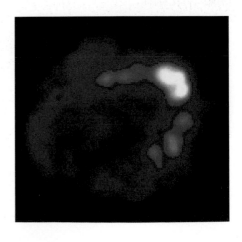

Supernovae produce photons with enormous energies. A gamma-ray camera captured this image of a supernova, with yellow and red regions showing the most energy.

Find out about:

▶ mapping stars on to the Hertzsprung–Russell diagram

▶ the structure of the Sun, and how energy leaves the Sun

4A Stars change

Looking at the night sky, you see stars of different brightnesses and colours. By the beginning of the 20th century, astronomers had worked out how to make sense of this:

▶ Stars might be dim because they were a long way off. Knowing the distance to a dim star, they could work out its luminosity.

▶ Stars are different colours because they are different temperatures. Red is cool, blue is hot.

A Danish astronomer called Ejnar Hertzsprung set about finding if there was any connection between luminosity and temperature. He gathered together published data and drew up a chart, which he published in 1911.

An American, Henry Russell, came up with the same idea independently. He was unaware of Hertzsprung's chart, which had been published in a technical journal of photography. Today, the chart is known as the Hertzsprung–Russell diagram, or H–R diagram. A modern version is shown below.

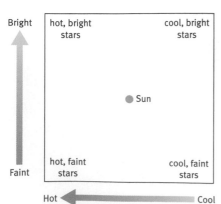

Explaining the axes on the Hertzsprung–Russell diagram.

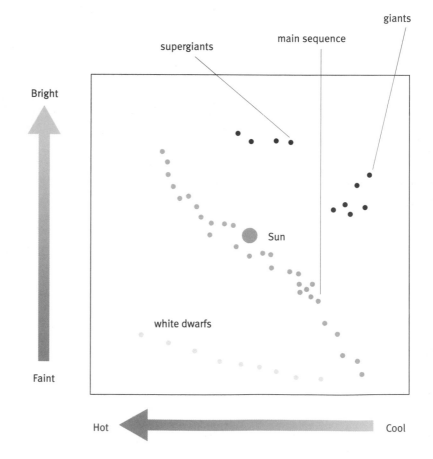

Data for stars – the H–R diagram

Understanding the H–R diagram

This chart has luminosity on the vertical axis and temperature on the horizontal axis. It is usually drawn as shown, with temperature *decreasing* along the *x*-axis. The Sun is roughly at the middle of the chart.

By 1924, over 200 000 stars had been catalogued. When plotted on the H–R diagram, these stars fell into three groups:

▸ About 90% of stars (including the Sun) fell along a line running diagonally across the diagram. This is known as the main sequence.

▸ About 10% of stars were white dwarfs, small and hot.

▸ About 1% of stars were red giants or supergiants, bright but not very hot.

What the H–R diagram reveals

The stars which appear on the H–R diagram are a representative selection of all stars. A first guess might be that there are simply three different, unrelated types of star. However, astronomers now believe that an individual star changes during its lifetime. They interpret the H–R diagram like this:

▸ Since most stars fall on the main sequence, this suggests that an average star spends most of its lifetime as a main-sequence star.

▸ A star may spend a small part of its lifetime as a red giant, and/or as a white dwarf.

Astronomers cannot watch individual stars change through a lifetime, because the process is much too slow to see. Instead, they link their observations of star populations to models of how stars work.

In the rest of this section, you will learn how astronomers think stars change, and how this is reflected in the H–R diagram.

Questions

1 List the colours of stars, from coolest to hottest.

2 If the Sun became dimmer and cooler, how would its position on the H–R diagram change?

3 A star in the bottom left-hand corner of the H–R diagram is dim but hot. Why does this suggest that it is small?

Main-sequence stars

Spacecraft such as *SOHO* have allowed scientists to look in great detail at the surface of the Sun and to measure the rate at which it is pouring energy out into space. Its colour indicates that the surface temperature of the Sun is about 5 500 K – which is far too 'cold' for nuclear fusion reactions to take place.

Inside the Sun

You cannot tell exactly what is inside the Sun. However, there are some clues that can help physicists to make intelligent guesses:

> Nuclear fusion, the source of the Sun's energy, requires temperatures of millions of degrees.

> Energy leaves the Sun from its surface layer, the **photosphere**, whose temperature is about 5 500 K.

> The photosphere has a granular appearance (see the photo), which is continually changing. Something is going on under the surface.

> A star like the Sun can burn steadily for billions of years, so it must radiate energy at the same rate that it generates it from fusion reactions.

Physicists can use these ideas to develop models of the inside of a star. The diagram below shows how they picture the internal structure of the Sun, based on such models.

The surface of the Sun, photographed by the *SOHO* satellite, showing the granularity caused by the presence of convective cells.

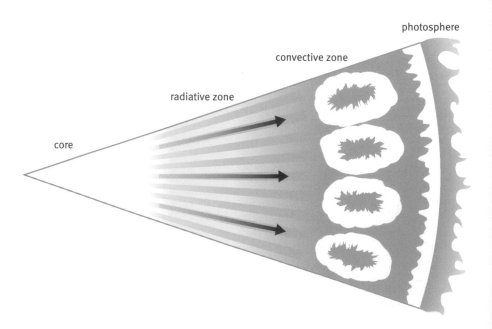

The internal structure of a star like the Sun.

Layer upon layer

▶ The **core** is the hottest part, with a temperature of the order of 14 million K. This is where nuclear fusion reactions occur. Hydrogen nuclei are fused together to form helium nuclei, releasing energy.

▶ Photons travel outwards through the **radiative zone**.

▶ Close to the surface temperature fall to just 1 million K. Matter can flow quite readily, and convection currents are set up, carrying heat energy to the photosphere. This is the **convective zone**. It is the tops of the convective 'cells' that cause the granular appearance of the Sun's surface.

▶ Electromagnetic radiation is emitted by the photosphere and radiates outwards through the solar atmosphere.

The lifetime of a star depends on its mass and the rate that it radiates energy.

> **Key words**
> core
> radiative zone
> convective zone
> photosphere

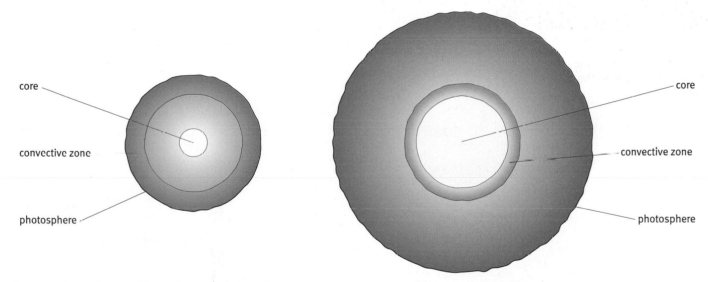

Cross-sections of stars with 1 solar mass and 5 solar masses.

> ## Questions
>
> 4 A star like the Sun burns for billions of years, with a steady brightness and temperature. What does this tell you about its position on the H–R diagram?
>
> 5 Why is the long-term stability of the Sun important for us?
>
> 6 Of what two elements is the Sun mainly composed?
>
> 7 Why does hydrogen gas have to be hot for fusion to take place?
>
> 8 The diagrams compare the inner structures of a star like the Sun and one which has 5 times the mass. What differences can you identify between them?

Find out about:

▶ How stars and planetary systems form

4B Protostars

How does a star form? The raw material of stars is hydrogen, and there has been plenty of that since the early days of the Universe. Here is a simplified version of how astronomers think that a star forms:

▶ A cloud of gas and dust in space starts to contract, pulled together by gravity. Each particle attracts every other particle, so that the cloud collapses towards its centre. It forms a rotating, swirling disc.

▶ Recall that the temperature of a gas increases when it is compressed. The material at the centre gets hotter and hotter, so that it starts to glow.

▶ Eventually, the temperature of this material is hot enough for fusion reactions to occur, and a star is born.

▶ Material further out in the disc clumps together to form planets.

So planets form at the same time as the star that they orbit. In these early stages, as the star forms, it is known as a **protostar**. This stage in the Sun's life is thought to have lasted 100 000 to 1 million years.

A protostar at the centre of a new planetary system.

Getting warmer

Here are two ways to think about when a protostar gets hot enough for fusion to start.

▸ The *gas* idea. The star starts from a cloud of gas. As you saw on page 238, when a gas is compressed, its temperature rises. In this case, the force doing the compressing is gravity.

▸ The *particle* idea. Every particle in the cloud attracts every other particle. As they 'fall' inwards, they move faster (gravitational potential energy is being converted to kinetic energy). The particles collide with each other, sharing their energy. The fastest particles are at the centre of the cloud (they have fallen furthest), and fast-moving particles mean a high temperature.

Note that these are *not* competing explanations. They are just different ways of describing what is going on.

Seek and find

Computer models of star formation can help to explain why the (roughly) spherical material from which a star forms collapses to form a flattened disc. Such models suggest that we will always find that the planets orbiting a star lie in a plane, just as in the Solar System.

Some models of star formation predict that, as a protostar forms, it spins faster and faster. Eventually, it blows out giant jets of hot gas, at right angles to the planetary disc. Large telescopes now have sufficient resolution to allow us to see this going on, as shown in the photo below. Planets travelling around distant stars are generally too small to see directly, but the gas jets travel far out into space and can occasionally be spotted.

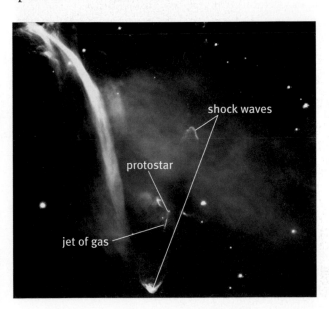

A protostar is forming at the centre of this image. One bright jet of gas can be seen coming downwards from it. Two symmetrical shock waves spread out in opposite directions. Photo taken by the Very Large Telescope in Chile.

Key words
protostar

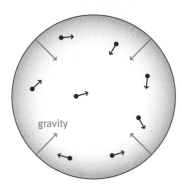

Explaining why a protostar gets hot.

Questions

1 From what materials does a protostar form?

2 If astronomers see a protostar glowing, does this indicate that nuclear fusion is taking place?

3 Imagine a sky-rocket exploding in the night sky. A small, hot explosion results in material being thrown outwards.

  a Describe the energy changes that are going on.

  b Now imagine the same scene, but in reverse. How is this similar to the formation of a protostar? How does it differ?

Find out about:

▶ what happens when hydrogen fusion ends

▶ how a supernova leaves a neutron star or a black hole

4C Death of a star

Many generations into the future, people can expect the Sun to keep releasing energy at a steady rate. Fusion reactions will continue in its core, as hydrogen is converted to helium. As this happens, the Sun's mass decreases very, very slowly. Einstein's equation $E = mc^2$ says that, if an object radiates energy E, its mass will decrease by an amount m. The constant c is the speed of light.

But this cannot go on for ever, because eventually all of the hydrogen in the Sun's core will be used up. What happens then?

As fusion slows down in the core of any star, its core cools down and there is less pressure, so the core collapses. The star's outer layers, which contain hydrogen, fall inwards, becoming hot. This causes new fusion reactions, making the outer shell expand. At the same time, the surface temperature falls, so that the colour changes from yellow to red. This produces a red giant.

In the case of the Sun, calculations suggest that it may expand sufficiently to engulf the three nearest planets – Mercury, Venus, and Earth.

An artist's impression of the view from a planet when its star has become a red giant. A moon is also shown, for comparison.

Inside a red giant

While the outer layers of a red giant star are expanding, its core is contracting and heating up, to 100 million K. This is hot enough for new fusion reactions to start. Helium nuclei have a bigger positive charge than hydrogen nuclei, so there is greater electrical repulsion between them. If they are to fuse, they need greater momentum to overcome this repulsion. When helium nuclei do fuse, they form heavier elements such as carbon, nitrogen, and oxygen, releasing energy.

400 million km   RED GIANT STAR

orbit of Mars   CORE OF STAR

helium-burning shell

hydrogen-burning shell

carbon–oxygen core

The structure of a red giant.

After a relatively short period of time (a few million years), the outer layers cool and drift off into space. The collapsed inner core remains as a white dwarf, which gradually becomes less bright and hot as fusion stops.

More massive stars

The Sun is a relatively small star. Bigger stars, greater than about 8 solar masses, also expand, to become red supergiants. In these, core temperatures may exceed 3 billion degrees, and more complex fusion reactions can occur, forming even heavier elements and releasing yet more energy. What happens next is described on the next page.

Moving about on the H–R diagram

Picture the life of a star like the Sun on the Hertzsprung–Russell diagram.

- Protostars are to the right of the main-sequence. As it heats up, a protostar moves to a point on the main-sequence, where it stays for billions of years.

- When it becomes a red giant, it moves above the main sequence.

- Finally, as a white dwarf, it appears below the main sequence.

Questions

1 At what point in its life does a star become a red giant?

2 What determines whether a star becomes a red giant or a red supergiant?

3 How many helium-4 nuclei must fuse to give a nucleus of carbon-12? And to give a nucleus of oxygen-16?

4 Use a periodic table to help you decide:

   a What element is formed when two helium nuclei fuse?

   b And when five fuse?

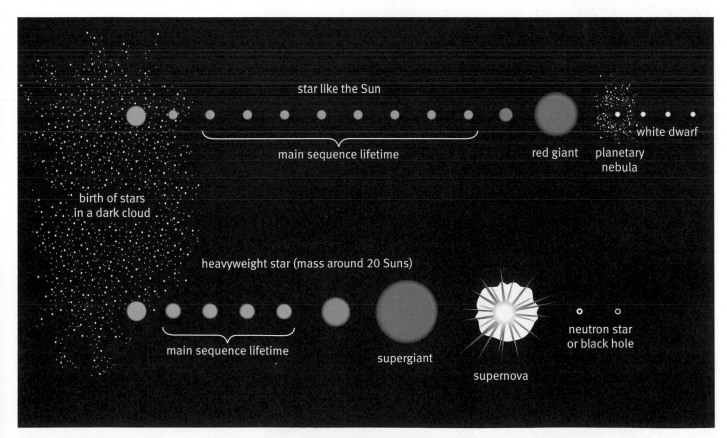

The life and death of a star mainly depends on its mass. The most massive stars have the shortest lives and most spectacular deaths.

A supernova explosion

What happens after the red supergiant phase of a large star is one of the most dramatic events in nature. By fusing lighter elements, the supergiant's core has become largely composed of iron. Iron nuclei absorb energy when they fuse, and so the process slows down. Now the drama starts.

The outer layers of the star are no longer held up by the pressure of the core, and they collapse inwards. The core has become very dense, and the outer material collides with the core and bounces off, flying outwards. The result is a huge explosion called a **supernova**. This is what Tycho Brahe saw in 1572 (page 243)

In the course of the explosion, temperatures rise to 10 billion K, enough to cause the fusion of medium-weight elements and thus form the heaviest elements of all – up to uranium in the periodic table. For a few days, a supernova can outshine a whole galaxy.

The remnants of a supernova in the constellation of Cassiopeia. The cloud is about 10 light-years across. This is a composite image, made using three telescopes to capture infrared, visible, and X-ray data.

Supernova remnants

Supernovas are rare. They are seen about once every century in a typical galaxy. But there are some 100 billion galaxies in the Universe. When astronomers search with their telescopes, they can identify the remnants of supernovas that occurred hundreds or thousands of years ago.

The photograph on the left shows the remnants of a supernova that happened in about 1660. You can see the expanding sphere of dust and gas, formed from the star's outer layers. This material contains all of the elements of the periodic table. As it becomes distributed through space, it may become part of another contracting cloud of dust and gas. A protostar may form with new planets orbiting it, and the cycle starts over again.

Dense and denser

The core of an exploding supernova remains. If its mass is less than about 2.5 solar masses, this central remnant becomes a **neutron star**. This is made almost entirely of neutrons, compressed together like a giant atomic nucleus, perhaps 30 km across.

A more massive remnant collapses even further under the pull of its own gravity, to become a **black hole**. Within a black hole, the pull of gravity is so strong that not even light can escape from it.

Neutron stars are thought to explain the pulsars, discovered by Jocelyn Bell and Anthony Hewish (page 181). As the core of a star collapses to form a neutron star, it spins faster and faster. Its magnetic field becomes concentrated, and this results in a beam of radio waves coming out of its magnetic poles. As the neutron star spins round, this beam sweeps across space and is detected as a regular series of pulses at an observatory on some small, distant planet.

Key words
supernova
neutron star
black hole

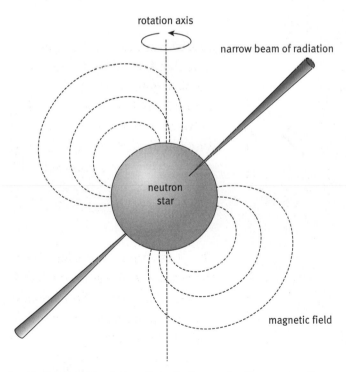

A spinning neutron star sends out a beam of radio waves – the origin of a pulsar.

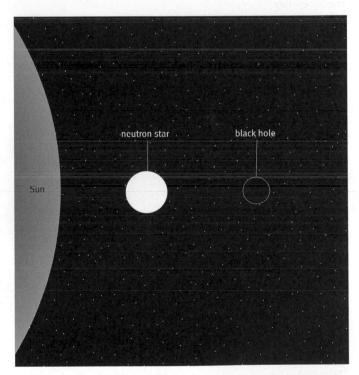

The neutron star and the black hole shown here have the same mass as the Sun.

Questions

5 Put these objects in order, from least dense to most dense:

neutron star, protostar, red supergiant, black hole, main-sequence star

6 Draw a diagram to show the complete life cycle of stars, starting from a protostar. Indicate how stars of different masses end differently.

Astronomers working together at ESO

There are parts of the sky that are not visible from the northern hemisphere. So 11 European countries have set up three observatories in the Atacama Desert high up in the Andes mountains, Chile. Together they, and the organization for astronomical research that runs them, are known as the European Southern Observatory (ESO). Two of ESO's sites are at heights of about 2500 m above sea level, but one, the ALMA array of radio telescopes, is on a 5000 m-high mountain. These remote locations are chosen because the atmosphere is both clear and dry there. This reduces the effects of absorption and refraction of radiation, and of light pollution.

Aerial view of La Silla Observatory, Chile. 'La Silla' means 'the saddle', after the shape of the mountain-top on which it stands

Remote control

Each year, over 1000 astronomers make observations using the ESO telescopes. Half of them do this from their home base in Europe.

ESO does this by making great use of the power of computers and the Internet. The telescopes in Chile are remote. It takes two days of travel to reach them, and two days to get home again. So many of the astronomers who need observations to be made send in their requests, and these are programmed into the ESO control system. Local operators ensure that the observations are made, and the results are sent back to Europe.

One benefit of this is to avoid the 'weather lottery'. Some observations are so sensitive that they require the clearest of skies, which might only be available on 10% of nights in the year. Imagine travelling to Chile for three nights' observing, only to find that the skies were never clear enough! ESO's computer control ensures that your observations are postponed to a later date, while another astronomer's observations are brought forward to take advantage of the available time.

In 2005, ESO's data management system won a top award from Computerworld magazine. The system makes use of the latest database software, and is described as 'end-to-end', because it gathers, stores, and distributes data in a continuous operation. Data is collected, transferred to ESO's headquarters in Germany, and checked for quality. Individual astronomers can access their data over the Internet. They have the exclusive right to use their data for one year after it has been collected, after which it becomes available to any researcher anywhere in the world.

By 2010, the data archive is expected to contain a petabyte of data – that is, 10^{15} bytes of information. It will be accessible via the Grid, the advanced successor to the Internet.

La Silla Hotel, which accommodates visiting astronomers

The archive of DVDs at the ESO headquarters near Munich, Germany

Control room for the new 3.5m New Technology Telescope

Douglas Pierce-Price

ESO people

Douglas Pierce-Price is a British astronomer based in Germany.

How many people work for ESO?

'Technically, I work for the European Organisation for Astronomical Research in the Southern Hemisphere. This organization employs 320 staff members from around the world (many of us work in Germany), as well as 160 local staff recruited in Chile. This means that the organization provides work for local people.

'In addition, there are about 100 students and research fellows who are attached to the organization. So, for UK students, it is possible to join a research team here once they have completed an undergraduate degree.'

What is it like to live and work in a desert on top of a mountain?

'The observatory staff live and work in the Residencia, a futuristic building built partly underground and with a 35-metre-wide glass dome in the roof. It is part of the VLT's "base camp" facility, situated a short distance below the summit of Cerro Paranal.

'Astronomical conditions at Paranal are excellent, but they come at a price. It's a forbidding desert environment; virtually nothing can grow outside. The humidity can be as low as 10%, there are intense ultraviolet rays from the Sun, and the high altitude can leave people short of breath. The nearest town is two hours away, so there is a small paramedic clinic at the base camp.

'Living in this extremely isolated place feels like visiting another planet. Within the Residencia, a small garden and a swimming pool are designed to increase the humidity inside. The building provides visitors and staff with some relief from the harsh conditions outside: there are about 100 rooms for astronomers and other staff, as well as offices, a library, cinema, gymnasium, and cafeteria.'

Up all night

Monika Petr-Gotzens is a German astronomer working at the European Southern Observatory. She is studying how stars form in dense clusters. She is particularly interested in the formation of binary stars. These are pairs of stars that orbit one another. More than half of all stars are in binary pairs.

Monika uses both radio telescopes and optical (light) telescopes in her work.

What is it like to work with a telescope at the top of a mountain?

'The work "at the telescope", i.e. observing during the night, is not as romantic as you might think. The control over the telescope and instrument is 100% computer based and carried out from the control room. These control rooms are hundreds of metres away from the telescope, and you don't even see the telescope during your observation, unless you actively walk into the dome (from where you can't control anything). So it isn't the freezing cold which keeps you awake during the observing night, but the smell of coffee and cookies.'

What part do computers play in your work?

'Modern astronomy without computer control is unthinkable. It sharpens our view of the Universe by directing the telescope very accurately. Computers also process the data gathered by the telescope to give much higher-quality images and measurements.'

Astronomers today usually work in collaborative teams. Why is this?

'International collaborations are very important. Nowadays, it is not a single clever observation that solves one of the grand questions of the Universe. They are answered through major efforts. For example, surveys of stars across large areas of the sky may be carried out using bigger and bigger telescopes. It is often impossible for individuals to deal with the huge amount of data accumulated from such surveys.'

The ESO telescopes are sited high on mountains. Why is this?

'The factors that influence the choice of site for an observatory depend on the kind of observatory: optical, infrared, millimetre, or radio waves. For optical observatories, a low-turbulent atmosphere (i.e. very good seeing), a dark sky without light pollution, and a high number of clear sky nights are important factors. It's easier for radio telescopes – they can see through clouds.

'The size of the telescope is also important. Independent of the working wavelength, the rule applies that the larger the telescope, the less windy a site must be. Wind means that the density of the air is changing, and this causes radiation to be refracted. (That's why stars appear to twinkle in the night sky.)

'On top of that, sites must also have a reasonable logistical supply. It must be reasonably easy for astronomers to travel to the observatory, and they need accommodation, food, and drink. Natural springs, for example, to be used for the water supply, are an advantage, although not an absolute requirement.

Monica Petr-Gotzens

P7 Observing the Universe

Summary

Topic 1 Observatories and telescopes

- Astronomical objects are so distant that their light is effectively parallel.

- Converging (convex) lenses and concave mirrors can be used to focus parallel rays of light.

- power of a lens (in D) = $\dfrac{1}{\text{focal length (in m)}}$

- A converging lens forms a real image of a distant source of light.

- A simple telescope uses two converging lenses. The eyepiece is more powerful than the objective.

- magnification = $\dfrac{\text{focal length of objective}}{\text{focal length of eyepiece}}$ H

- Most astronomical telescopes have concave mirrors as their objectives.

- A large telescope is needed to collect the weak radiation from a faint or distant source.

- The aperture of a telescope must be much larger than the wavelength of radiation it detects. H

- Many telescopes are sited on mountains or in space to reduce the effects of the atmosphere, which refracts and absorbs electromagnetic radiation.

- International collaboration can share the cost of an astronomical project, and allows expertise to be shared.

- When an observatory is planned, non-astronomical factors such as cost, environmental impact, and working conditions must be taken into account.

Topic 2 Naked-eye astronomy

- The apparent movements of the Sun, Moon, and stars across the sky can be explained in terms of the rotation of the Earth, the orbit of the Moon around the Earth, and the orbits of the Earth around the Sun.

- Seen from the Earth, the planets move in irregular patterns relative to the fixed stars.

- The apparent motions of the planets can be explained in terms of their orbits around the Sun. H

- The phases of the Moon, and eclipses of the Sun and Moon, can be explained in terms of the relative positions of the Sun, Moon, and Earth.

- Solar eclipses are rare because the orbit of the Moon is tilted relative to the Earth's orbit plane. H

- Different stars are seen in the night sky through a year, as the Earth travels around its orbit.

- A sidereal day is 4 minutes less than a solar day. H

- Nearby stars show parallax: they appear to move relative to more distant stars over the course of a year.

- A parsec is a measure of distance, similar in magnitude to a light-year. Neighbouring stars are typically separated by a few parsecs, galaxies by megaparsecs.

- The luminosity of a star depends on its temperature and size. Observed brightness also depends on distance from Earth.

- Cepheid variables are stars whose brightness varies regularly. The most luminous have the longest periods.

- The changing luminosity of Cepheids allows astronomers to measure their distances, and so measure distances to the galaxies they are in.

- In 1920 two American astronomers took part in a public debate about the scale of the Universe. Within a few years, new evidence conclusively showed that there are galaxies beyond the Milky Way

- Light from distant galaxies is red-shifted. This shows that they are moving away:
speed of recession = Hubble constant × distance

Topic 3 Inside stars

- The spectrum of a star has a continuous range of frequencies, plus lines that indicate the chemical elements present.
- Line spectra (emission and absorption) arise when electrons within atoms change their energy levels.
- A molecular model can be used to explain why the pressure and volume of a gas vary with temperature.

   temperature in K = temperature in °C + 273

- The alpha scattering experiment showed that an atom has a small, massive, positive nucleus.
- The protons and neutrons in a nucleus are held together by the strong nuclear force, which acts against the electrical repulsion between protons.

Topic 4 The lives of stars

- A protostar forms when gravity compresses a cloud of gas, so that it becomes hot. Planets form around the new star.
- Hydrogen nuclei can fuse together to produce helium, if they are brought close together.
- Hydrogen fusion occurs in the core of a star like the Sun. At later stages in a star's life, further fusion reactions can occur.
- Energy is transferred from a star's core to its surface by a convective zone, and radiated from its photosphere.
- When there is insufficient hydrogen in the core, a star expands to become a red giant or supergiant. When helium fusion ends, a red giant becomes a hot white dwarf, which then fades.
- Fusion stops in a massive star when the core has mostly become iron. The star explodes as a supernova. What remains is a neutron star or a black hole.

Glossary

ABO blood type All people can be divided into four groups depending on the antigens which are carried on their red blood cells. These may be type A, type B, both A and B, or neither. This way of classifying people's blood type is the ABO system.

absolute zero Extrapolating from the behaviour of gases at different temperatures, the theoretically lowest possible temperature, −273 °C. In practice, the lowest temperature achievable is about a degree above this.

absorption spectrum (of a star) Consists of dark lines superimposed on a continuous spectrum. It is created when light from the star passes through a cooler gas that absorbs photons of particular energies.

accuracy How close a quantitative result is to the true or 'actual' value.

activation energy The minimum energy needed in a collision between molecules if they are to react. The activation energy is the height of the energy barrier between reactants and products in a chemical change.

aerobic respiration Respiration which uses oxygen.

alcohols Alcohols are organic compounds containing the reactive group —OH. Ethanol is an alcohol. It has the formula C_2H_5OH

alkane Alkanes are hydrocarbons found in crude oil. All the C—C bonds in alkanes are single bonds. Ethane is an alkane. It has the formula C_2H_6.

anaerobic respiration Respiration which does not use oxygen.

angular magnification (of a refracting telescope) The ratio of the angle subtended by an object when seen through the telescope to the angle subtended by the same object when seen with the naked eye. It can be calculated as

$$\frac{\text{focal length of objective lens}}{\text{focal length of eyepiece lens}}$$

antagonistic pair Two muscles which work to move the same bone in opposite directions, e.g. the biceps and triceps muscles.

aperture (of a telescope) The light-gathering area of the objective lens or mirror.

aqueous aqueous solution is a solution in which water is the solvent.

astrolabe An instrument used for locating and predicting the positions of the Sun, Moon, planets, and stars, as well as navigating and telling the time.

atom economy A measure of the efficiency of a chemical process. The atom economy for a process shows the mass of product atoms as a percentage of the mass of reactant atoms.

ATP ATP (adenosine triphosphate) is a chemical used by living things to store and transfer energy during chemical reactions.

atrium (plural atria) One of the upper chambers in the heart. The two atria pump blood to the ventricles.

autoradiology Gene probes are often made using radioactive DNA bases. The radioactivity blackens X-ray film, which shows whether the gene probe has bound to the DNA sample.

autotroph An organism which produces its own organic compounds.

bacteriophage A type of virus which infects bacteria.

black hole A mass so great that its gravity prevents anything escaping from it, including light. Some black holes are the collapsed remnants of massive stars.

blood transfusion Transfer of blood from one person to another.

bulk chemicals Chemicals made by industry on a scale of thousands or millions of tonnes per year. Examples are sulfuric acid, nitric acid, sodium hydroxide, ethanol, and ethanoic acid.

burette A graduated tube with taps or valves used to measure the volume of liquids or solutions during quantitative investigations such as titrations.

by-products Unwanted products of chemical synthesis. By-products are formed by side-reactions that happen at the same time as the main reaction, thus reducing the yield of the product required.

capillary network Large numbers of narrow blood vessels which pass through each organ in the body. Capillaries receive blood from arteries and return it to veins. Capillary walls are only one cell thick.

carbohydrate A natural chemical made of carbon, hydrogen, and oxygen. The hydrogen and oxygen are present in the proportions as water. An example is glucose $C_6H_{12}O_6$. Carbohydrates includes sugars, starch, and cellulose.

carbon cycle The cycling of the element carbon in the environment between the atmosphere, biosphere, hydrosphere, and lithosphere. The element exists in different compounds in these spheres. In the atmosphere it is mainly present as carbon dioxide.

carboxylic acid Carboxylic acids are organic compounds containing the reactive group —COOH. Ethanoic acid (acetic acid) is an example. It has the formula CH_3COOH.

carrier gas The mobile phase in gas chromatography.

cartilage Tough, flexible tissue found at the end of bones and in joints. It protects the end of bones from rubbing together and becoming damaged.

cellulose The chemical which makes up most of the fibre in food. The human body cannot digest cellulose.

Cepheid variable A star whose brightness varies regularly, over a period of days.

chlorophyll A green pigment found in chloroplasts. Chlorophyll absorbs energy from sunlight for photosynthesis.

chloroplast An organelle found in some plant cells where photosynthesis takes place.

chromatography An analytical technique in which the components of a mixture are separated by the movement of a mobile phase through a stationary phase.

circulatory system The heart and blood vessels. The circulatory system transports useful chemicals and waste products around the body.

codominant Some genes have two alleles which are neither dominant or recessive. If a person has a copy of both these alleles, they will both be expressed and show up in that person. These alleles are co-dominant.

commensalism A relationship between two organisms of different species where one organism gains, and the other neither gains or loses from the relationship.

compensation point Respiration uses glucose in a plant, photosynthesis produces glucose in a plant. When respiration and photosynthesis are taking place in a plant at the same rate, there is no net gain or loss of glucose. This is the compensation point.

constellation A group of stars that form a pattern in the night sky. Patterns recognized are cultural and historical, and are not based on the actual positions of the stars in space.

consumers Organisms which eat others in a food chain. This is all the organisms in a food chain except the producer(s).

convective zone (of a star) The layer of a star above its radiative zone, where energy is transferred by convective currents in the plasma.

converging lens A lens that changes the direction of light striking it, bringing the light together at a point.

core The Earth's core is made mostly from iron, solid at the centre and liquid above.

decomposers Organisms which feed on dead organisms. They break down the complex organic chemicals in their bodies, releasing nutrients back into the ecosystem to be used by other living organisms.

deoxygenated Blood in which the haemoglobin is not bound to oxygen molecules.

diasystolic The blood pressure when all parts of the heart muscle are relaxed and the heart is filling with blood.

diffraction What happens when waves hit the edge of a barrier or pass through a gap in a barrier. They bend a little and spread into the region behind the barrier.

dioptre Unit of lens power, equivalent to a focal length of 1 metre.

dislocation An injury where a bone is forced out of its joint.

diverging lens A lens that changes the direction of light striking it, spreading it into a wider cone of light.

DNA fingerprinting A DNA fingerprint uses gene probes to identify particular sequences of DNA bases in a person's genetic make-up. The pattern produced in a DNA fingerprint can be used to identify family relationships.

DNA profiling A DNA profile is produced in the same way as a DNA fingerprint, but fewer gene probes are used. DNA profiling is used in forensic science to test samples of DNA left at crime scenes.

DNA technology Any process which uses our knowledge of DNA to solve a problem or make a new product.

donor A person who gives blood to another person.

double circulation A circulatory system where the blood passes through the heart twice for every complete circulation of the body.

drying agent A chemical used to remove water from moist liquids or gases. Anhydrous calcium chloride and anhydrous sodium sulfate are examples of drying agents.

dynamic equilibrium Chemical equilibria are dynamic. At equilibrium the forward and back reactions are still continuing but at equal rates so that there is no overall change.

electromagnetic spectrum The 'family' of electromagnetic waves of different frequencies and wavelengths.

emission spectrum (of an element) The electromagnetic frequencies emitted by an excited atom as electron energy levels fall.

end point The point during a titration at which the reaction is just complete. For example, in an acid–alkali titration, the end point is reached when the indicator changes colour. This happens when exactly the right amount of acid has been added to react with all the alkali present at the start.

endothermic An endothermic process takes in energy from its surroundings.

energy level diagram A diagram to show the difference in energy between the reactants and the products of a reaction.

equilibrium A state of balance in a reversible reaction when neither the forward nor the backward reaction is complete. The reaction appears to have stopped. At equilibrium reactants and products are present and their concentrations are not changing.

esters An organic compound made from a carboxylic acid and an alcohol. Ethyl ethanoate is an ester. It has the formula $CH_3COOC_2H_5$.

ethanol Waste product from anaerobic respiration in plants and yeast.

exothermic An exothermic process gives out energy to its surroundings.

extended object An astronomical object made up of many points, for example the Moon or a galaxy. By contrast, a star is a single point.

eyepiece lens (of an optical telescope) The lens nearer the eye, which will have a higher power. Often called a telescope 'eyepiece'.

fats Fats are esters of glycerol with long-chain carboxylic acids (fatty acids). The fatty acids in animal fats are mainly saturated compounds.

feedstocks A chemical, or mixture of chemicals, fed into a process in the chemical industry.

fermenter A large vessel in which microorganisms are grown to make a useful product.

fine chemicals Chemicals made by industry in smaller quantities than bulk chemicals. Fine chemicals are used in products such as food additives, medicines, and pesticides.

focal length The distance from the optical centre of a lens or mirror to its focus.

Focus (of a lens mirror) The point at which rays arriving parallel to its principal axis cross each other. Also called the 'focal point'.

focusing Adjusting the distance between lenses, or between the eyepiece lens and a photographic plate (or CCD), to obtain a sharp image of the object.

functional group A reactive group of atoms in an organic molecule. The hydrocarbon chain making up the rest of the molecule is generally unreactive with common reagents such as acids and alkalis. Examples of functional groups are —OH in alcohols and —COOH in carboxylic acids.

gas exchange The exchange of oxygen and carbon dioxide that takes place in the lungs.

gene probe A short piece of single-stranded DNA used in a genetic test. The gene probe has complementary bases to the allele which is being tested for.

genetic modification (GM) Altering the characteristics of an organism by introducing the genes of another organism into its DNA.

globular cluster A cluster of hundreds of thousands of old stars.

glycerol Glycerol is an alcohol with three —OH groups. Its chemical name is propan-1,2,3-triol. Its formula is CH_2OH—$CHOH$—CH_2OH.

haemoglobin The protein molecule in red blood cells. Haemoglobin binds to oxygen and carries it around the body. It also gives blood its red colour.

heat under reflux Heating a reaction mixture in a flask fitted with a vertical condenser. Vapours escaping from the flask condense and flow back into the reaction mixture.

heterotroph An organism which must eat other organisms for its source of organic compounds.

host An organism who's body is infected with a parasite.

Hubble constant The ratio of the speed of recession of galaxies to their distance, with a value of about 72 km/s per Mpc.

hydrocarbon A compound of hydrogen and carbon only. Ethane, C_2H_4, is a hydrocarbon.

hyphae A network of fine threads which form the body of a fungus.

interdependence The relationships between different living things which they rely on to survive.

inverted image An image that is upside down compared to the object.

joint A point where two or more bones meet.

Kelvin scale A scale of temperature in which 0 K is absolute zero, and the triple point of water (where solid, liquid, and gas phases co-exist) is 273 K.

kinetic model of matter The idea that a gas consists of particles (atoms or molecules) that move around freely, colliding with each other and with the walls of any container, with most of the volume of gas being empty space.

lactic acid Waste product from anaerobic respiration in animals.

ligament Tissue which joins two or more bones together.

limiting factor The factor which prevents the rate of photosynthesis from increasing at a particular time. This may be light intensity, temperature, carbon dioxide concentration, or water availability.

locating agent A chemical used to show up colourless spots on a chromatogram.

Luminosity (of a star) The amount of energy radiated into space every second. This can be measured in watts, but astronomers usually compare a star's luminosity to the Sun's luminosity.

lunar eclipse When the Earth comes between the Moon and the Sun, and totally or partially covers the Moon in the Earth's shadow as seen from the Earth's surface.

Magnification (of an optical instrument) The process of making something appear closer than it really is.

measurement uncertainty Variations in analytical results owing to factors that the analyst cannot control. Measurement uncertainty arises from both systematic and random errors.

Megaparsec (Mpc) A million parsecs.

mitochondria An organelle in plant cells where respiration takes place.

mobile phase The solvent that carries chemicals from a sample through a chromatographic column or sheet.

multifactorial disease A disease caused by several different factors, including genetic and environmental factors.

mutualism An association where both organisms seem to benefit.

neutron star The collapsed remnant of a massive star, after a supernova explosion. Made almost entirely of neutrons, they are extremely dense.

non-aqueous A solution in which a liquid other than water is the solvent.

normal An imaginary line drawn at right angles to the point at which a ray strikes the boundary between one medium and another. Used to define the angle of the ray that strikes or emerges from the boundary.

objective lens (of an optical telescope) The lens nearer the object, which will have a lower power. Often called a telescope 'objective'.

observed brightness (of a star) A measure of the light reaching a telescope from a star.

organic chemistry The study of carbon compounds. This includes all the natural carbon compounds from living things and synthetic carbon compounds.

organic compound d A chemical which contains carbon in its molecules.

osmotic balance If a cell contains too high a level of dissolved chemicals it will gain too much water by osmosis. If a cell's level of dissolved chemicals is too low, it will lose too much water by osmosis. When the cell has the correct level of dissolved chemicals, it is osmotically balanced.

oxygen debt After a period of anaerobic respiration the body uses oxygen to break down the lactic acid. The amount of oxygen which is needed to do this is the oxygen debt.

oxygenated Blood in which the haemoglobin is bound to oxygen molecules (oxyhaemoglobin).

parallax The apparent shift of an object against a more distant background, as the position of the observer changes. The further away an object is, the less it appears to shift. This can be used to measure how far away an object is, for example to measure the distance to stars.

parallax angle When observed at an interval of six months, a star will appear to move against the background of much more distant stars. Half of its apparent angular motion is called its parallax angle.

parasite An organism that lives in or on another organism.

Parsec (pc) A unit of astronomical distance, defined as the distance of a star which has a parallax angle of one arcsecond. Equivalent to 3.1×10^{12} km.

peak frequency The frequency with the greatest intensity.

penumbra An area of partial darkness in a shadow, for example places in the Moon's path where the Earth only partially blocks off sunlight. Some sunlight still reaches these places because the Sun has such a large diameter.

percentage yield A measure of the efficiency of a chemical synthesis.

$$\text{percentage yield} = \frac{\text{actual yield}}{\text{theoretical yield}}$$

phases (of the Moon) Changing appearance, due to the relative positions of the Earth, Sun, and Moon.

photons Tiny 'packets' of electromagnetic radiation. All electromagnetic waves are emitted and absorbed as photons. The energy of a photon is proportional to the frequency of the radiation.

photosphere The visible surface of a star, which emits electromagnetic radiation.

photosynthesis The process in green plants which uses energy from sunlight to convert carbon dioxide and water into the sugar glucose.

pipette A pipette is used to measure small volumes of liquids or solutions accurately. A pipette can be used to deliver the same fixed volume of solution again and again during a series of titrations.

planet A very large, spherical object that orbits the Sun, or other star.

plasma The clear straw-coloured fluid part of blood.

plasmids Small circle of DNA found in bacteria. Plasmids are not part of a bacterium's main chromosome.

polymer A material made up of very long molecules. The molecules are long chains of smaller molecules.

polymerase chain reaction (PCR) A technique used to make many copies of a sample of DNA.

power In an electric circuit, the rate at which work is done by the battery or power supply on the components in a circuit. Power is equal to current voltage.

precision A measure of the spread of quantitative results. If the measurements are precise all the results are very close in value.

pressure (of a gas) The force a gas exerts per unit area on the walls of its container.

principal axis An imaginary line perpendicular to the centre of a lens or mirror surface.

producers Organisms found at the start of a food chain. Producers are autotrophs, able to make their own food.

protein Chemicals in living things that are polymers made by joining together amino acids.

proton A positively charged particle found in the nucleus of atoms. The relative mass of a proton is 1 and it has one unit of charge.

protostar The early stages in the formation of a new star, before the onset of nuclear fusion in the core.

protozoan A type of single-celled organism.

pyramid of biomass A chart which shows the relative amount of living mass (biomass) at different levels in a food chain.

pyramid of numbers A chart which shows the relative number of organisms at different levels in a food chain.

qualitative Qualitative analysis is any method for identifying the chemicals in a sample. Thin-layer chromatography is usually a qualitative method of analysis.

quantitative Quantitative analysis is any method for determining the amount of a chemical in a sample. An acid–base titration is an example of quantitative analysis.

quarks Fundamental particles that make up neutrons, protons, and other sub-atomic particles.

radiative zone (of a star) The layer of a star surrounding its core, where energy is transferred by photons to the convective zone.

ray diagram A way of representing how a lens or telescope affects the light that it gathers, by drawing the rays (which can be thought of as very narrow beams of light) as straight lines.

recipient A person who receives blood from another person.

recombination Recombination happens during meiosis. Pairs of chromosomes exchange sections of DNA. This produces chromosomes in sex cells that have a unique mixture of alleles.

red blood cells Blood cells containing haemoglobin, which binds to oxygen so that it can be carried around the body by the bloodstream.

reference materials Known chemicals used in analysis for comparison with unknown chemicals.

reflection What happen when a wave hits a barrier and bounces back off it. If you draw a line at right angles to the barrier, the reflected wave has the same angle to this line as the incoming wave. For example, light is reflected by a mirror.

reflector A telescope that has a mirror as its objective. Also called a reflecting telescope.

refraction Waves change their wavelength if they travel from one medium to another in which their speed is different. For example, when travelling into shallower water, waves have a smaller wavelength as they slow down.

refractor A telescope that has a lens as its objective, rather than a mirror.

renewable resource Resources that can be replaced as quickly as they are used. An example is wood from the growth of trees.

rennin An enzyme which acts on a protein in milk, causing it to form solid clumps. Rennin is used in cheese-making. Traditionally rennin is obtained from the stomachs of young mammals, but now over half the rennin used in cheese-making is produced by a genetically engineered yeast.

replicate sample Two or more samples taken from the same material. Replicate samples should be as similar as possible and analysed by the same procedure to help judge the precision of the analysis.

representative sample A sample of a material that is as nearly identical as possible in its chemical composition to that of the larger bulk of material sampled.

resolving power The ability of a telescope to measure the angular separation of different points in the object that is being viewed. Resolving power is limited by diffraction of the electromagnetic waves being collected.

respiration A series of chemical reactions in cells which release energy for the cell to use.

restriction enzymes   A group of natural enzymes which cut DNA at particular places. Each restriction enzyme cuts DNA at a specific base sequence.

retardation factor   A retardation factor, R_f, is a ratio used in paper or thin-layer chromatography. If the conditions are kept the same, each chemical in a mixture will move a fixed fraction of the distance moved by the solvent front. The R_f value is a measure of this fraction.

retention time   In chromatography, the time it takes for a component in a mixture to pass through the stationary phase.

retrograde motion   An apparent reversal in a planet's usual direction of motion, as seen from the Earth against the background of fixed stars. This happens periodically with all planets beyond the Earth's orbit.

reversible processes   A change which can go forwards or backwards depending on the conditions. Many reversible processes can reach a state of equilibrium.

RICE   RICE stands for Rest, Ice, Compression, Elevation. This is the treatment for a sprain.

sample   A small portion collected from a larger bulk of material for laboratory analysis (such as a water sample or a soil sample).

saturated   In the molecules of a saturated compound, all of the bonds are single bonds. The fatty acids in animal fats are all saturated compounds.

sickle-cell anaemia   A disease in which a large number of red blood cells are sickle shaped and cannot carry oxygen properly.

sidereal day   The time taken for the Earth to rotate 360°: 23 hours and 56 minutes.

single-cell protein (SCP)   A microorganism grown as a source of food protein. Most single-cell protein is used in animal feed, but one type is used in food for humans.

skeletal-muscular system   All the bones and muscles which work together to move the body.

skeleton   The bones that form a framework for the body. The skeleton supports and protects the internal organs, and provides a system of levers that allow the body to move. Some bones also make red blood cells.

solar day   The time taken for the Earth to rotate so that it fully faces the Sun again: exactly 24 hours.

solar eclipse   When the Moon comes between the Earth and the Sun, and totally or partially blocks the view of the Sun as seen from the Earth's surface.

solvent front   The furthest position reached by the solvent during paper or thin-layer chromatography

spectrometer   An instrument that divides a beam of light into a spectrum and enables the relative brightness of each part of the spectrum to be measured.

speed of recession   The speed at which a galaxy is moving away from us.

sprain   An injury where ligaments are located.

starch   A type of carbohydrate found in bread, potatoes, and rice. Plants produce starch to store the energy food they make by photosynthesis. Starch molecules are a long chain of glucose molecules.

stationary phase   The medium through which the mobile phase passes in chromatography.

strong (nuclear) force   A fundamental force of nature that acts inside atomic nuclei.

strong acid   A strong acid is fully ionized to produce hydrogen ions when it dissolves in water.

supernova   A dying star that explodes violently, producing an extremely bright astronomical object for weeks or months.

synovial fluid   Fluid found in the cavity of a joint. The fluid lubricates and nourishes the joint, and prevents two bones from rubbing against each other.

systolic   The blood pressure when the blood is pumped from the left ventricle to the rest of the body.

tapeworm   A parasitic worm which lives primarily in the gut of other living organisms, such as humans.

telescope (from Greek, meaning 'far-seeing')   An instrument that gathers electromagnetic radiation, to form an image or to map data, from astronomical objects such as stars and galaxies. It makes visible things that cannot be seen with the naked eye.

tendon   Tissue that joins muscle to a bone.

tissue fluid   Plasma that is forced out of the blood as it passes through a capillary network. Tissue fluid carries dissolved chemicals from the blood to cells.

titration   An analytical technique used to find the exact volumes of solutions that react with each other.

trophic levels   The different steps in a food chain.

umbra   An area of total darkness in a shadow. For example, places in the Moon's path where the Earth completely blocks off sunlight.

universal donor   People with a blood type that can be given to any other person, whatever their blood type.

universal recipient   People who can receive blood of any type in a transfusion.

unsaturated   There are double bonds in the molecules of unsaturated compounds. There is no spare bonding. The fatty acids in vegetable oils include a high proportion of unsaturated compounds.

UV   Ultraviolet (UV) radiation is a type of radiation that we cannot see. It is beyond the violet end of the visible spectrum.

valves   Flaps of tissue which act like one-way gates, only letting blood flow in one direction around the body. Valves are found in the heart and in veins.

vector   A method of transfer. Vectors are used to transfer genes from one organism to another.

vegetable oil   Vegetable oils are esters of glycerol with fatty acids (long-chain carboxylic acids). More of the fatty acids in vegetable oils are unsaturated when compared with the fatty acids in animal fats.

ventricle   One of the lower chambers of the heart. The right ventricle pumps blood to the lungs. The left ventricle pumps blood to the rest of the body.

vertebrate An animal with a spinal column (backbone).

vinegar A sour-tasting liquid used as a flavouring and to preserve foods. It is a dilute acetic (ethanoic) acid made by fermenting beer, wine, or cider.

weak acids Weak acids are only slightly ionized to produce hydrogen ions when they dissolve in water.

white blood cells Cells in the blood that fight microorganisms. Some white blood cells digest invading microorganisms. Others produce antibodies.

yield The crop yield is the amount of crop that can be grown per area of land.

Index

Acknowledgements

Publisher's Acknowledgments

pp8/9 Galen Rowell/Corbis UK Ltd.; p10 Paul A. Souders/Corbis UK Ltd.; **p40** Stuart Boreham/Cephas Picture Library/Alamy; **p43b** Cordelia Molloy/Science Photo Library; **p64** Andrew Warburton/Alamy; **p66r** Klaus Guldbrandsen/Science Photo Library; **p68** David Stoecklein/Corbis UK Ltd.; **p70t** Kimimasa Mayama/Reuters/Corbis UK Ltd.; **p74r** blickwinkel/Alamy; **p85b** Clive Brunskill/Getty Images; **p88t** Jim Cummins/Corbis UK Ltd., **p94b** Corbis UK Ltd, **p94t** Christine Osborne/CORBIS; **p97** Andrew Lambert Photography/Science Photo Library; **p100** Imagebroker/Alamy; **p110t&b** Zooid Pictures; **p112** Corbis UK Lrd; **p113b** Getty Images; **p114** Corbis UK Ltd; **p116** Martin Bond/Science Photo Library; **p120b** Crown Copyright Health & Safety Laboratory/Science Photo Library; **p121** Corbis UK Ltd; **p123** Science Photo Library; **p127** National Portrait Gallery; **p128l** Zooid Pictures, **p128r** Lou Chardonnay/Corbis UK Ltd.; **p129** Zooid Pictures; **p130t** Maximilian Stock Ltd/Science Photo Library, **p130b** Photo courtesy of LGC; **p131t** Pullman, **p131b** Nick Laham/Allsport/ Getty Images; **p132** Bayer AG; **p133** www.ars.usda.gov; **p134t&b** Zooid Pictures; **p135l** Adrian Arbib/Corbis UK Ltd., **p135r** Zooid Pictures; **p136** Environmental Health Department, London Borough of Camden/ Oxford University Press; **p135l** BBC Photograph Library, **p137r** David Stoecklein/ Corbis UK Ltd.; **p140** Analtech Inc.; **p141** Analtech Inc.; **p142l&r** CAMAG; **p144** Wellcome Trust; **p145** James Holmes/Thomson Laboratories/Science Photo Library; **p150t&b** Anna Grayson; **p151t&b** Anna Grayson; **p152t&b** Anna Grayson; **p156** Maximilian Stock Ltd/Science Photo Library; **p157** R. Estall/Robert Harding Picture Library Ltd/Alamy; **p159t** Steve Bicknell/The Steve Bicknell Style Library/Alamy, **p159b** William Taufic/Corbis UK Ltd.; **p160b** Laurance B. Aiuppy/Stock Connection/Alamy; **p161** Du Pont (UK) Ltd; **p164** Zooid Pictures; **p166** Nigel Cattlin/Holt Studios International; **p167** Alamy; **p170t** Leslie Garland/Leslie Garland Picture Library/Alamy, **p170b** Huntsman Tioxide, **p171** Tony Jones/Huntsman Tioxide, **p176/177** JPL/NASA, **p178** Charles O'Rear/Corbis, **p178b** Paul A. Sonders/Corbis UK Ltd, **p179t** David Parker/Science Photo Library, **p179r** Justyn Willsmore Photography/Photographersdirect.com. **p179b** Courtesy of Spaceguard Foundation, **p180tr** Eckard Slawik/Science Photo Library, **p180bl** Gabe Palmer/Corbis, **p180br** European Space Agency, **p181t** Hencoup Enterprses Ltd/Science Photo Library, **p181b** European Space Agency, **p182b** NASA/Science Photo Library, **p183** Robin Scagell/Science Photo Library, **p185** Mark Seymour/Oxford University Press, **p186l** Mark Seymour/Oxford University Press, **p186b** Science Photo Library, **p188** Mark Seymour/Oxford University Press, **p189** D. A. Calvert, Royal Greenwich Observatory/Science Photo Library, **p191t** Gregory Dimijian/Science Photo Library, **p191b** David Parker/Science Photo Library, **p193** STSci/NASA; Roger Ressmeyer/Corbis, **p194t** (uncredited), **p194b** Martin Bond/Science Photo Library, **p195l** John Mead/Science Photo Library, **p195r** Jodrell Bank/Science Photo Library, **p196** Dr Seth Shostak/Science Photo Library, **p198** NASA, **p199** Courtesy of the Campaign to Protect Rural England, **p200tl** David Malin, **p200tr** David Malin, **p200bl&br** Institute of Astronomy/University of Cambridge, **p201** Anglo-Australian Observatory, **p202** Adam Hart-Davis/Science Photo Library, **p203tr** Institute of Astronomy/University of Cambridge, **p203cr** Institute of Astronomy/University of Cambridge, **p203bl** Jerry Lodriguss / Science Photo Library, **p204** US Geological Survey/Science Photo Library, **p210t** Dr Fred Espenak/Science Photo Library, **p210b** George Bernard/Science Photo Library, **p211t** Fred Espenak/Science Photo Library, **p211b** Dr Fred Espenak/Science Photo Library, **p212** Mark Seymour/Oxford University Press, **p216t** Eckhard Slawik/Science Photo Library, **p216b** Dr Juerg Alean/Science Photo Library, **p219** Harvard College Observatory/Science Photo Library, **p221** ESA/NASA, **p222** NASA/JPL-Caltech/R. Hurt (SSC), **p223** (uncredited), **p224** Emilio Segre Visual Archives/American Institute of Physics/Science Photo Library, **p226cr** NASA/Science Photo Library, **p226bl** Mary Evans Picture Library, **p227tl** John K. Davies/Science Photo Library, **p227tr** David Parker/Science Photo Library, **p227b** David Parker/Science Photo Library, **p228** Physics Dept., Imperial College/Science Photo Library, **p234** Courtesy of CERN, **p235t&b** Courtesy of CERN, **p244l** Herman Heyn/Science Photo Library, **p244r** CCI Archives/Science Photo Library, **p245t** Royal Observatory, Edinburgh/Science Photo Library, **p245b** Courtesy HESS Collaboration http://www.mpi-hd.mpg.de/hfm/HESS/HESS.html, **p248** European Space Agency/Science Photo Library, **p251** European Space Agency/Science Photo Library, **p252** David A. Hardy, Futures: 50 Years In Space/Science Photo Library, **p254** NASA/Science Photo Library, **p256** Courtesy ESO, **p257t&l&r** Courtesy ESO, **p258** Courtesy ESO, **p259** Courtesy ESO.

OXFORD
UNIVERSITY PRESS

Great Clarendon Street, Oxford OX2 6DP

Oxford University Press is a department of the University of Oxford.
It furthers the University's objective of excellence in research, scholarship,
and education by publishing worldwide in

Oxford   New York

Auckland   Cape Town   Dar es Salaam   Hong Kong   Karachi
Kuala Lumpur   Madrid   Melbourne   Mexico City   Nairobi
New Delhi   Shanghai   Taipei   Toronto

With offices in

Argentina   Austria   Brazil   Chile   Czech Republic   France   Greece
Guatemala   Hungary   Italy   Japan   Poland   Portugal   Singapore
South Korea   Switzerland   Thailand   Turkey   Ukraine   Vietnam

British Library Cataloguing in Publication Data

Data available

ISBN 978-0-19-915215-5

10 9 8 7 6 5 4 3 2 1

Printed in Spain by Cayfosa.

Illustrations by IFA Design, Plymouth, UK

These resources have been developed to support teachers and students undertaking a new OCR suite of GCSE Science specifications, Twenty First Century Science.

Many people from schools, colleges, universities, industry, and the professions have contributed to the production of these resources. The feedback from over 75 Pilot Centres was invaluable. It led to significant changes to the course specifications, and to the supporting resources for teaching and learning.

The University of York Science Education Group (UYSEG) and Nuffield Curriculum Centre worked in partnership with an OCR team led by Mary Whitehouse, Elizabeth Herbert, and Emily Clare to create the specifications, which have their origins in the *Beyond 2000* report (Millar & Osborne, 1998) and subsequent Key Stage 4 development work undertaken by UYSEG and the Nuffield Curriculum Centre for QCA. Bryan Milner and Michael Reiss also contributed to this work, which is reported in: *21st Century Science GCSE Pilot Development: Final Report* (UYSEG, March 2002).

Sponsors
The development of Twenty First Century Science was made possible by generous support from:
• The Nuffield Foundation
• The Salters' Institute
• The Wellcome Trust

THE SALTERS' INSTITUTE